U.S.
Military Museums,
Historic Sites
&
Exhibits

by

Bryce D. Thompson

Military Living Publications
P. O. Box 2347
Falls Church, Virginia 22042-0347
(703) 237-0203
(703) 237-2233 FAX

NOTICE

This book is published by Military Marketing Services, Inc., a private business in no way connected with the U.S. Federal or any other government. This book is copyrighted by Bryce D. Thompson. Opinions expressed by the author are his own and are not an official expression by any government agency or official.

Back cover photographs by Bond A. Williams copyright © 1989 by the photographer. Cover photograph of members of "B" Troop, 4th Cavalry Regiment, provided by the Fort Huachuca, Arizona, Public Affairs Office. Cover design by Cover to Cover, Falls Church, Virginia.

Library of Congress Cataloging-in-Publication Data

```
Thompson, Bryce D.
    U.S. military museums, historic sites & exhibits / by Bryce D.
Thompson.
       p.   cm.
    Includes index.
    ISBN 0-914862-18-9 : $23.95. -- ISBN 0-914862-19-7 (pbk.) : $13.95
    1. Military museums--United States--Directories.  2. Military
parks--United States--Directories.  3. Historic sites--United
States--Directories.  4. Historic ships--United States--Directories.
I. Title.  II. Title: US military museums, historic sites &
exhibits.
U13.U6T48  1989
355'.0074'73--dc20                                         89-9324
                                                              CIP
```

ISBN 0-914862-18-9 (Hardcover)
ISBN 0-914862-19-7 (Softcover)

For

Teresa Mullin

Nec tecum possum vivere nec sine te.

Martial

KEY TO BACK COVER PHOTOGRAPHS

From top to bottom: A Stearman N25-3 Trainer at the U.S. Marine Corps Air-Ground Museum; 7-inch Naval Gun Mark II 1918 mounted on a 7-inch Naval Tractor Mount Mark V at the U.S. Marine Corps Air-Ground Museum; F-102 Jet Fighter on the grounds at Peterson Air Force Base; the M4A3 Sherman Medium Tank that was used in the filming of the James Garner film "Tank," on temporary loan from the Smithsonian Institution to the U.S. Marine Corps Air-Ground Museum; the USS *Barry*, a Forest Sherman-class destroyer permanantly anchored in the Anacostia River in front of the Navy Memorial Museum.

INTRODUCTION & ACKNOWLEDGEMENTS

This book is probably the most comprehensive guide to American military museums and sites ever published. It includes Army, Navy, Air Force, Marine Corps, Coast Guard and N.O.A.A. museums in the U.S. and overseas; other military museums; relevant aviation and maritime museums; sites associated with the history of all military powers in the U.S. and its territories; historic U.S. warships, submarines and boats; and NASA visitor centers and space museums. I looked for Public Health Service museums or exhibits, hoping to have all seven of this nation's uniformed services represented in this book, but I located none.

The **Visitor Information** section in each listing contains location information, driving directions, mailing address, contact telephone number(s), hours of operation and admissions fee information. The **Items-on-Display** section lists the categories of artifacts and memorabilia on display and the types of exhibits found at the museum, visitor center or site. If you have a special interest in particular types of military artifacts—unit patches, field equipment, edged weapons and so on—the Items-on-Display section will tell you which museum, visitor center or battle site has them.

The text that follows the Items-on-Display section for a museum provides information about a museum's mission and major themes and describes artifacts of exceptional interest to visitors. The textual section of a listing about a battlefield site generally places the battle in its historical context and examines the battle's causes and consequences. Exhibits and artifacts on display in visitor centers at battlefield sites and parks are examined as well. Listings about historic warships and submarines provide capsule histories of the vessels and highlight their most important engagements, missions and accomplishments.

Everyone who uses this book should realize that any given museum's status is subject to change without notice. Over the past few years, museums have closed at Fort Carson, Fort Drum, Fort Belvoir and the Naval Surface Weapons Center at Dahlgren. Other closings will almost certainly occur if bases that have recently been targeted for closure do indeed close. Chanute Air Force Base, the Presidio of San Francisco and Mather Air Force Base, to name only a few, have museums and are on the list of bases/posts that will be deactivated sometime in the near future. But the news isn't all bad. Efforts are currently underway to develop new museums in many locations across the country. The Virginia National Guard hopes to have a museum open by the early 90s, as does the Army's 6th Infantry Division (Light) after it moves its headquarters from Fort Richardson to Fort Wainwright, Alaska. The bottom line is: call

Introduction, continued

before going.

As you thumb through this book, you'll notice that some museums, battle sites and so on have only their names, mailing addresses and phone numbers listed at the end of a state, territory or country section. Space limitations and an occasional absence of detailed information about a museum or site made this necessary.

No one puts together a book like this on his own. Hundreds of museum curators, assistant curators, site and park superintendents, park rangers and others provided essential information during the nearly two years I spent researching and writing this book. I gratefully acknowledge their contributions.

I would also like to thank the following: Dr. William R. Crawford, Col., USA (Ret.), who suggested I write this book; his wife, Ann Crawford, who provided me with valuable leads during my research; my brother, Robert E. Thompson, Jr., who contributed much to my knowledge of display ships on the Eastern Seaboard; Bond A. Williams, a good friend and a fine photographer, who spent days with me (when she couldn't really afford the time) looking for, and finding, interesting items to photograph; my parents, Robert E. Thompson, Sr. and Betty Lee Thompson, for their unflagging support and encouragement, and for proofreading the manuscript; Anna Belle and Gordon Causey, for proofreading sections of the manuscript; and Stacey Wing, for the many invaluable corrections she made and suggestions she offered while proofreading the manuscript. I also want to thank Cheryl Lynn Cunningham, for all the good times.

Bryce Thompson
Falls Church, Virginia
July 1989

CONTENTS

UNITED STATES

ALABAMA

ALASKA

ARIZONA

ARKANSAS

CALIFORNIA

CALIFORNIA (continued)

GEORGIA (continued)

HAWAII

IDAHO

ILLINOIS

INDIANA

IOWA

KANSAS

MINNESOTA

MISSISSIPPI

MISSOURI

MONTANA

NEBRASKA

NEVADA

NEW HAMPSHIRE

NEW JERSEY

NEW JERSEY (continued)

NEW MEXICO

NEW YORK

NORTH CAROLINA

NORTH DAKOTA

OHIO

OHIO (continued)

OKLAHOMA

OREGON

PENNSYLVANIA

RHODE ISLAND

SOUTH CAROLINA

SOUTH DAKOTA

TENNESSEE

TEXAS

UTAH

VERMONT

VIRGINIA

GERMANY (continued)

UNITED STATES

ALABAMA

ALABAMA SPACE & ROCKET CENTER

Visitor Information: Located off I-65 west of downtown Huntsville. Take the Huntsville exit (Highway 20) off I-65. Mailing Address: One Tranquility Base, Huntsville, Alabama 35807. Telephone: 1-800-633-7280 (outside Alabama); 1-800-572-7234 (in Alabama); or call (205) 837-3400. Hours: 9:00 am to 5:00 pm daily during the fall, winter and spring; 8:00 am to 6:00 pm during June, July and August. Closed Christmas. Admission: $10.00 per adult, $6.00 per child, senior citizen and military member. Special rates available for groups.

Items on Display: Rockets, Missiles, Space Craft, Space Exploration Displays, Satellites/Satellite Communications Displays.

Historic artifacts, hands-on exhibits, live demonstrations of astronaut training equipment and film presentations pertaining to the past, present and future of America's space program are all part of the country's largest space museum, the Alabama Space and Rocket Center. The Apollo XVI command module and the Sigma 7 Mercury Spacecraft in which astronaut Wally Schirra orbited the Earth in 1962 are on display in the space museum, along with a vast number of other space-related artifacts and exhibits. The Rocket Park outside contains a number of early Army missiles and NASA rockets from the entire history of manned and unmanned space flight. The massive Saturn V rocket on display, which NASA engineers developed for the Apollo program, is the first Saturn V ever built and the only rocket ever designated a National Historic Landmark by the federal government.

The centerpiece of the center's Shuttle Park is the "Pathfinder," a full-size mockup of the shuttle orbiter that NASA built for clearance testing at nearby Marshall Space Flight Center. Bus tours of the Space Flight Center, where America's space station is currently being designed, depart from the Space and Rocket Center's entrance on a regular basis throughout the day.

ALABAMA

FORT CONDÉ

Visitor Information: Located at 150 South Royal Street in Mobile. From I-10 east take the Water Street exit. From I-10 west take the Canal Street exit. Follow signs to the fort. Mailing Address: 150 South Royal Street, Mobile, Alabama 36602. Telephone: (205) 434-7304. Hours: 8:00 am to 5:00 pm daily. Admission: free.

Items on Display: Historic Structure (reconstructed French fort).

Initially constructed as a temporary wooden stockade by the French in 1711, Fort Condé served the military purposes of three European powers before its capture by American forces during the War of 1812. By 1735 the French had constructed a permanent, brick-and-mortar fort within the stockade and had given the fort the name it bears today. In 1763 the English supplanted the French and in 1780 the Spanish seized the fort from the English. In 1813, President James Monroe ordered American troops to take the fort by force and thus end Spanish aid to the British invaders. Belief in the fort's military importance dwindled and in 1820 it was torn down. The city of Mobile reconstructed the fort based on original drawings and blueprints. It opened in time for the 1976 Bicentennial celebrations and now serves as Mobile's Visitor and Welcome Center. Artifacts excavated at the site are on display.

FORT GAINES HISTORIC SITE

Visitor Information: Located on the extreme east end of Dauphin Island near the mouth of Mobile Bay. From I-10 take AL-163 south to Dauphin Island. Turn left at Bienville Boulevard and proceed to the fort. Mailing Address: P. O. Box 97, Dauphin Island, Alabama 36528. Telephone: (205) 861-6992. Hours: 9:00 am to 5:00 pm daily. Admission: $2.00 per adult, $1.00 per child ages 6-12.

Items on Display: Uniforms, Field Equipment, Dioramas, Edged Weapons, Side Arms, Shoulder Arms, Ordnance, Coast-Defense Artillery, Historic Structure (fort).

Fort Gaines was built in 1857 and remained in use until the end of World War II. The fort was attacked and recaptured by Union forces in 1864 during the Battle of Mobile Bay and was used as a base of operations by Union troops during the campaign for Mobile in 1865. Eight of the original cannon used during the Civil War and several fine examples of Confederate ironcladding are on display, in addition to numerous artifacts, most from the Civil War era.

ALABAMA

FORT MORGAN

Visitor Information: Located 22 miles west of Gulf Shores, Alabama, near the mouth of Mobile Bay. From I-10 take AL-59 south to Gulf Shores. In Gulf Shores take AL-180 west for 22 miles to the fort. Mailing Address: Route 1, Box 3540, Highway 180, Gulf Shores, Alabama 36542. Telephone: (205) 540-7125. Hours: 9:00 am to 5:00 pm daily. Closed Thanksgiving, Christmas and New Year's Day. Admission: $2.00 per adult, $1.00 per child ages 6-18.

Items on Display: Uniforms, Unit Patches, Field Equipment, Personal Documents, Official Documents, Maps, Photographs, Paintings/Drawings, Flags (replicas), Medals, Edged Weapons, Side Arms, Shoulder Arms, Ordnance, Field Artillery, Coast-Defense Artillery, Scale Models (ships/boats), Historic Structures (fort, concrete batteries).

Fort Morgan is one of the most architecturally impressive brick coast-defense fortifications ever constructed in the U.S. Built between the years 1819 and 1833, the fort was garrisoned from the 1830s until 1923, when it was abandoned until the outbreak of World War II. Confederate forces seized the fort from Union control in the early days of the Civil War and used the fort's strategically placed guns to aid Confederate supply ships as they forged through the Union blockades in Mobile Bay. Confederate forces held the fort until 1864, when heavy bombardment from the ships of Admiral David Farragut's Gulf Squadron necessitated its surrender. The Fort Morgan Museum's collection consists largely of artifacts from the Civil War era through World War II, with items from the War of 1812 and earlier periods also on display.

MILITARY POLICE CORPS REGIMENTAL MUSEUM

Visitor Information: Located in Building 3182 on Fort McClellan, three miles northwest of Anniston, Alabama. Mailing Address: Fort McClellan, Alabama 36205-5000. Take AL-21 north at the Anniston/Oxford exit and proceed 10 miles north to Fort McClellan and Summerall Gate. Follow signs to the museum. Telephone: (205) 848-3522/3050. Hours: 8:00 am to 4:00 pm Monday through Friday. Weekends by appointment. Closed federal holidays. Admission: free.

Items on Display: Uniforms, Unit Patches, Field Equipment, Personal Documents, Official Documents, Maps, Photographs, Paintings/Drawings, Flags, Battle Streamers, Medals, Edged Weapons, Side Arms, Shoulder Arms, Machine Guns, Rockets/Rocket Launchers, Aircraft (rotary wing), Ships/Boats, Wheeled Vehicles.

ALABAMA
Military Police Corps Regimental Museum, continued

Displays at the museum focus upon the history of the Military Police Corps and depict the duties of Military Police personnel from ancient times to the present. Of special interest are Vietnam prisoner-of-war artifacts, a Vietnam-era helicopter gun ship, a river patrol boat and combat art from World War I to Vietnam.

U.S. ARMY AVIATION MUSEUM

Visitor Information: Located in buildings 6007, 6008, 6009 and 6013 at the U.S. Army Aviation Center on Fort Rucker. Take US-231 north from Dothan to AL-249 and follow signs. Mailing Address: P. O. Box 610, Fort Rucker, Alabama 36362-5134. Hours: 9:00 am to 4:00 pm Monday through Friday, 1:00 pm to 5:00 pm weekends and holidays. Closed Christmas. Admission: free.

Items on Display: Aircraft (fixed wing, rotary wing).

The largest collection of rotary-wing aircraft in the free world is on display at the Army Aviation Museum. Alongside the many helicopters from the 40-plus year history of Army aviation are numerous fixed-wing aircraft, including the C-121A used by General MacArthur at Bataan.

U.S. ARMY CHEMICAL CORPS MUSEUM

Visitor Information: Located in Building 2299 on Fort McClellan, three miles northwest of Anniston. Mailing Address: Fort McClellan, Alabama 36205-5000. From I-20 take AL-21 north for ten miles to the Baltzell Gate and follow signs to the museum. Telephone: (205) 848-3355/4449. Hours: 7:30 am to 4:00 pm Monday through Friday. Closed federal holidays. Admission: free.

Items on Display: Uniforms, Field Equipment, Paintings/Drawings, Ordnance, Chemical/Biological Weapons Displays.

Though the special weapons it develops, tests and holds in readiness have proven to be more controversial than the neutron bomb, the Chemical Corps of today remains an active and vital part of the United States' defense posture. The Chemical Corps began in the World War I era as the 30th Engineers-Gas and Flame Regiment. The regiment transferred to the Chemical Warfare Service in 1918 and by the end of World War II had assumed its present designation. The special mortars, smoke-generating devices and flame throwers that the Corps developed and employed in World War II and in

ALABAMA

U.S. Army Chemical Corps Museum, continued

Korea had a significant impact on the overall outcome of both conflicts.

In 1973, as political leaders began to question the suitability of chemical and biological weapons activities, the Chemical Corps was disestablished; however, mounting evidence of Soviet capabilities and advances in the chemical/biological weapons arena lead to the reversal of the disestablishment directive in 1976.

The Chemical Corps Museum houses more than 4000 artifacts that depict the history of chemical and biological warfare and of the U.S. Army Chemical Corps.

USS *ALABAMA* BATTLESHIP MEMORIAL PARK

Visitor Information: Located off Battleship Parkway (US-90). Take I-10 east from Mobile to exit 27 onto US-90 to the park. Mailing Address: USS *Alabama* Battleship Commission, P. O. Box 65, Mobile, Alabama 36601. Telephone: (205) 433-2703. Hours: 8:00 am to sunset daily. Closed Christmas. Admission: $5.00 per adult, $2.50 per child ages 6-11.

Items on Display: Uniforms, Unit Patches, Field Equipment, Personal Documents, Official Documents, Maps, Photographs, Paintings/Drawings, Dioramas, Flags, Battle Streamers, Medals, Edged Weapons, Side Arms, Shoulder Arms, Machine Guns, Mines, Field Artillery, Air-Defense Artillery, Rockets, Aircraft (fixed wing, rotary wing), Ships, Submarines/Submersible Vehicles, Tracked Vehicles, Scale Models (aircraft).

Anchored just off shore from the USS *Alabama* Battleship Memorial Park are two of the most distinguished fighting ships of the World War II era: the park's namesake, the USS *Alabama*, a South Dakota Class battleship; and the submarine USS *Drum*. During its 37 months of active service, the *Alabama* shot down 22 Japanese planes while earning nine battlestars in campaigns in the Pacific Theatre. The *Drum* earned 12 battlestars while sinking 15 enemy vessels during its wartime career. Both ships are open to the public for self-guided tours.

The visitor center on shore contains a variety of 20th-century military artifacts. Outdoor displays include tracked vehicles, a towering Redstone rocket, artillery pieces and a number of historic aircraft, including the Boeing B-52D Stratofortress, a North American

ALABAMA
USS *Alabama* Battleship Memorial Park, continued

P-51D Mustang and a prototype model of the Republic F-105B Thunderchief.

WOMEN'S ARMY CORPS MUSEUM

Visitor Information: Located in Building 1077 on Fort McClellan, three miles northwest of Anniston, Alabama. Mailing Address: Fort McClellan, Alabama 36205-5000. From I-20 take AL-21 north for ten miles to the Galloway Gate. Telephone: (205) 848-3512/5559. Hours: 7:30 am to 4:00 pm Monday through Friday. Weekends by appointment for large groups. Closed federal holidays. Admission: free.

Items on Display: Uniforms, Field Equipment, Photographs, Communications Equipment.

The Women's Army Corps Museum is the only museum in the Army museum system devoted exclusively to the developing role of women in the Army. The WAC was established in May, 1942, as the Women's Army Auxiliary Corps. At that time, women in the Corps did not have official military status and lacked the military and veterans' benefits received by men who served. This changed in the summer of '43 when Congress granted full military status to women and removed "auxiliary" from the Corps' official name. WACs provided communications, clerical and administrative support while serving all over the world and had active roles in all of the United States' military conflicts from World War II to Vietnam. By the mid-1970s, because the role of women in the Army had expanded into all areas except those involving combat or other forms of hazardous duty, the need for a separate women's corps had diminished. The Women's Army Corps was disestablished by act of Congress in 1978.

Other Military Museums, Historic Sites & Exhibits in Alabama

First White House of the Confederacy, 644 Washington Avenue, Montgomery, Alabama 36104. Telephone: (205) 261-4624.

Fort Toulouse-Jackson Park, Route 6, Box 6, Wetumpka, Alabama 36092. Telephone: (205) 567-3002.

Horseshoe Bend National Military Park, Route 1, Box 103, Daviston, Alabama 36256. Telephone: (205) 234-7111.

ALABAMA

Other Military Museums in Alabama, continued

NASA/Marshall Space Flight Center, Marshall Space Flight Center, Alabama 35812. Telephone: (205) 837-3400.

Warrant Officer Candidate Hall of Fame, C Company, 1/145th Aviation, 1st Aviation Brigade, Fort Rucker, Alabama 36362-5000. Telephone: (205) 255-4006.

ALASKA

SITKA NATIONAL HISTORICAL PARK

Visitor Information: Located at 106 Metlakatla Street in Sitka, south of Juneau on the Pacific Coast. Call for driving directions. Mailing Address: P. O. Box 738, Sitka, Alaska 99835. Telephone: (907) 747-6281. Hours: 8:00 am to 6:00 pm daily from mid-April to mid-September, 8:00 am to 5:00 pm Monday through Saturday from mid-September to mid-April. Admission: free.

Items on Display: A complete list was unavailable at press time, but the visitor center is known to contain the following: Maps, Paintings/Drawings, Edged Weapons, Shoulder Arms.

Tlingit Indians and Russian troops met in battle in 1804 near the present-day town of Sitka. Exhibits about the battle and Russian and Indian artifacts are on display in the park's visitor center. The center's 1,000-volume library on Alaskan history is open to the public.

Other Military Museums, Historic Sites & Exhibits in Alaska

Eagle Historical Society Museum, P. O. Box 26, Eagle City, Alaska 99738. Telephone: (907) 547-2230.

Fort Kenay Historical Museum, Senior Court, P. O. Box 361, Kenai, Alaska 99611. Telephone: (907) 283-7294.

ARIZONA

ARIZONA MILITARY MUSEUM

Visitor Information: Located at 5636 East McDowell Road, Phoenix, Arizona 85008-3495. Take I-10 to the McDowell Road east exit. Continue to 52nd Street and the Papago Park Military Reservation (Arizona National Guard). Telephone: (602) 267-2676. Hours: 9:30 am to 2:00 pm Tuesday and Thursday, 1:00 pm to 4:00 pm weekends. Admission: free.

Items on Display: Uniforms, Unit Patches, Field Equipment, Personal Documents, Official Documents, Maps, Photographs, Paintings/Drawings, Flags, Battle Streamers, Medals, Edged Weapons, Side Arms, Shoulder Arms, Machine Guns, Flame Throwers, Mines, Ordnance, Field Artillery, Rockets/Rocket Launchers, Chemical/Biological Weapons Displays, Aircraft (rotary wing), Communications Equipment, Tracked Vehicles, Scale Models (aircraft, tracked vehicles).

Artifacts at the Arizona Military Museum depict the military history of Arizona from the time of the Spanish Conquistadors to the present. Items on display relate to the participation of Arizona residents in the Indian Wars, the Mexican Border Service, early Arizona militia units, the Arizona National Guard and all of the nation's major armed conflicts.

CHAMPLIN FIGHTER MUSEUM

Visitor Information: Located at 4636 Fighter Aces Drive, Mesa, Arizona 85205. Take the Superstition Freeway (AR-360) exit east off I-10. Turn left onto Country Club Drive to McKellips Road. Turn right on McKellips to Falcon Drive. Turn left onto Falcon to Fighter Aces Drive and the museum on the left. Telephone: (602) 830-4540. Hours: 10:00 am to 5:00 pm daily. Admission: $5.00 per adult, $2.50 per child ages 14 and under.

Items on Display: Photographs, Paintings/Drawings, Side Arms, Shoulder Arms, Machine Guns, Aircraft (fixed wing).

Nearly 30 fighter aircraft from World War I through Vietnam are on display at the Champlin Fighter Museum. World War I-era aircraft include the English Sopwith Camel and Spad XIII, the German Fokker D-VII and D-VIII and the Albatross D-Va. World War II-era aircraft include the Messerschmitt 109E, the Spitfire MK 1X and the Grumman FM-2 Wildcat. A Soviet MiG-17 jet fighter is on display as

ARIZONA
Champlin Fighter Museum, continued

well.

The museum serves as headquarters for the American Fighter Aces Association, which has put together the largest collection of fighter ace memorabilia in the country. More than 700 autographed photos of aces from 15 different countries and personal belongings of famous aces such as Germany's Baron von Richthofen are on display, as is an extensive automatic weapons collection.

FORT BOWIE NATIONAL HISTORIC SITE

Visitor Information: Located 11 miles south of Bowie. Take I-10 to Bowie and turn south on Apache Pass Road. The parking area for the site is 11 miles ahead (nine miles of the road is unpaved). Wear comfortable walking shoes since the fort itself is a one and a half mile hike from the parking area over moderate terrain. Mailing Address: P. O. Box 158, Bowie, Arizona 85605. Telephone: (602) 847-2500. Hours: 8:00 am to 4:30 pm daily. Closed Christmas. Admission: free.

Items on Display: Uniforms, Unit Patches, Field Equipment, Personal Documents, Official Documents, Photographs, Flags, Medals, Edged Weapons, Side Arms, Shoulder Arms, Field Artillery, Communications Equipment, Historic Structure (fort ruins).

Fort Bowie's history is the history of the Indian Wars of the Southwest in microcosm. The Indian uprising that began near here in 1860 led to many years of bloody, intermittent warfare between U.S. Army soldiers and the Chiricahua Apaches, who were led first by Cochise and then by Geronimo.

The fort was established in 1862 near the spring at Apache Pass, the only reliable source of water for many miles and a vital waystation on the Butterfield Overland Trail between St. Louis and San Francisco. Many campaigns of attrition were launched from Fort Bowie against the Apaches until the final surrender of Geronimo in 1886. When the fort was disestablished on October 17, 1894, an endlessly fascinating, yet tragic, period in American history came to an end. Pamphlets available at the fort museum tell the story of Fort Bowie in detail. Period military and Indian artifacts are on display.

FORT HUACHUCA MUSEUM

Visitor Information: Located at the corner of Boyd and Grierson Streets on Fort Huachuca, 70 miles south of Tucson off AZ-90. Take I-10 east from Tucson to AZ-90 south to the fort. Mailing Address: P. O. Box 766, Fort Huachuca, Arizona 85613-6000. Telephone: (602) 533-5736. Hours: 9:00 am to 4:00 pm Monday through Friday, 1:00 pm to 4:00 pm weekends. Admission: free.

Items on Display: Uniforms, Field Equipment, Official Documents, Maps, Photographs, Paintings/Drawings, Flags, Edged Weapons, Side Arms, Shoulder Arms, Ordnance, Field Artillery, Historic Structure (fort buildings).

Displays at Fort Huachuca's post museum focus upon the cavalry soldier's role in the taming of the American Southwest and upon southwestern history in general. Post-Civil War-period uniforms, weapons and other items from the fort's history are on display.

Fort Huachuca is home to "B" Troop, 4th Regiment, U.S. Cavalry (Memorial). Formed in the early 1970s as a ceremonial unit, "B" Troop members are uniformed and outfitted as cavalry soldiers of the 1880s. The troop performs on post at selected times and off post throughout the Southwest.

FORT LOWELL MUSEUM

Visitor Information: Located at the corner of Craycroft Road and Fort Lowell Road in Tucson, a short drive east of I-10. Mailing Address: 949 East 2nd Street, Tucson, Arizona 85719. Telephone: (602) 885-3832. Hours: 10:00 am to 4:00 pm Wednesday through Saturday. Admission: free.

Items on Display: Uniforms, Field Equipment, Maps, Photographs, Dioramas, Edged Weapons, Side Arms, Shoulder Arms, Communications Equipment, Historic Structures (ruins of fort, reconstructed commanding officer's quarters, reconstructed kitchen building).

Exhibits and artifacts at the Fort Lowell Museum focus on Army activities in the Southwest in the latter half of the 19th century, with particular emphasis on the Army's campaigns against the Apaches. The commanding officer's quarters and a kitchen building, in which military and other period artifacts are on display, have been reconstructed among the fort's ruins. As with Fort Bowie, Fort Lowell's importance as a military outpost waned after the capture of

ARIZONA
Fort Lowell Museum, continued

Geronimo in 1886 and it was abandoned in 1891.

FORT VERDE STATE HISTORIC PARK

Visitor Information: Located approximately 50 miles south of Flagstaff off I-17. Take I-17 north from Phoenix or south from Flagstaff to the Camp Verde exit. The fort is on Lane Street in Camp Verde. Mailing Address: P. O. Box 397, Camp Verde, Arizona 86322. Telephone: (602) 567-3275. Hours: 8:00 am to 5:00 pm daily. Closed Christmas. Admission: $1.00 per adult, under age 17 admitted free.

Items on Display: Uniforms, Field Equipment, Personal Documents, Official Documents, Maps, Photographs, Paintings/Drawings, Medical Equipment, Historic Structures (officers' quarters in three buildings, administration building).

In 1865 Army troops garrisoned Camp Verde in response to the growing hostility between Indians and settlers. Camp Verde became Fort Verde a few years later and, until its abandonment in 1891, was a focal point for military ventures against the Indians of the Southwest. A small museum in the old administration building houses military artifacts and displays about the Indian Wars. Three officers' quarters, furnished as they were in the 1880s, are open to the public.

PIMA AIR MUSEUM

Visitor Information: Located at 6000 East Valencia Road in Tucson. From I-10 take the Valencia Road exit east to the museum. Mailing Address: Tucson Air Museum Foundation, 6000 East Valencia Road, Tucson, Arizona 85706. Telephone: (602) 574-9658. Hours: 9:00 am to 5:00 pm daily. Closed Christmas. Admission: $4.00 per adult, $3.00 for seniors, groups and military personnel, $2.00 for children ages 10-17, under age ten admitted free.

Items on Display: Uniforms, Field Equipment, Missiles, Aircraft (fixed wing, rotary wing), Scale Models (aircraft).

One of the largest privately funded air museums in the world, the Pima Air Museum's collection spans more than 80 years of aviation history. Among the more than 130 aircraft on display: a full-scale replica of the Wright Brothers Wright Flyer, a World War II-era North American B-25 medium-range bomber, a Lockheed F-104B jet fighter and a mock-up of the famous X-15.

ARIZONA

TITAN MISSILE MUSEUM

Visitor Information: Located a short distance south of Tucson. Take I-19 south from Tucson to exit 69. Go west one tenth of a mile past La Canada and turn right to the museum. All tours are guided. For safety reasons, high-heeled shoes cannot be worn in the missile silo. Mailing Address: Green Valley, Arizona 85014. Telephone: (602) 791-2929. Hours: 9:00 am to 5:00 pm (last tour begins at 4:00 pm) Wednesday through Sunday from May 1 to October 31; open daily from November 1 to April 30. Closed Christmas. Admission: $4.00 per adult, $3.00 for seniors and military personnel, $2.00 for children ages 10-17, under age ten admitted free. Group rates are available.

Items on Display: Missiles, Missile Silos/Installation.

A part of the 390th Strategic Missile Wing headquartered at Davis-Monthan Air Force Base, this Titan Missile Complex came on line in 1963. In use until July 31, 1984, it was one of 18 missile complexes located in the Tucson area. All Titan missile sites, with this one exception, have been or will soon be deactivated and destroyed. This is truly a one-of-a-kind museum.

Other Military Museums, Historic Sites & Exhibits in Arizona

Fort Apache, White Mountain Apache Culture Center, P. O. Box 507, Fort Apache, Arizona 85926. Telephone: (602) 338-4625.

ARKANSAS

PEA RIDGE NATIONAL MILITARY PARK

Visitor Information: Located approximately 20 miles north of Fayetteville near the town of Pea Ridge. From I-40 go north on US-71 through Fayetteville to Rogers. Turn east onto US-62 and proceed ten miles to the park. Mailing Address: Pea Ridge, Arkansas 72751. Telephone: (501) 451-8122. Hours: 8:00 am to 5:00 pm daily. Closed Thanksgiving, Christmas and New Year's Day. Admission: $1.00 per person or $3.00 per family; age 12 and under or 62 and over admitted free.

Items on Display: Uniforms, Field Equipment, Personal Documents, Maps, Photographs, Paintings/Drawings, Flags, Edged Weapons, Shoulder Arms, Ordnance, Field Artillery, Historic Structure (restored tavern).

The only major Civil War engagement in which native American troops served as combatants occurred at Pea Ridge. Roughly one thousand Cherokee Indians from the Indian Territory fought on the Confederate side until the devastating effects of Union cannon forced their retreat. The Union victory at Pea Ridge was assured only when Confederate forces ran out of artillery ammunition. The Elkhorn Tavern served as a field hospital for both sides at different times during the engagement. Period artifacts are on display in the visitor center and tavern.

PRAIRIE GROVE BATTLEFIELD STATE PARK

Visitor Information: Located just off US-62 eight miles west of Fayetteville. Signs are posted. Mailing Address: P. O. Box 306, Prairie Grove, Arkansas 72753. Telephone: (501) 846-2990. Hours: 8:00 am to 10:00 pm daily (park); 8:00 am to 5:00 pm daily (museum). Closed Thanksgiving, Christmas and New Year's Day. Admission: free.

Items on Display: Uniforms, Field Equipment, Personal Documents, Official Documents, Maps, Photographs, Dioramas, Flags, Medals, Edged Weapons, Side Arms, Shoulder Arms, Field Artillery.

On December 7, 1862, 18,000 Confederate and Union troops clashed eight miles outside Fayetteville. The battle claimed 2,500 casualties before a dwindling supply of ammunition forced the Confederate Army to withdraw, its goal of forcing Union troops from Northwest Arkansas unfulfilled. A museum at the site displays artifacts and

Prairie Grove Battlefield State Park, continued

ARKANSAS

memorabilia from the battle.

Other Military Museums, Historic Sites & Exhibits in Arkansas

Fort Smith National Historic Site, P. O. Box 1406, Fort Smith, Arkansas 72902. Telephone: (501) 783-3961.

Jenkins' Ferry, Marks' Mill and Poison Spring Battlefields, c/o Arkansas State Parks, One Capitol Mall 4A-900, Little Rock, Arkansas 72201. Telephone: (501) 371-1191.

Phillips County Museum, 623 Pecan Street, Helena, Arkansas 72342. Telephone: (501) 338-3567.

CALIFORNIA

AMPHIBIAN VEHICLE MUSEUM

Visitor Information: Located just north of Oceanside on Camp Pendleton between Los Angeles and San Diego. From I-5, take the Camp Pendleton exit and enter at the main gate. Follow Vandergrift Boulevard for eight miles. Turn right at Rattlesnake Canyon Road and drive to the top of the hill. The museum is an outdoor display on the left before the traffic light. The Marine Corps asks that you do not exit your vehicle before arriving at the museum parking area and that no photographs be taken in the vicinity of the Marine Corps Air Facility. Stopping your vehicle near the Air Facility is also prohibited. The driver must have valid license, vehicle registration and proof of insurance. Mailing Address: Marine Corps Base, Building 1160, Joint Public Affairs Office, Camp Pendleton, California 92055-5001. Telephone: (619) 725-5566. Hours: daylight hours daily. Admission: free.

Items on Display: Amphibious Landing Craft.

The most extensive collection of amphibious vehicles in the free world is on outdoor display at the Amphibian Museum. More than 30 LVTs (Landing Vehicles, Tracked) dating from World War II through Vietnam illustrate the development of the amphibious landing craft as a sea-to-shore assault and river-forging craft. Experimental LVTs in the collection include a huge 176,000 pound cargo carrier and an LVT with a water speed of over 40 miles per hour. By way of comparison, the original LVT1s used in the Pacific in World War II weighed 17,300 pounds and moved along at about six miles per hour.

ANGEL ISLAND STATE PARK

Visitor Information: Located on Angel Island in San Francisco Bay. Take US-101 north from San Francisco over the Golden Gate Bridge for approximately five miles to CA-131 east. Drive approximately five miles to the town of Tiburon. Take the Tiburon ferry in town to Angel Island. Mailing Address: P. O. Box 318, Tiburon, California 94920. Telephone: (415) 435-1915. Hours: 8:00 am to sunset daily. Admission: $1.00 per person.

Items on Display: Field Equipment, Personal Documents, Official Documents, Maps, Photographs, Dioramas, Flags, Edged Weapons, Shoulder Arms, Mines, Ordnance, Field Artillery, Missile Silos/Installations, Amphibious Landing Craft, Historic Structures (concrete batteries, fort and P.O.W.-camp buildings).

Angel Island State Park, continued

The visitor center on Angel Island displays artifacts from the island's long and varied military history. Over the years, Angel Island was the site of a major in- and out-processing station for military personnel, an immigration station and a detention center for suspected or potential enemy sympathizers during wartime. During World War II, hundreds of Japanese P.O.W.s were temporarily detained on the island. After the war, a Nike missile base was installed on the island's south side. The base remained active until 1962. Today, old gun emplacements and buildings once used by the military, the Immigration Service and the U.S. Public Health Service can all be reached by walking trails. The Nike missile base, though it can be seen from a distance, is as yet closed to the public.

CASTLE AIR MUSEUM

Visitor Information: Located 60 miles north of Fresno on Castle Air Force Base. Take CA-99 to Atwater, then take the Buhach exit to Buhach Road to Santa Fe Drive. Turn left on Santa Fe. The museum entrance is 200 yards from the base's main gate. Mailing Address: P. O. Box 488, Atwater, California 95301. Telephone: (209) 723-2178/2177. Hours: 10:00 am to 4:00 pm daily. Admission: free.

Items on Display: Uniforms, Unit Patches, Field Equipment, Personal Documents, Maps, Photographs, Paintings/Drawings, Flags, Medals, Edged Weapons, Side Arms, Shoulder Arms, Aircraft (fixed wing, rotary wing).

More than 30 aircraft are on outdoor display at the Castle Air Museum, including a B-17 Flying Fortress, a Mitchell B-25, a B-52 Stratofortress, a B-45 Tornado, a B-47 Stratojet and a British B-2 Vulcan, the first of its kind ever displayed at a museum outside the United Kingdom. The museum building itself houses over 600 artifacts from the history of military aviation.

CEC/SEABEE MUSEUM

Visitor Information: Located 40 miles northwest of Los Angeles on the Naval Construction Battalion Center, Port Hueneme. From US-101 north or south, take the Wagon Wheel off-ramp south onto Ventura Boulevard. The base is approximately eight miles ahead. The guard at the gate will issue a pass for the museum. Mailing Address: Code 22M, Naval Construction Battalion Center, Port Heuneme, California 93043-5000. Telephone: (805) 982-5163. Hours: 8:00 am to 5:00 pm Monday through Friday, 9:00 am to 4:30 pm Saturday, 12:30

CALIFORNIA
CEC/Seabee Museum, continued

pm to 4:30 pm Sunday. Closed national holidays. Admission: free.

Items on Display: Uniforms, Unit Patches, Field Equipment, Personal Documents, Official Documents, Photographs, Paintings/Drawings, Dioramas, Flags, Battle Streamers, Medals, Edged Weapons, Side Arms, Shoulder Arms, Machine Guns, Ordnance, Field Artillery, Rockets/Rocket Launchers, Amphibious Landing Craft, Communications Equipment, Medical Equipment, Tracked Vehicles.

An extensive collection of artifacts and memorabilia from the storied history of the Seabees and the Navy Civil Engineer Corps is on display at the CEC/Seabee Museum. Selected exhibits contain cultural artifacts from many of the locations where Seabees have served, including Alaska, China, the South Pacific and Vietnam. Two exhibits display German and Japanese military artifacts from World War II. Another focuses on Seabee activities at the North and South Poles. Extensive medal, uniform and arms exhibits and numerous plaques, posters, sculptures, carvings and other items make this one of the finest Navy museums in the country.

DRUM BARRACKS CIVIL WAR MUSEUM

Visitor Information: Located south of Los Angeles at 1952 Banning Boulevard, Wilmington, California 90744. Take the Harbor Freeway south to the Pacific Coast Highway. Go left on the PCH to Avalon. Turn right on Avalon to M Street. Turn left on M to Banning Boulevard. Turn right on Banning to the museum. Telephone: (213) 548-7509. Hours: 9:00 am to 1:00 pm Monday through Friday, 12:30 pm to 3:00 pm weekends. Admission: $1.00 donation.

Items on Display: Uniforms, Field Equipment, Personal Documents, Official Documents, Maps, Photographs, Paintings/Drawings, Flags, Edged Weapons, Side Arms, Shoulder Arms, Machine Guns, Field Artillery.

A wide variety of Civil War-era artifacts is on display in the Civil War Museum, most of which pertain to the history of Camp Drum, once garrisoned by as many as 7,000 troops. Included in the museum's collection is a scale model of the camp in its heyday; old maps of the surrounding area; a Gatling gun designed for use in the "camel corps," which was phased out in 1863; two rooms of Civil War-period furnishings; and a selection of unique books from the 1860s.

EDWARD F. BEALE MUSEUM

Visitor Information: Located in Building 2471 on Beale Air Force Base, 35 miles northeast of Sacramento. Take CA-70 north from Sacramento to the North Beale Highway east to the base. Mailing Address: 9 SRW/CCX, Building 2471, Beale Air Force Base, California 95903-5000. Telephone: (916) 634-2038/4453. Hours: 9:00 am to 5:00 pm Monday through Friday, 10:00 am to 4:00 pm Saturday. Admission: free.

Items on Display: Uniforms, Unit Patches, Field Equipment, Personal Documents, Official Documents, Maps, Photographs, Paintings/Drawings, Dioramas, Flags, Battle Streamers, Medals, Edged Weapons, Side Arms, Shoulder Arms, Machine Guns, Mines, Ordnance, Field Artillery, Aircraft (fixed wing), Navigational Equipment, Communications Equipment, Tracked Vehicles, Wheeled Vehicles, Scale Models (aircraft, tracked vehicles).

Exhibits at the Edward F. Beale Museum chronicle the history of Beale Air Force Base from its beginnings as Camp Beale in 1942. Twentieth-century military artifacts on display include pressure suits worn aboard U-2 reconnaissance planes and SR-71s, a full-scale mock-up of an early barracks at Camp Beale, World War II-era bombs and German and American mines. Five aircraft, including the B-25 and the B-57, are on static display outdoors.

FORT HUMBOLDT STATE HISTORIC PARK

Visitor Information: Located at 3431 Fort Avenue, Eureka, California 95501. Take US-101 north from San Francisco to Highland Avenue east in Eureka. Turn north on Fort Avenue to the park. Telephone: (707) 445-6567. Hours: 9:00 am to 5:00 pm daily. Closed Thanksgiving, Christmas and New Year's Day. Admission: free.

Items on Display: Uniforms, Field Equipment, Maps, Photographs, Paintings/Drawings, Edged Weapons, Side Arms, Shoulder Arms, Field Artillery, Historic Structures (original post hospital, reconstructed surgeon's quarters).

Between 1853 and 1866, Fort Humboldt served as a supply depot and prison camp for the Army in Northern California. The original post hospital building still stands and houses a small museum containing pre-Civil War military artifacts. Muskets, side arms, bayonets and the uniforms and field equipment used by soldiers of the 1850s are on display. The post surgeon's quarters, originally built in 1853, was reconstructed in 1984.

CALIFORNIA

FORT POINT NATIONAL HISTORIC SITE

Visitor Information: Located at the southern end of Golden Gate Bridge in San Francisco. From the south, take US-101 north to the Golden Gate Bridge Toll Plaza. Take the exit marked "View Area - Presidio-Golden Gate NRA", then take the first right. Turn left onto Lincoln Boulevard then left again at Long Avenue. From the north, take US-101 south across the Golden Gate Bridge. After passing the Toll Plaza, turn right at 25th Avenue. Keep to the right while passing under the Toll Plaza and continue on to Lincoln Boulevard. Turn left at Lincoln Boulevard, then left again at Long Avenue to the fort. Mailing Address: Box 29333, Presidio of San Francisco, California 94129. Telephone: (415) 556-1693/2857. Hours: 10:00 am to 5:00 pm daily. Closed Thanksgiving, Christmas and New Year's Day. Admission: free.

Items on Display: Uniforms, Ordnance, Coast-Defense Artillery, Historic Structure (fort).

Army engineers built Fort Point between the years 1853 and 1861. Originally the site of a Spanish fort, Fort Point successfully guarded the entrance to San Francisco Bay for over twenty years. No hostile foreign vessels ever attempted to cross the fort's formidable line of fire. Its ten-inch Columbiad cannon could fire a 128-pound ball for over two miles. The development of rifled cannon during the Civil War made brick forts like Fort Point vulnerable to artillery assaults from both land and sea and in 1886 its garrison was withdrawn. The last of its cannon were removed in 1900.

The fort became a training and then a storage facility in the ensuing years, then served as a base of operations during the construction of the Golden Gate Bridge. During World War II about 100 soldiers re-garrisoned the fort, operating searchlights and manning rapid-fire cannon in support of the submarine net that spanned the entrance to San Francisco Bay.

Today Park Service Rangers hold cannon demonstrations on a regular basis during which they frequently enlist the aid of visitors as they load, aim and fire Civil War cannon.

MARCH FIELD MUSEUM

Visitor Information: Located several miles southeast of Riverside on March Air Force Base. Take I-215 south from Riverside to the March Air Force Base exit in Moreno Valley. Mailing Address: 22 AREFW/CVM, March Air Force Base, California 92518-5000.

March Field Museum, continued

Telephone: (714) 655-3725. Hours: 10:00 am to 4:00 pm Monday through Friday, 12:00 noon to 4:00 pm Saturday and Sunday. Closed Thanksgiving, Christmas and New Year's Day. Admission: free.

Items on Display: Uniforms, Unit Patches, Field Equipment, Personal Documents, Official Documents, Maps, Photographs, Paintings/Drawings, Dioramas, Flags, Battle Streamers, Medals, Edged Weapons, Side Arms, Shoulder Arms, Ordnance, Rockets/Rocket Launchers, Missiles, Aircraft (fixed wing, rotary wing), Space Exploration Displays, Scale Models (aircraft).

March Field history and technological developments in aviation since World War I are the subjects of chronologically arranged displays at the March Field Museum. More than 30 historic aircraft and missiles stand inside and outside the museum building, with many different types of aircraft represented, including tankers, transports, fighters, medium- and long-range bombers and trainer aircraft.

McCLELLAN AVIATION MUSEUM

Visitor Information: Located northeast of Sacramento off I-80 on McClellan Air Force Base. From I-80 take the Watt Avenue exit north to gate 3 at the base. A visitor's pass will be issued at the gate. Mailing Address: P. O. Box X, McClellan Air Force Base, California 95652-5990. Telephone: (916) 643-3192. Hours: 9:00 am to 3:00 pm Monday through Saturday. Closed on national holidays. Admission: free.

Items on Display: Uniforms, Unit Patches, Field Equipment, Photographs, Medals, Edged Weapons, Machine Guns, Ordnance, Aircraft (fixed wing), Scale Models (aircraft).

Displays and artifacts at the McClellan Aviation Museum depict the history of the base from its origins at Rockwell Field, San Diego, in 1914 to the present. One indoor display focuses on the evolution of the Army Air Force/United States Air Force uniforms worn by both male and female personnel. An extensive collection of AAF/USAF decorations and service medals beginning with the first Medal of Honor awarded during the Civil War is on display as well. The Airpark contains numerous aircraft from the Korean War and the Vietnam era, including F-104 and F-105 jet fighters. Other items on display: a 700-pound general purpose bomb with low altitude fins, German bayonets from World War II, survival equipment from World War II to Vietnam and a .50 caliber machine gun and gunmount

CALIFORNIA
McClellan Aviation Museum, continued

used in the B-17G long-range bomber.

PRESIDIO ARMY MUSEUM

Visitor Information: Located on the Presidio of San Francisco. In San Francisco, follow Lombard into the Presidio. Turn right when Lombard ends at Lincoln Boulevard and proceed to the museum at the intersection with Funston Avenue. Mailing Address: Building 2, Presidio of San Francisco, California 94129-5000. Telephone: (415) 561-4115/3319. Hours: 10:00 am to 4:00 pm Tuesday through Sunday. Special tours can be arranged. Admission: free.

Items on Display: Uniforms, Unit Patches, Field Equipment, Personal Documents, Official Documents, Maps, Photographs, Paintings/Drawings, Dioramas, Flags, Battle Streamers, Medals, Edged Weapons, Side Arms, Shoulder Arms, Machine Guns, Ordnance, Field Artillery, Coast-Defense Artillery, Missiles, Communications Equipment, Medical Equipment, Tracked Vehicles, Scale Models (aircraft, tracked vehicles).

The military history of the San Francisco Presidio area is a rich and storied one, dating back to 1776 when the Spanish flag was raised at the present site of nearby Fort Point. The Presidio Army Museum was established to preserve that history, to examine the Presidio's impact on the surrounding civilian community and to exhibit artifacts from the history of Army participation in armed conflicts both in the U.S. and abroad.

The museum's 19th-century collection of military artifacts includes several examples of rare uniforms and head gear and an extensive standard and color display. Endicott-period coast-artillery displays include models, medals, original photographs and uniforms. Items from the 20th century focus on the two world wars. Full-scale mock-ups of a World War I trench and a World War II bunker, an extensive recruiting-poster collection and numerous weapons, uniforms and models are on display.

The museum's outstanding coast-defense artillery collection includes a Spanish 9-pounder cast in Peru in 1627, the oldest dated bronze cannon in the New World. Other Spanish bronze guns are on display, as is a French gun manufactured in 1754, which was captured by U.S. troops in Cuba in 1898. The museum's collection also includes Civil War-era and 20th-century artillery pieces.

Presidio Army Museum, continued

CALIFORNIA

One of the museum's truly unique displays centers on the famous San Francisco earthquake of 1906 and the Army's role in the aftermath of the disaster. Two cottages used by refugees from the quake have been restored. A tent used by refugees and photographs and other memorabilia from the disaster complete the exhibit.

7TH INFANTRY DIVISION & FORT ORD MUSEUM

Visitor Information: Located seven miles north of Monterey on Fort Ord. Take US-101 south to CA-156, turn right and proceed ten miles to the main gate. Go to the visitors center to obtain a permit and a map containing directions to the museum. Mailing Address: ATTN: AFZW-PTM-Museum Branch, Building 1040, 1st Avenue, Ford Ord, California 93941-5111. Telephone: (408) 242-4905. Hours: 9:00 am to 12:00 noon and 1:00 pm to 4:00 pm Monday through Friday. Closed federal holidays. Admission: free.

Items on Display: Uniforms, Field Equipment, Photographs, Side Arms, Shoulder Arms, Machine Guns, Field Artillery, Amphibious Landing Craft.

Exhibits at the museum chronicle the history of Fort Ord from its beginnings as a maneuver area in 1917 to its construction by the 7th Infantry Division as a post in 1940. Displays featuring 7th Infantry Division history begin with World War I and continue through the Korean-War era. The Japanese field gun and mountain-infantry gun on display were captured by the division on Attu during World War II. The DUK-W amphibious landing craft on outdoor display was used by the division during the Pacific campaigns.

SILVER WINGS AVIATION MUSEUM

Visitor Information: Located 12 miles east of Sacramento on Mather Air Force Base. Take CA-99 to CA-50 east to the Mather Air Force Base exit. Or take I-5 to CA-50 east to the Mather exit. Mailing Address: 323 FTW/PAW, Mather Air Force Base, California 95655-5000. Telephone: (916) 364-2177. Hours: 10:00 am to 4:00 pm Monday through Friday, 12:00 noon to 4:00 pm weekends. Admission: free.

Items on Display: Uniforms, Unit Patches, Field Equipment, Personal Documents, Maps, Photographs, Flags, Machine Guns, Ordnance, Missiles, Aircraft (fixed wing), Navigational Equipment, Scale Models (aircraft).

CALIFORNIA
Silver Wings Aviation Museum, continued

Exhibits at the Silver Wings Aviation Museum focus on a variety of aviation-related topics: local aviation and Mather Air Force Base history, Air Force aviation in war and peace, the evolution of navigation equipment and technology, early women aviators, Black airmen and other subjects. One of the aircraft engines on display is the General Electric I-16 Turbojet, America's first jet engine, built in 1942 for the P-59A. Also on display is a 1934 Corbin Superace, a racing and sport aircraft. This Superace was built by Elton James, a former Mather Air Force Base commander, and is said to be the only surviving example of this aircraft in the United States.

TRAVIS AIR FORCE BASE MUSEUM

Visitor Information: Located approximately 40 miles northeast of San Francisco near the city of Fairfield on Travis Air Force Base. From I-80 in Fairfield, take the Airbase Parkway exit. The parkway leads directly to the main gate at Travis. Mailing Address: P. O. Box 1565, Travis Air Force Base, California 94535-5000. Telephone: (707) 424-5605. Hours: 9:00 am to 4:00 pm Monday through Friday, 9:00 am to 5:00 pm weekends. Admission: free.

Items on Display: Uniforms, Unit Patches, Field Equipment, Personal Documents, Official Documents, Photographs, Paintings/Drawings, Aircraft (fixed wing, rotary wing), Space Craft, Space Exploration Displays, Scale Models (aircraft).

Indoor and outdoor displays at the Travis Air Force Base Museum focus on Air Force airlift activities and military life in general from World War I to the present. A B-52 bomber and a C-124 cargo plane are among the 20 aircraft on outdoor display. Indoors, flight-related displays range from a 1912 Gonzales Brothers biplane to a Gemini space capsule and NASA displays about the Gemini, Apollo and Space Shuttle programs.

TREASURE ISLAND MUSEUM

Visitor Information: Located in Building 1 on Treasure Island Naval Station in San Francisco Bay. Take the Treasure Island exit off the San Francisco-Oakland Bay Bridge. Mailing Address: Building 1, Treasure Island, San Francisco, California 94130-5000. Telephone: (415) 765-6182. Hours: 10:00 am to 3:30 pm daily. Closed Easter, Thanksgiving, Christmas and New Year's Day. Admission: free.

CALIFORNIA

Treasure Island Museum, continued

Items on Display: Uniforms, Field Equipment, Official Documents, Maps, Photographs, Paintings/Drawings, Edged Weapons, Side Arms, Shoulder Arms, Machine Guns, Flame Throwers, Space Exploration Displays, Scale Models.

In 1981, when the Coast Guard joined the Navy and Marine Corps in exhibiting artifacts at the Treasure Island Museum, the museum became the only facility in the country dedicated to the history of all three sea-going services. Museum exhibits focus on the activities of the three services in the Pacific and on the history of Treasure Island itself. On display are original documents from Commodore Perry's expedition to Japan in 1854; artifacts from the Marine Corps' involvement in the Boxer Rebellion in China in the early 20th century; uniforms and weapons from World War II; items from the Apollo XII moon mission, which boasted an all-Navy crew; and many other permanent and rotating exhibits.

U.S. ARMY MUSEUM

Visitor Information: Located in Building 113 on Corporal Ewing Road on the Presidio of Monterey. In downtown Monterey, enter through the Artillery Street gate off Pacific Street and follow signs to the museum three blocks inside the gate. Mailing Address: ATTN: AFZW-DC-P-Museum, Presidio of Monterey, California 93944-5006. Telephone: (408) 647-5414. Hours: 9:00 am to noon and 1:00 pm to 4:00 pm Monday through Friday. Closed federal holidays. Admission: free.

Items on Display: Uniforms, Field Equipment, Photographs, Paintings/Drawings, Dioramas, Edged Weapons, Side Arms, Shoulder Arms, Field Artillery.

Artifacts and exhibits at the Army Museum outline the history of the Presidio of Monterey area prior to World War II, beginning with the Native American period and continuing through the Spanish, Mexican and American eras. Special displays focus on the days of the horse cavalry and on horse-drawn field artillery.

CALIFORNIA

Other Military Museums, Historic Sites & Exhibits in California

American Society of Military History Heritage Park, c/o American Society of Military History, Patriotic Hall, 1816 South Figueroa Street, Los Angeles, California 90015. Telephone: (213) 746-1776.

Edwards Air Force Base Museum, 6500 ABW/CCM, Edwards Air Force Base, California 93523-5000. Telephone: (805) 277-8050.

Fort Ross State Historic Park, 19005 Coast Highway 1, Jenner, California 95450. Telephone: (707) 847-3286.

Fort Tejon State Historic Park, 35251 Fort Tejon Road, Lebec, California 93243. Telephone: (805) 248-6692.

Marines Memorial Club Library and Museum, 609 Sutter Street, San Francisco, California 94102-5000. Telephone: (415) 673-6672.

Military Medal Museum and Research Center, 448 North San Pedro Street, San Jose, California 95110. Telephone: (408) 298-1100.

NASA/Ames Research Center, Public Information Office, Mail Stop 204-12, Moffet Field, California 94035. Telephone: (415) 694-5091.

NASA/Dryden Flight Research Facility, Box 273, ATTN: ISF, Building 4825, Edward Air Force Base, California 93523-5000. Telephone: (805) 258-3273.

NASA/Jet Propulsion Laboratory, 4800 Oak Grove Drive, ATTN: Visitor Control, Building 249, Pasadena, California 91109. Telephone: (818) 354-5533.

Planes of Fame Museum, 7000 Merrill Avenue, Box 17, Chino, California 91719. Telephone: (714) 597-3514.

Point Mugu Pacific Missile Test Center Missile Park, ATTN: Public Affairs Office, Point Mugu, California 93042-5000. Telephone: (805) 989-1110.

San Diego Aerospace Museum, 2001 Pan American Plaza, Balboa Park, San Diego, California 92101. Telephone: (619) 234-8291.

CALIFORNIA

Other Military Museums in California, continued

SS *Jeremiah O'Brien* (Liberty Ship), c/o Superintendent, Golden Gate National Recreation Area, Fort Mason, San Francisco 94123-5000. Telephone: (415) 556-0560.

Sutter's Fort State Historic Monument, 2701 L Street, Sacramento, California 95814. Telephone: (916) 445-4422.

USS *Pampanito* (Submarine), c/o National Maritime Museum Association, Building 275, Presidio of San Francisco, San Francisco, California 94129. Telephone: (415) 441-5819 or 929-0202.

USS *Roncador* (Submarine), c/o American Society of Military History, Patriotic Hall, 1816 South Figueroa Street, Los Angeles, California 90015. Telephone: (213) 746-1776.

COLORADO

EDWARD J. PETERSON SPACE COMMAND MUSEUM

Visitor Information: Located six miles southeast of Colorado Springs on Peterson Air Force Base. Take US-24 (Platte Avenue) east from Colorado Springs to the Peterson AFB exit. Turn right on Peterson Road, which enters the base, then turn left at the fifth intersection, Ent Avenue. The museum is on the corner. Mailing Address: 3rd Space Support WING/PACM, Peterson Air Force Base, Colorado 80914-5000. Telephone: (719) 554-4915. Hours: 8:30 am to 4:30 pm Tuesday through Friday, 9:30 am to 4:30 pm Saturday from October through April; 9:00 am to 5:00 pm Tuesday through Friday, 10:00 am to 5:00 pm Saturday from May through September. Admission: free.

Items on Display: Uniforms, Unit Patches, Personal Documents, Photographs, Paintings/Drawings, Flags, Missiles, Aircraft (fixed wing), Satellites/Satellite Communications Displays, Scale Models (aircraft).

Exhibits at the Space Command Museum chronicle the history of Air Force aviation at Peterson Air Force Base, as well as the histories of NORAD and the Space Command. Memorabilia from the career of Lt. Edward J. Peterson are on display, along with numerous artifacts from the World War II era, including flying suits and survival kits. Space-related artifacts include a radiation-detection satellite and a space suit. More than 200 model aircraft are on display along with a collection of more than 1300 unit patches from World War II to the present.

Nike Ajax, Bomarc, Hawk and Nike Hercules missiles are on display outdoors along with a number of aircraft from World War II to Vietnam.

LOWRY HERITAGE MUSEUM

General Information: Located six miles east of Denver on Lowry Air Force Base. From I-70 take I-225 south to the 6th Avenue exit, then west to the main gate. Security personnel will provide directions to the museum. Mailing Address: LTTC/LHM, Lowry Air Force Base, Colorado 80230-5000. Telephone: (303) 370-3028/3230. Hours: 9:00 am to 4:30 pm Monday through Friday, 10:00 am to 4:00 pm Saturday. Closed Sundays and holidays. Admission: free.

COLORADO

Lowry Heritage Museum, continued

Items on Display: Uniforms, Unit Patches, Field Equipment, Official Documents, Photographs, Paintings/Drawings, Flags, Medals, Edged Weapons, Ordnance, Missiles, Aircraft (fixed wing), Military Intelligence/Covert Operations Displays, Scale Models (aircraft).

Exhibits at the Lowry Heritage Museum interpret the history of Lowry Air Force Base and examine its development into one of the major technical training centers for the U.S. Armed Forces. The building that houses the museum formerly served as the offices for the Commandant of the Air Force Academy when the Academy was located at Lowry between 1954 and 1959. An exhibit about the Academy's years at Lowry and its first four graduating classes is one of the museum's central exhibits. Another exhibit traces the history of military photography from the Civil War to the space age, and includes the Goddard aerospace photographic collection, gun cameras, spy cameras and cameras used for mapping and night photography.

F-104, F-105 and F-4C jet fighters are among the more than 15 aircraft on display at Lowry, as are the B-52 Stratofortress long-range bomber and the B-29 Superfortress.

U.S. AIR FORCE ACADEMY

General Information: Located five miles north of Colorado Springs. Take I-25 north from Colorado Springs to the Air Force Academy exit. Mailing Address: HQ USAFA/XPAG, United States Air Force Academy, Colorado Springs, Colorado 80840-5241. Telephone: (719) 472-2555. Hours: 9:00 am to 6:00 pm daily. Admission: free.

Items on Display: Uniforms, Personal Documents, Paintings/Drawings, Medals, Aircraft (fixed wing), Scale Models (aircraft).

Though as yet no museum has been built at the Air Force Academy, there is still much for the visitor to see and enjoy in the Academy's cadet area. The Barry Goldwater Visitor Center opened in June of 1986 and houses exhibits about cadet life and about the history of the Academy, in addition to a theatre, cafeteria and gift shop. A nature trail leads from the visitor center to the cadet chapel, an elegantly futuristic structure that is Colorado's most frequently visited man-made attraction. The chapel is open to visitors Monday through Saturday from 9:00 am to 5:00 pm.

COLORADO
U.S. Air Force Academy, continued

Arnold Hall, the cadet activities building, houses several displays about notable figures in Air Force history. The Major Louis J. Sebille display honors the first member of the Air Force to win the Medal of Honor. The Jacqueline Cochrane display contains models of aircraft that Cochrane flew, trophies that she won, her World War II Women Air Force Service Pilots' uniform, and the numerous medals she earned during her Air Force career.

Nearby, the Academy's planetarium offers public shows year round, with reservations accepted from groups of 25 or more. Interested parties should call ahead for scheduling information. The number is (719) 472-2779.

Other Military Museums, Historic Sites & Exhibits in Colorado

Old Fort Garland, P. O. Box 368, Fort Garland, Colorado 81133. Telephone: (719) 379-3512.

CONNECTICUT

HMS *ROSE*

Visitor Information: Located at Captain's Cove Seaport in Bridgeport, a maritime center with full marina services, a restaurant, shops and cruise vessels. Take I-95 to exit 26 and follow signs. Mailing Address: 1 Bostwick Avenue, Bridgeport, Connecticut 06605. Telephone: (203) 335-1433. Hours: Captain's Cove Seaport operates year round. The *Rose* is open for tours from April through October when in port. Admission: fee charged.

Items on Display: Ships/Boats.

The HMS *Rose* is a replica of the British 24-gun frigate whose actions against colonial smuggling operations lead to the formation of the American Navy. According to HMS *Rose* Foundation officials, "Newport had become one of the richest cities in America by perfecting the art of smuggling to the point where it had become the city's principle industry, and Rhode Islanders had already destroyed a number of Royal Navy vessels that had been sent to put an end to smuggling. The *Rose*, being consideraly larger than the vessels sent previously, was able to reduce the smuggling to zero and the resulting unemployment caused Newport to lose four-fifths of her population by mid-1775. Therefore, the Rhode Island General Assembly sent a bill to the Continental Congress to establish a national Navy to deal with the *Rose*. The bill...passed on October 13, 1775, thus making *Rose* directly responsible for the founding of the American Navy."

The replica on display, built in 1970, was originally berthed in Newport. By the late 70s, the ship had fallen in disrepair. In 1984, Kaye Williams bought the ship and founded the HMS *Rose* Foundation. Restoration work began in 1985 and was largely completed by 1989. The *Rose* is now the largest operational wooden sailing vessel in the world. In 1989, the Coast Guard certified the ship as the largest sailing school vessel in the United States. Crew members are on hand in season to give lectures and guided tours.

MEMORIAL MILITARY MUSEUM

Visitor Information: Located at 61 Center Street, Bristol Connecticut National Guard Armory, Bristol, Connecticut 06010. Take exit 31 off I-84 east or exit 33 off I-84 west in Plainville, Connecticut. Telephone: (203) 583-5466. Hours: 7:00 pm to 9:00 pm on Friday evenings during the summer. Other times by appointment.

CONNECTICUT
Memorial Military Museum, continued

Admission: free.

Items on Display: Uniforms, Field Equipment, Personal Documents, Official Documents, Photographs, Paintings/Drawings, Flags, Edged Weapons, Side Arms, Shoulder Arms, Machine Guns, Scale Models (aircraft).

The director of Bristol's only military museum describes the museum's collection, located in a former classroom in the local National Guard Armory, as "small by most standards, but with a little of everything, with a home-town flavor." Most of the artifacts on display were donated or loaned by area veterans or by their families, so the emphasis here is on 20th-century military history, especially World War II, though items from the Civil War period up to Vietnam are also on view. Of special interest are parts from Japanese aircraft shot down at Pearl Harbor; POW items from Bataan and Corregidor; and an alarm bell from the USS *Maine*, whose sinking led to America's declaration of war against Spain in 1898.

NAUTILUS MEMORIAL/SUBMARINE FORCE LIBRARY & MUSEUM

Visitor Information: Located on the Naval Submarine Base in Groton. From I-95 take exit 86 north onto CT-12 to the Naval Submarine Base. Mailing Address: Box 571, Croton, Connecticut 06349-5000. Telephone: (203) 449-3174. Hours: 9:00 am to 5:00 pm Wednesday through Monday from April 15 to October 14; 9:00 am to 3:30 pm Wednesday through Monday from October 15 to April 14. Admission: free.

Items on Display: Official Documents, Maps, Photographs, Ships/Boats, Submarines/Submersible Vehicles, Submarine Equipment Displays, Scale Models (ships/boats).

Commissioned as a U.S. Navy ship on September 30, 1954, the USS *Nautilus* was the world's first nuclear-powered submarine. She established a number of continuous-submerged-time and speed records during her years of active service. In 1958, when Commander William R. Anderson and crew guided her under the ice pack from the Bering Stait to the Greenland Sea, she became the first ship ever to reach the geographic North Pole.

After years of superlative service, the *Nautilus* was decommissioned in 1980. Now a part of the the Submarine Force Library & Museum's

Nautilus Memorial, continued

CONNECTICUT

holding, the *Nautilus* is open for self-guided tours year round. The museum itself houses exhibits about the history and development of the submarine force, including an authentic submarine control room, working periscopes, an extensive scale-model display and several foreign-made miniature submarines.

NEW ENGLAND AIR MUSEUM

Visitor Information: Located at Bradley International Airport, Windsor Locks, Connecticut 06096. From I-95 take exit 40 west to CT-75 north for two miles. Signs will direct you to the museum on the left. Telephone: (203) 623-3305. Hours: 10:00 am to 5:00 pm daily. Closed Thanksgiving, Christmas and New Year's Day. Admission: $5.00 per adult, $4.00 per senior, $2.00 per child ages 6-12. Group rates are available.

Items on Display: Aircraft (fixed wing, rotary wing), Scale Models (aircraft).

The New England Air Museum's collection of over 75 aircraft spans the history of military and civilian aviation from a reproduction of a 1896 Chanute glider to a Vietnam-era Republic F-105B Thunderchief jet fighter. The Boeing B-29A Superfortress bomber, the Douglas A-26C Invader bomber and the Lockheed F-8K Crusader jet fighter are only a few of the many fixed-wing military aircraft on exhibit. A number of rotary-wing aircraft are on display as well, including the Bell UH-1B Huey used in Vietnam and the Korean War-era Hiller OH-23G Raven.

Aviation-related exhibits at the museum focus upon the early days of ballooning, the first helicopters and aircraft engines between 1908 and 1911. A flight demonstrator and cockpit simulator are popular with visitors of all ages.

U.S. COAST GUARD MUSEUM

Visitor Information: Located one mile north of I-95 on CT-32 in New London, Connecticut. Signs are posted. Mailing Address: U.S. Coast Guard Academy, New London, Connecticut 06320. Telephone: (203) 444-8511. Hours: 8:00 am to 5:00 pm Monday through Friday year round, 10:00 am to 5:00 pm on weekends from April 9 through October 31 only. Admission: free.

CONNECTICUT
U.S. Coast Guard Museum, continued

Items on Display: Uniforms, Field Equipment, Photographs, Paintings/Drawings, Ships/Boats, Scale Models (aircraft, ships/boats).

Today's Coast Guard had three predecessors: the Revenue-Cutter Service, the Lighthouse Service and the Life-Saving Service. Exhibits at the Coast Guard Museum examine the origins, activities and contributions of all three and portray the history of the modern Coast Guard. Visitors will learn that the Coast Guard is one of seven uniformed services but is not an armed force, at least not during peacetime, when it falls under the jurisdiction of the Department of Transportation; however, during wartime, the Coast Guard falls under the direction of the Secretary of the Navy and becomes responsible for coastal defense in addition to its peacetime duties, which involve water safety, search and rescue and contraband interdiction.

Other Military Museums, Historic Sites & Exhibits in Connecticut

Company of Military Historians Headquarters and Museum, North Main Street, Westbrook Connecticut 06498. Telephone: (203) 399-9460.

Fort Griswold State Park, 57 Fort Street, Groton, Connecticut 06340. Telephone: (203) 445-1729.

Purple Heart Museum, Old Town Hall, Enfield Street, Enfield, Connecticut 06082. Telephone: (203) 745-1729.

Putnam Memorial State Park (Colonial Museum), RFD 1, West Redding, Connecticut 06896. Telephone: (203) 938-2285.

76th Infantry Division Museum, 700 South Quaker Lane, West Hartford, Connecticut 06110. Telephone: (203) 232-4593.

Submarine Library Museum, 440 Washington Street, Middletown, Connecticut 06457. Telephone: (203) 346-0388.

DELAWARE

DOVER AIR FORCE BASE HISTORICAL CENTER

Visitor Information: Located on Dover Air Force Base, five miles southeast of Dover off US-113. Signs are posted. Mailing Address: 436 MAW, P. O. Box 03050, Dover Air Force Base, Delaware 19902-5000. Telephone: (302) 678-6614. Hours: variable. Call ahead. Admission: free.

Items on Display: A complete list was unavailable at press time, but the center's collection is known to include the following: Shoulder Arms, Aircraft (fixed wing).

The Dover Air Force Historical Center's collection of military and aviation-related artifacts is relatively small at present, but will continue to grow through the on-going efforts of museum personnel. A Boeing B-17 was added to the museum's collection of historic aircraft in June, 1989, bringing the total number of planes on indoor display to six. A Cessna O-2 Skymaster, nicknamed "Bird Dog" by U.S. service personnel in Vietnam, is in the collection as well. A forward fire control and reconnaissance aircraft, the O-2 has a "push/pull" configuration, with engines at the front and back of its fuselage.

U.S. COAST GUARD CUTTER *MOHAWK*

Visitor Information: Located at 901 Washington Street, Wilmington, Delaware 19801. From I-95 north or south in Wilmington, take the Maryland Avenue exit and follow signs to the Amtrak Station on Martin Luther King Jr. Drive. At the station turn right onto King Street. The ship is one block directly ahead. Telephone: (302) 656-0400. Hours: 9:00 am to 3:00 pm Saturdays or by appointment. Admission: free.

Items on Display: Coast Guard Cutter.

The Coast Guard Cutter *Mohawk* (WPG 78) was launched on October 23, 1934, from the Pusey and Jones shipyard and officially commissioned after sea trials in January of 1935. Originally designed for ice-breaking and rescue duties in the North Atlantic and Great Lakes areas, the *Mohawk* was modified during World War II for anti-submarine warfare and convoy-escort duties. After performing admirably in a variety of vital capacities during World War II, the cutter was decommissioned and placed in reserve in 1948. In 1981, the task of restoring the cutter to its wartime appearance began. In

DELAWARE
U.S. Coast Guard Cutter *Mohawk*, continued

1983, the *Mohawk* was rededicated as a floating museum and memorial to those men and women who took part in the Battle of the North Atlantic.

Other Military Museums, Historic Sites & Exhibits in Delaware

Fort Delaware, P. O. Box 1251, Wilmington, Delaware 19899. Telephone: (302) 834-7941.

DISTRICT OF COLUMBIA

MARINE CORPS MUSEUM

Visitor Information: Located in Building 58 on the grounds of the Washington Navy Yard in southeast Washington. Follow signs posted on I-395 to the 9th Street gate. Ask the guard for directions. Mailing Address: Marine Corps Historical Center, Washington Navy Yard, Building 58, 9th & M Streets, S.E., Washington, D.C. 20374-5000. Telephone: (202) 433-3840/3267/3534. Hours: 10:00 am to 4:00 pm weekdays and Saturdays, 12:00 noon to 5:00 pm Sundays and holidays. Closed Christmas, New Year's Day and Inauguration Day. Admission: free.

Items on Display: Uniforms, Unit Patches, Field Equipment, Personal Documents, Official Documents, Maps, Photographs, Paintings/Drawings, Dioramas, Flags, Battle Streamers, Medals, Edged Weapons, Side Arms, Shoulder Arms, Machine Guns, Field Artillery, Communications Equipment, Scale Models (aircraft, ships/boats, tracked vehicles).

The Marine Corps Museum features a series of chronologically arranged displays of period uniforms, weapons and other items that focus upon different aspects of Marine involvement in American military history, beginning with the formation of the Corps in 1775 and continuing through Corps participation in the Vietnam conflict.

The famous flag raised by five Marines and one Navy man at the summit of Mt. Suribachi on February 23, 1945, is the centerpiece of the museum's Iwo Jima display. Combat photographer Joe Rosenthal captured the event on film. His photograph won the Pulitzer Prize and inspired Felix de Weldon's bronze cast of the flag raising that stands near Arlington National Cemetery, an enduring symbol of the determination and tenacity of American combat personnel in World War II. The famous flag was actually the second flag raised by American servicemen that day on Mt. Suribachi. The first, raised two hours earlier to signal the capture of a key position and to bolster the morale of the embattled men on the island, is also on display, as is a scale model of the island and busts of the three men who participated in the flag raising and survived the war.

The Iwo Jima "Victory Flag," raised some three weeks after the capture of Mt. Suribachi when the island was finally secured, is down the hall from the Iwo Jima display. The battle for Iwo Jima produced over 28,000 American casualties. Nearly 7,000 Americans were killed or listed as missing in action. Japanese losses were considerably higher.

DISTRICT OF COLUMBIA

NATIONAL ARCHIVES

Visitor Information: Located between Constitution and Pennsylvania Avenues and 7th and 9th Streets, just north of the Mall. Parking is limited in the area. Visitors are encouraged to use the Metro System. The Archives Station serves the National Archives. For Metro information call (202) 637-7000. Mailing Address: National Archives and Records Administration, Washington, D.C. 20408. Telephone: (202) 523-3000. Hours: 8:45 am to 10:00 pm Monday through Friday, 8:45 am to 5:15 pm Saturday (Central Research and Microfilm Research Rooms); 10:00 am to 9:00 pm daily during spring, summer and fall, 10:00 am to 5:30 pm daily during winter (Exhibition Hall). Admission: free.

Items on Display: Personal Documents, Official Documents, Maps, Photographs, Video Tapes.

At first glance, the National Archives may seem out of place in a book about U.S. military history. Nothing could be further from the truth. The Archives is, according to government publications, "the official depository for records of military personnel separated from the U.S. Air Force, Army, Coast Guard, Marine Corps and Navy. The records are housed in three locations: the National Archives Building, Washington, D.C., the Washington National Records Center, Suitland, Maryland, and the National Personnel Records Center, St. Louis, Missouri." The Archives also contains records relating to volunteer service between the years 1775 and 1902 and to "persons who rendered military service for the Confederate States government in its armed forces from 1861 through 1865."

The Archives is an endlessly fascinating collection of personal and official military documents, treaty documents dating back to the 18th century, military maps and tens of thousands of photographs depicting all aspects of the nation's military history beginning with the Civil War. Some years ago while scanning a role of microfilm, I happened upon a number of letters written by the famous (and infamous) Confederate guerilla William Quantrill and several of his followers. Unexpected but welcome discoveries of this kind are a commonplace at the Archives.

The Archives collection also includes captured Japanese and German military records; files from the history of the Office of Special Services, the precursor of today's C.I.A.; and a large number of video tapes that may be viewed in specially equipped booths. Eva Braun's Home Movies; the United States Air Force's Project Bluebook, which documents the Air Force's investigation of "flying saucer" phenomena;

National Archives, continued

DISTRICT OF COLUMBIA

a 59-minute film about Nazi concentration camps that was shown at the Nürnberg war trials; and an 18-minute film about the Battle of Midway are only a few of the video tapes available.

The Declaration of Independence, the Constitution and the Bill of Rights are on display in the Archives Exhibition Hall, along with other important documents pertaining to the formation of the United States of America.

NATIONAL GUARD HERITAGE GALLERY

Visitor Information: Located two blocks east of the I-395/Massachusetts Avenue interchange at 1 Massachusetts Avenue. Take the Washington Metro (subway) Red Line to Union Station. The Heritage Gallery is a two minute walk from the station. Mailing Address: The Historical Society of the Militia and National Guard, 1 Massachusetts Avenue, N.W., Washington, D.C. 20001. Telephone: (202) 789-0031, extension 31. **Note: The Heritage Gallery closed temporarily** at the end of 1988 so that a new museum building could be constructed on the same site. The museum is expected to re-open in 1990.

Items on Display: Uniforms, Unit Patches, Field Equipment, Official Documents, Maps, Photographs, Paintings/Drawings, Flags, Medals, Edged Weapons, Side Arms, Shoulder Arms, Machine Guns, Ordnance, Field Artillery, Scale Models (aircraft).

Part of the National Guard Association, the National Guard Heritage Gallery "was established in 1975 to promote a better understanding of the role played by America's Citizen Soldiers' in both peace and war," in the words of museum officials. The Guard, which celebrated its 350th anniversary in 1986, is not only decades older than any of the nation's uniformed services—it is decades older than the nation itself. Artifacts, relics and memorabilia from Guard members' participation in armed conflicts beginning with the American Revolution and continuing through Vietnam are on display.

DISTRICT OF COLUMBIA

NATIONAL MUSEUM
OF HEALTH & MEDICINE
(OF THE ARMED FORCES INSTITUTE OF
PATHOLOGY)

Visitor Information: Located in Building 54 on the grounds of Walter Reed Army Medical Center. From I-495 (Beltway) take the Georgia Avenue exit south to the Walter Reed Army Medical Center. Enter through the main gate, take the first right and drive to the rear of the hospital. Turn right at the end of the road, then turn left and proceed around to the museum on the right. Parking is limited during the week, unlimited on weekends. Mailing Address: Armed Forces Institute of Pathology, Walter Reed Army Medical Center, Building 54, 6825 16th Street N.W., Washington, D.C. 20306-6000. Telephone: (202) 576-2348. Hours: 9:30 am to 5:00 pm Monday through Friday, 11:30 am to 5:30 pm weekends and holidays from May 1 to October 31; 9:30 am to 4:30 pm Monday through Friday, 11:30 am to 4:30 pm weekends and holidays from November 1 to April 30. Admission: free.

Items on Display: Medical Equipment, Health-Related Displays.

Pick up a pamphlet after you enter the National Museum of Health and Medicine for a map of the museum and a brief history. You'll learn that "the Medical Museum contains extensive collections of medical, surgical, and diagnostic instruments and related items as well as materials representing many of the health conditions which affect humans." A good place to begin your tour is at the rear of Brinton Hall, where a display titled "What is Pathology?" explains the meaning of pathology, outlines its history and profiles those who made key contributions to its development. Display cases containing cross-sections of different organs, each affected by one or more pathological conditions, are located at the center of Brinton Hall. Cigarette smokers should pay special attention to the lung display.

Two of the most compelling displays in Hammond Hall focus on Lincoln and Garfield, two of this nation's three assassinated Presidents. The Lincoln display contains a cutting of Lincoln's hair taken from the wound area, Lincoln's life mask, the probe used to locate the steel ball that killed him and cuffs from the shirt of a man named Curtis, stained with Lincoln's blood. The Garfield display contains, among other items, the section of Garfield's spine through which his assassin's bullet passed. A genuine shrunken head from Ecuador, South America, is also on display in Hammond Hall. The head, a war trophy, was reduced to its present size by removing the skull and treating the tissues that remained with hot sand and

DISTRICT OF COLUMBIA
National Museum of Health & Medicine, continued

steam. An undated mummified Egyptian head is just below the shrunken head.

Billings Hall houses the most comprehensive collection of microscopes in the U.S. Silliphant Hall houses the surgical-instrument display, which includes early-20th century German surgical instruments used in World War I, mid-20th century Japanese surgical instruments used in World War II, autopsy kits and a variety of dental instruments.

NAVY MEMORIAL MUSEUM

Visitor Information: Located in Building 76 on the grounds of the Washington Navy Yard in southeast Washington. Follow signs posted on I-395 to the 9th Street gate. Ask the guard for directions. Mailing Address: 9th & M Streets, S.E., Building 76, Washington Navy Yard, Washington, D.C. 20374-5000. Telephone: (202) 433-4882. Hours: 9:00 am to 4:00 pm Monday through Friday (till 5:00 pm during the summer), 10:00 am to 5:00 pm weekends and holidays. Closed Thanksgiving, Christmas Eve and Day and New Year's Eve. Admission: free.

Items on Display: Uniforms, Unit Patches, Field Equipment, Personal Documents, Official Documents, Maps, Photographs, Paintings/Drawings, Flags, Medals, Edged Weapons, Side Arms, Shoulder Arms, Mines, Ordnance, Field Artillery, Coast-Defense Artillery, Rockets/Rocket Launchers, Missiles, Nuclear Weapons Displays, Aircraft (fixed wing), Ships/Boats, Navigational Equipment Displays, Submarines/Submersible Vehicles, Submarine Equipment Displays, Deep-Sea Exploration Displays, Space Craft, Space Exploration Displays, Communications Equipment, Scale Models (aircraft, ships/boats, amphibious vehicles, tracked vehicles), Historic Structure (munitions factory).

Permanent and rotating exhibits at the Navy Memorial Museum trace the history of the Navy from Revolutionary times to the present, with key exhibits focusing on the Navy's participation in this country's major armed conflicts and upon the lasting contributions of Navy personnel in many fields of endeavor.

The museum's centerpiece is the "fighting top" from the frigate *Constitution*, the oldest commissioned ship in the Navy. When it was positioned on the foremast some 70 feet above the deck, the three-and-a-half ton structure was used as a vantage point by

DISTRICT OF COLUMBIA
Navy Memorial Museum, continued

sharpshooters who took aim at key opposition crew members, such as helmsmen and powderboys. Throughout the museum, intricately detailed scale models of ships and planes, past and present, illustrate the development of Naval sea and air power. The space exhibit documents Naval involvement in the U.S. space program. The space suit worn by Captain John Young, USN, during the Apollo XVI voyage which he commanded and a replica of an early space capsule into which visitors can climb are on display.

The centerpiece of the undersea-exploration exhibit is a full-size model of the *Trieste*, a bathyscaphe, or deep-sea submersible vehicle, developed by Swiss balloonist August Picard and sold to the U.S. in 1958. The *Trieste* made 128 dives before it was retired in 1963. Its most famous dive occurred on January 10, 1960, when it explored the depths of the Marianas Trench between Guam and the Philippines, the deepest place in the oceans. During Trieste's 20-minute stay at the trench's floor, researchers on board made an astounding discovery—a flat fish adapted to the enormous pressure of eight tons per square inch.

Other items on display include a World War II Corsair dive-bomber, suspended from the ceiling at an angle as if coming in for a strafing run; a Japanese kamikaze suicide plane and the bullet-riddled wing of a kamikaze that crashed into the USS *Enterprise* in 1945; a 40mm quad gun and mount removed from the Battleship *Dakota*; the fife rail and wheel from the USS *Hartford*, the flagship of Admiral David ("Damn the torpedoes!") Farragut's Gulf Squadron from 1861 to 1865; an extensive Navy medals display, including a fine Medals of Honor collection; and the submarine room and exhibit, which traces the history and development of submarines with photographs, plaques, patches, models and pieces of equipment used on board submarines, including three operational periscopes.

After leaving the museum, have a look at the big guns, missiles, rockets, anchors, mines and other artifacts on the museum grounds. Then walk over to the Submarine Museum, housed in the Taylor building off to the left as you face the river. The museum contains an old German Seehund submarine, an Italian wet sub, a Japanese Kaiten submarine and other items.

No visit to the museum would be complete without a self-guided tour of the USS *Barry*, a Forrest Sherman-class destroyer permanently anchored in the Anacostia River about 100 yards in front of the museum building. The *Barry* was launched in 1955 and during its years of service participated in the Naval blockade of Cuba during

Navy Memorial Museum, continued

DISTRICT OF COLUMBIA

the Cuban Missile Crisis of 1962. It also served in Vietnam and was credited with destroying over 1000 enemy structures. Navy personnel are stationed at various points along the tour route to answer questions. Tour highlights include a destroyer museum, a look at the combat information center and a trip to the ship's bridge.

PENTAGON

Visitor Information: Located on the south bank of the Potomac River in Arlington, Virginia. Take I-395 south to Boundary Drive to the visitor parking entrance. Guided-tours office is on the Concourse. Mailing Address: Pentagon, ATTN: OASD-PA-Pentagon Tours, Washington, D.C. 20310-5000. Telephone: (703) 695-1776. Hours: 9:00 am to 3:30 pm Monday through Friday. Closed on national holidays. Admission: free.

Items on Display: Photographs, Paintings/Drawings, Flags, Medals.

With 3.7 million square feet of space, the Pentagon is one of the world's largest office buildings and is headquarters for the Secretaries of the Department of Defense and the Joint Chiefs of Staff. A guided tour includes stops in the Commander-in-Chief Corridor, the Executive Corridor, the Time-Life Corridor and the Pentagon's Hall of Heroes.

SMITHSONIAN INSTITUTION

Visitor Information: The Museum of American History and the Air and Space Museum are located on the Mall in Northwest D.C. Parking in the vicinity is extremely limited, especially during the spring and summer. Visitors are encouraged to use the Metro system. The Smithsonian Station serves the museums on the Mall. For Metro information call (202) 637-7000. The Air and Space Museum's Paul E. Garber Facility is located at the corner of Old Silver Hill Road and Silver Hill Road in Suitland, Maryland. The facility is open daily by appointment only. Call (202) 357-1400 at least two weeks ahead of time. Mailing Address: Visitor Information and Associates' Reception Center, Smithsonian Institution, Washington, D.C. 20560. Telephone: (202) 357-2700; (202) 357-1729 (for the hearing impaired). Hours: most Smithsonian museums are open daily from 10:00 am through 5:30 pm. Spring and summer hours may be extended. Admission: free.

DISTRICT OF COLUMBIA
Smithsonian Institution, continued

Items on Display: Uniforms, Field Equipment, Personal Documents, Official Documents, Maps, Photographs, Paintings/Drawings, Dioramas, Flags, Battle Streamers, Medals, Edged Weapons, Side Arms, Shoulder Arms, Machine Guns, Ordnance, Field Artillery, Rockets/Rocket Launchers, Missiles, Aircraft (fixed wing, rotary wing), Space Craft, Space Exploration Displays, Satellites/Satellite Communications Displays, Ships/Boats, Navigational Equipment, Scale Models (aircraft, ships/boats).

The Smithsonian's Air and Space Museum and its Paul E. Garber Facility in Suitland, Maryland, collectively house the nation's most important collection of military and civilian aviation and space-related artifacts. Exhibits in the museum's galleries focus on different aspects of aviation and space exploration history, including World War I aviation, World War II aviation, sea-air operations, planetary exploration, vertical flight, rocketry and space flight and the Apollo moon missions. The following are but a few of the outstanding items on display: the Wright Flyer piloted by Orville Wright during the first successful flight by man in a machine-powered, heavier-than-air craft; the Apollo XI Command Module that carried Armstrong, Aldrin and Collins to the Moon and back in July, 1969; Charles Lindbergh's Spirit of St. Louis, in which Lindbergh made the first solo, non-stop, transatlantic flight in 1927; a German Messerschmitt Me 262, the first jet fighter ever used in combat; and a Japanese Mitsubishi A6M5 Zero. Items on display at the museum's Paul E. Garber Facility in Suitland include the Enola Gay, the Boeing B-29 Superfortress that dropped the first atomic bomb; a Curtiss JN-4D Jenny; a Vought F4U-ID Corsair and many other fighter aircraft from World War II.

If you enter the Smithsonian's Museum of American History from the Mall, the first object you see is the famous flag that flew over Fort McHenry during the British naval bombardment of 1814. The sight of the flag flying over the fort during the bombardment inspired Francis Scott Key to write the poem that was later adopted as the words to our national anthem. The museum's Armed Forces History wing is located on the third floor. Exhibits in the wing chronicle the origins and evolution of America's armed forces. The USS *Philadelphia* Gondola Gunboat in the wing dates from 1776 and is the oldest extant U.S. combat vessel. George Washington's field headquarters tent is also on display.

DISTRICT OF COLUMBIA

Other Military Museums, Historic Sites & Exhibits in the District

Combat Art Gallery, Washington Navy Yard, Washington, D.C. 20374-5000. Telephone: (202) 433-4882 (Navy Memorial Museum).

Museum of the District of Columbia Militia and National Guard, 2001 East Capitol Street, Washington, D.C. 20003-1719. Telephone: (202) 433-5180.

FLORIDA

AIR FORCE ARMAMENT MUSEUM

Visitor Information: Located outside the main gate of Eglin Air Force Base, 24 miles east of Fort Walton Beach. From I-10 east or west take FL-85 north to the intersection with FL-189 and the base. Mailing Address: 3201 ABG/AM, Eglin Air Force Base, Florida 32542-5000. Telephone: (904) 882-4062. Hours: 9:30 am to 4:30 pm daily. Closed Easter, Christmas and New Year's Day. Admission: free.

Items on Display: Uniforms, Field Equipment, Personal Documents, Official Documents, Maps, Photographs, Paintings/Drawings, Dioramas, Flags, Medals, Edged Weapons, Side Arms, Shoulder Arms, Machine Guns, Flame Throwers, Mines, Ordnance, Chemical/Biological Weapons Displays, Field Artillery, Rockets/Rocket Launchers, Missiles, Aircraft (fixed wing), Space Craft (replica), Scale Models (aircraft).

Artifacts and exhibits at the Air Force Armament Museum illustrate the history and technological development of Air Force armament and ordnance capabilities since the establishment of the Air Force as a separate department in 1947. Aircraft on display include the B-17 Flying Fortress, the F-4 Phantom II, the P-47 Thunderbolt, the P-51 Mustang and the F-105 Thunderchief. Many missiles, rockets and rocket launchers are on display, in addition to many types of modern ordnance, including several types rarely found in museums, such as firebombs and mustard bombs. Though it is the only museum in the nation dedicated to the acquisition and display of Air Force armament, the Air Force Armament Museum houses numerous military artifacts which pre-date the establishment of the Air Force and its precursor, the Army Air Corps. Artifacts dating back to the War of 1812 are on display.

AIR FORCE SPACE MUSEUM

Visitor Information: Located on Cape Canaveral Air Force Station. All tours are scheduled through the Kennedy Space Center Visitor Center and are conducted on buses that depart the Visitor Center at designated times. Visitors may not enter the station unless they are on one of the tour buses. See the NASA/John F. Kennedy Space Center listing for driving directions. Mailing Address: AF Space Museum, c/o ESMC/PA, Patrick Air Force Base, Florida 32925-5000. Telephone: (407) 494-5933 (Patrick AFB Public Affairs Office). Hours: daylight hours daily. Admission: $4.00 per person.

FLORIDA

Air Force Space Museum, continued

Items on Display: Nuclear Weapons Displays, Rockets, Missiles, Space Craft, Space Exploration Displays, Satellites/Satellite Communications Displays, Tracked Vehicles, Scale Models (ships/boats), Historic Structures (NASA launch complexes).

On the night of January 31, 1958, America launched its first satellite, Explorer I, into orbit, and doggedly followed the upstart Soviets into the space age. Explorer's launch pad and the pads from which America's first two manned flights were launched are all part of the Air Force Space Museum, as are many examples of rockets and missiles that played strategic roles in the development of the U.S. space program.

A blockhouse control room at the launch complex has been authentically restored. The exhibits and displays it houses, as well as those in the adjacent exhibit hall, focus on the development of rocket science, rocket propulsion systems, Air Force involvement in America's space program and other related subjects.

FORT CLINCH STATE PARK

Visitor Information: Located at 2601 Atlantic Avenue, Fernandina Beach, Florida 32034. Take I-95 to A1A south to the park entrance. Telephone: (904) 261-4212. Hours: 9:00 am to 5:00 pm daily (fort); 8:00 am to sundown daily (park). Park Admission: $1.00 per car and driver, $0.50 for each additional person. Fort Admission: $1.00 per person over age five (June through September only).

Items on Display: Uniforms, Field Equipment, Personal Documents, Official Documents, Maps, Photographs, Dioramas, Edged Weapons, Side Arms, Shoulder Arms, Ordnance, Coast-Defense Artillery (replicas), Medical Equipment, Historic Structure (fort).

Displays at the Fort Clinch Interpretive Center detail the history of the U.S. fort system and of Fort Clinch itself, as well as Civil War-era military activities in Northeastern Florida and Spanish American War-era activities at the fort and on nearby Amelia Island. A shot rack contains various types of shot and shells. The fort cannon are replicas of 1861 Rodman 10-inch guns. A Civil War-era kitchen, prison, carpenter's shop, quartermaster/commissary office, barracks, blacksmith shop and hospital with original medical, dental and pharmacy equipment are within the fort.

FLORIDA

GULF ISLANDS NATIONAL SEASHORE

Visitor Information: Fort Pickens, Fort Barrancas and the Fort Barrancas Advanced Redoubt are located within the boundaries of the Gulf Islands National Seashore. To reach Fort Pickens, take US-98 east from Pensacola across Pensacola Bay to Gulf Breeze. From Gulf Breeze, take FL-399 south to Pensacola Beach. Take FL-399 west at Pensacola Beach to the fort. To reach Fort Barrancas and the Advanced Redoubt, take FL-292 south to FL-295 south to the main entrance to Pensacola Naval Air Station. Once on the island, bear left at the first fork in the road. Mailing Address: c/o National Park Service, 1801 Gulf Breeze Parkway, Gulf Breeze, Florida 32561. Telephone: (904) 934-2604. Hours: vary according to season and site. Call before visiting. Admission: free, except for the Fort Pickens area.

Items on Display: Uniforms, Field Equipment, Official Documents, Photographs, Edged Weapons, Field Artillery, Coast-Defense Artillery, Ordnance, Historic Structures (forts, batteries).

After Spain ceded the Florida territories to the United States in 1821, American military planners selected Pensacola Bay as the site for a U.S. Navy Yard, then set about designing and constructing an effective coast-defense system for the area surrounding Pensacola Harbor. The coastal forts and batteries that were the product of this years-long effort by the U.S. Army Corps of Engineers are now a part of the Gulf Islands National Seashore. Fort Pickens, Fort Barrancas and the Fort Barrancas Advanced Redoubt have been restored and should be visited by anyone with an interest in the brick-and-masonry fortifications that were the staple of this country's coast-defense strategy until the end of the Civil War, when the advent of rifled artillery made such fortifications obsolete. Pamphlets about the history of the area can be obtained at two visitor centers and three information stations located in the park. A museum at Fort Pickens houses artifacts from the sites and exhibits about the military history of Pensacola Bay.

LAND SURVIVAL EXHIBIT

Visitor Information: Located on Pensacola Naval Air Station, eight miles south of Pensacola. On I-10 from Mobile, take exit 2 south and follow signs to the NAS. On I-10 from Tallahassee, take exit 4 south to the Garden Street exit. Go west on Garden (US-98) and follow signs to the NAS. Mailing Address: Commanding Officer, Naval Aviation Schools Command, Naval Air Station Pensacola, Pensacola, Florida 32508-6800. Telephone: (904) 452-2249/2003. Hours: 8:00 am to 3:00 pm Tuesday through Friday, 12:00 noon to 4:00 pm

Land Survival Exhibit, continued

weekends. Admission: free.

Items on Display: Field Equipment, Official Documents, Paintings/Drawings, Aircraft (fixed wing).

The Navy established its Land Survival Division on November 6, 1944, to train Naval aviators in the techniques of land survival in a non-hostile, non-evasive environment. The Land Survival Exhibit at Pensacola NAS supplements the classroom-training aspect of the land survival course. The exhibit contains live animal displays, working trap and snare devices and many species of edible plant life, in addition to displays that focus on survival techniques in arctic, desert and seashore environments. Examples of personal survival gear normally found in Naval aircraft and two examples of Navy aircraft, a PBY Catalina and an F-4, complete the exhibit.

NASA/JOHN F. KENNEDY SPACE CENTER

Visitor Informtion: Located off US-1 north of the city of Cocoa and south of Titusville. Take US-1 to the NASA Parkway east through security gate 3 to the visitor center, Spaceport U.S.A., on the right. Note: follow the Kennedy Space Center signs, not the signs for Cape Canaveral Air Force Station. Mailing Address: Spaceport U.S.A., TW Recreational Services, Inc., Visitor Center-TWRS, Kennedy Space Center, Florida 32899. Telephone: (407) 452-2121 extension 260; (407) 452-2121 (reservations for charter and convention groups). Hours: varies with season. Admission: fees are charged for the bus tours of Kennedy Space Center (blue tour) and Cape Canaveral Air Force Station (Air Force Space Museum—listed separately in this book). Fees also charged for admission to the IMAX Theater.

Items on Display: Rockets, Space Craft, Space Exploration Displays, Satellites/Satellite Communications Displays, Scale Models.

The NASA/John F. Kennedy Space Center's Spaceport U.S.A. offers visitors a chance to tour two historic launch complexes, the Kennedy Space Center itself, where the shuttle launches are conducted, and the Air Force Space Museum on Cape Canaveral Air Force Station (listed separately in this book). Spaceport U.S.A., the Kennedy Space Center's visitor center, houses artifacts from the history of manned space flight with Mercury, Gemini, Apollo, Soyuz and Skylab space craft on display. Selected exhibits at the center focus on the planets, earth resources, space-based communications networks, weather-monitoring satellites and earth sciences. The Rocket Garden outside

FLORIDA
NASA/John F. Kennedy Space Center, continued

the center contains examples of launch vehicles from all phases of America's space program.

Tours of the two launch complexes are conducted on board air-conditioned buses. Live and recorded narration is provided and camera stops are scheduled throughout both tours. Free multimedia presentations occur daily in the Galaxy Theater and elsewhere in the center. A 37-minute film about the space program, narrated by Walter Cronkite, is shown daily on the five-and-a-half-story screen in the center's IMAX® Theater.

NAVAL AVIATION MUSEUM

Visitor Information: Located in Building 3465 on Pensacola Naval Air Station Pensacola, Pensacola, Florida 32508-6800. On I-10 from Mobile, take exit 2 south and follow signs to the NAS. On I-10 from Tallahassee, take exit 4 south to the Garden Street exit. Go west on Garden (US-98) then follow signs south to the NAS. Telephone: (904) 452-3604. Hours: 9:00 am to 5:00 pm daily. Closed Thanksgiving, Christmas and New Year's Day. Admission: free.

Items on Display: Uniforms, Unit Patches, Personal Documents, Official Documents, Maps, Photographs, Paintings/Drawings, Flags, Medals, Aircraft (fixed wing, rotary wing), Space Craft, Space Exploration Displays, Scale Models (aircraft, ships/boats).

The size, scope and variety of the Naval Aviation Museum's collection of historic Navy, Marine Corps and Coast Guard aircraft and related exhibits makes it one of country's exemplary military aviation museums. Artifacts from the entire history of Naval aviation are on display, from a full-scale replica of the Navy's first Curtiss Biplane to the original prototype of the Navy's newest jet fighter, the F-18. Also on exhibit is the Skylab Command Module, the NC-4 Flying Boat that made the first air crossing of the Atlantic and operational jet fighter and Huey helicopter cockpit trainers that visitors can try out for themselves.

OLUSTEE BATTLEFIELD STATE HISTORIC SITE

Visitor Information: Located off I-10 west of Jacksonville. From I-10 take the US-90 exit west to the park. Mailing Address: P. O. Box 40, Olustee, Florida 32072. Telephone: (904) 752-3866. Hours: 8:00 am to sunset daily (park); 9:00 am to 5:00 pm Thursday through Monday (interpretive center). Admission: free.

FLORIDA

Olustee Battlefield State Historic Site, continued

Items on Display: Uniforms, Field Equipment, Photographs, Flags, Edged Weapons, Shoulder Arms, Ordnance.

The Olustee Battlefield Site commemorates the most significant victory of the Civil War won by Confederate forces in Florida. In February of 1864, a Confederate force met Union troops that had landed in Jacksonville and moved west, primarily intent upon disrupting Confederate supply lines. The ensuing battle ended with a decisive Confederate victory. The Union force retreated to Jacksonville, where it largely remained for the duration of the conflict. An interpretive center at the park houses displays and exhibits that interpret the battle and the significance of the Confederate victory.

UDT/SEAL MUSEUM

General Information: Located at 3300 North A1A, North Hutchinson Island, Fort Pierce, Florida 34949. From I-95 at Fort Pierce take US-1 north to A1A north to the museum. Telephone: (407) 464-3764. Hours: 10:00 am to 4:00 pm Tuesday through Saturday, 12:00 noon to 4:00 pm Sunday. Admission: $1.00 per adult, $0.50 per child over age five.

Items on Display: Uniforms, Unit Patches, Field Equipment, Personal Documents, Official Documents, Maps, Photographs, Paintings/Drawings, Dioramas, Flags, Battle Streamers, Medals, Edged Weapons, Side Arms, Shoulder Arms, Machine Guns, Mines, Ordnance, Space Craft, Ships/Boats, Amphibious Landing Craft, Submersible Vehicles, Communications Equipment, Scale Models (ships/boats, submarines/submersible vehicles).

The UDT/SEAL Museum is the only museum in the country devoted exclusively to the activities of the U.S. Navy Underwater Demoliton Teams (UDTs) and the U.S. Navy Sea-Air-Land Special Forces (SEALs). Artifacts and equipment used by these elite Naval units dating from World War II to the present are on display. Of special interest are the demolition/explosives displays, booby trap devices, scuba (self-contained underwater breathing apparatus) diving equipment, anti-tank and -personnel mines, submersible swimmer-delivery vehicles and an Apollo space craft.

FLORIDA

Other Military Museums, Historic Sites & Exhibits in Florida

Camp Blanding Museum and Memorial Park of the Second World War, c/o Department of Military Affairs, State Arsenal, P. O. Box 1008, St. Augustine, Florida 32085-1008. Telephone: (904) 824-8461 extension 174.

Castillo de San Marcos National Monument, 1 Castillo Drive, St. Augustine, Florida 32084. Telephone: (904) 829-6506.

Dade Battlefield State Historic Site, Bushnell, Florida 33513. Telephone: (904) 793-4781.

Fort Caroline National Memorial, 12713 Fort Caroline Road, Jacksonville, Florida 32225. Telephone: (904) 641-7155.

Fort de Soto Park, Tierra Verde, Box 3, St. Petersburg, Florida 33715. Telephone: (813) 866-2484.

Fort Gadsden State Historic Site, P. O. Box 157, Sumatra, Florida 32335. Telephone: (904) 670-8988.

Fort Jefferson National Monument, c/o U.S. Coast Guard Base, Key West, Florida 33040. Telephone: (305) 247-6211.

Fort Mantanzas National Monument, 1 Castillo Drive, St. Augustine, Florida 32084. Telephone: (904) 829-6506.

Fort Zachary Taylor State Historic Site, P. O. Box 289, Key West, Florida 33040. Telephone: (305) 292-6713.

Lighthouse Military Museum, 938 Whitehead at Truman, Key West, Florida 33040. Telephone: (305) 294-0012.

Natural Bridge Battlefield, c/o Florida Department of Natural Resources, Office of Communications, 3900 Commonwealth Boulevard, Tallahassee, Florida 32399-3000. Telephone: (904) 925-6216.

San Marcos de Apalache State Historic Site, P. O. Box 27, St. Marks, Florida 32355. Telephone: (904) 925-6216.

State Headquarters Museum, c/o Department of Military Affairs, State Arsenal, P. O. Box 1008, St. Augustine, Florida 32085-1008. Telephone: (904) 824-8461 ext. 174.

FLORIDA

Other Military Museums in Florida, continued

Tovar House Museum: The Museum of Florida's Army, c/o Department of Military Affairs, State Arsenal, P. O. Box 1008, St. Augustine, Florida 32085-1008. Telephone: (904) 824-8461 extension 174.

USS *Requin* Submarine Memorial, P. O. Box 261704, Tampa, Florida 33685. Telephone: (813) 223-7981.

Yesterday's Air Force Museum, Fairchild Street, Clearwater, Florida 34622. Telephone: (813) 626-9462.

GEORGIA

A. H. STEPHENS STATE HISTORIC PARK & CONFEDERATE MUSEUM

Visitor Information: Located off I-20 west of Augusta. From I-20 at exit 55, take GA-22 north for two miles to the junction with US-278. Go east for one mile to Crawfordville. Turn left at the first and only traffic light onto Monument Street, which ends two blocks later in front of the museum. Mailing Address P. O. Box 235, Crawfordville, Georgia 30631. Telephone: (404) 456-2602 (park office); (404) 456-2221 (museum office). Hours: 9:00 am to 5:00 pm Tuesday through Saturday, 2:00 pm to 5:30 pm Sunday. Closed Mondays except when Mondays are federal holidays, Thanksgiving and Christmas. Admission: $1.00 per adult, $0.50 per child ages 12-17, under age 12 free.

Items on Display: Uniforms, Personal Documents, Photographs, Paintings/Drawings, Flags, Medals, Edged Weapons, Side Arms, Shoulder Arms, Ordnance, Medical Equipment, Historic Structures (estate and out-buildings).

A. H. Stephens State Historic Park was established to preserve the home of Alexander H. Stephens, who for many years served as Congressman from Georgia and then as Vice-President of the Confederacy under President Jefferson Davis. Stephens was elected Governor of Georgia four months prior to his death in 1883. Visitors may tour Mr. Stephens' second house at the site, Liberty Hall. The Confederate Museum, which houses an extensive collection of Confederate artifacts and memorabilia, stands beside Liberty Hall.

ANDERSONVILLE NATIONAL HISTORIC SITE

Visitor Information: Located between Albany and Macon off GA-49. From I-75 north, take GA-49 south to the site. From I-75 south, take US-280 west to Americus, then take GA-49 north to the site. Mailing Address: Route 1, Box 85, Andersonville, Georgia 31711. Telephone: (912) 924-0343. Hours: 8:00 am to 5:00 pm daily. Closed Christmas. Admission: $1.00 per person ages 17 to 61. Over age 61 admitted free.

Items on Display: Unit Patches, Field Equipment, Personal Documents, Official Documents, Maps, Photographs, Paintings/Drawings, Flags, Medals, Edged Weapons, Side Arms, Shoulder Arms, Historic Structures (earthworks).

Andersonville National Historic Site, continued

Located on the site of the most infamous prisoner-of-war camp on American soil, the Andersonville National Historic Site commemorates the sacrifices made by P.O.W.s in all wars that involved the U.S. Thousands of captured Union troops endured the nightmarish living conditions at Andersonville during the final 14 months of the Civil War. Thousands of others died because of them. Artifacts and exhibits at the visitor center interpret the Andersonville story. Exhibits at the site's P.O.W. Museum focus on American prisoners of war from the Revolution to Vietnam.

ATLANTA CYCLORAMA

Visitor Information: Located at 800 Cherokee Avenue, S.E., Atlanta, Georgia 30315. From I-20 east or west in Atlanta, take exit 26 south to the Cyclorama. Telephone: (404) 658-7625. Hours: 9:30 am to 5:30 pm daily from October through April, 9:30 am to 4:30 pm daily from May through September. Admission: $3.00 per person age 13 and older, $2.50 per person in groups of ten or more, $1.50 per child, $1.00 per child in groups of ten or more. Child under age six admitted free.

Items on Display: Uniforms, Field Equipment, Personal Documents, Maps, Photographs, Paintings/Drawings, Dioramas, Flags, Medals, Edged Weapons, Side Arms, Shoulder Arms, Field Artillery, Medical Equipment.

The Atlanta Cyclorama is a truly stupendous work of Civil War-inspired art. The circular painting of the Battle of Atlanta stands 42 feet high, is 358 feet in circumference, and weighs over 9,300 pounds. Painted by German and Polish artists in 1885-1886, the Cyclorama drew crowds of admirers all over the country until it became a permanent exhibit in the city whose destruction it depicts. Narration, music and sound effects all serve to enhance the visitor's appreciation of the Cyclorama and of the gravity of the events it portrays. A museum on the first and second floors houses Civil War artifacts.

CHICKAMAUGA & CHATTANOOGA NATIONAL MILITARY PARK

Visitor Information: Located a short distance south of Chattanooga. From I-75 take the Battlefield Parkway exit west to US-27 south. The park entrance is one mile ahead. For the Lookout Mountain

GEORGIA
Chickamauga & Chattanooga Natl. Military Park, continued

area, take I-24 into Chattanooga. Exit at Broad Street and continue
on Broad until it becomes the Scenic Highway which leads to the
Mountain Top and Point Park. Mailing Address: P. O. Box 2128, U.S.
Highway 27, Fort Oglethorpe, Georgia 30742. Telephone: (404)
866-9241. Hours: 8:00 am to 4:45 pm daily; till 5:45 pm June, July
and August. Admission: $1.00 per adult at the Cravens House, all
other park areas free.

Items on Display: Uniforms, Field Equipment, Personal Documents,
Official Documents, Maps, Photographs, Paintings/Drawings,
Dioramas, Flags, Medals, Edged Weapons, Side Arms, Shoulder
Arms, Field Artillery, Civil War Battle Wagon & Traveling Forge.

This 8,113-acre park was established in 1890 to preserve the
Chickamauga, Orchard Knob, Lookout Mountain and Missionary
Ridge Battlefields. It is the oldest and largest military park in the
U.S., with more than 1350 historic markers and monuments in place.
Union forces led by General William S. Rosecrans battled a
Confederate force led by General Braxton Bragg at Chickamauga
Creek, on Lookout Mountain and at Missionary Ridge, where General
Ulysses S. Grant let the ultimately victorious Union force. Two visitor
centers, one at Chickamauga and the other at Lookout Mountain,
display Civil War artifacts, including an extensive shoulder-arms
collection and a signaling exhibit. Slide presentations are given at
both centers.

CONFEDERATE NAVAL MUSEUM

Visitor Information: Located on US-80/280 west at 202 4th Street
in Columbus. From I-85, take US-280/431 east toward Columbus
until it becomes US-80/280 to the museum on the west side of
Columbus. Mailing Address: P. O. Box 1022, Columbus, GA 31902.
Telephone: (404) 327-9798. Hours: 10:00 am to 5:00 pm Tuesday
through Friday, 1:00 pm to 5:00 pm weekends. Admission: free.

Items on Display: Uniforms, Field Equipment, Personal Documents,
Official Documents, Photographs, Paintings/Drawings, Dioramas,
Flags, Edged Weapons, Side Arms, Shoulder Arms, Mines, Ordnance,
Coast-Defense Artillery, Ships/Boats, Scale Models (ships/boats).

The remains of two very different types of Confederate warships are
on display at the Confederate Naval Museum. An ironclad ram, the
CSS *Jackson* is an example of one of the Civil War eras most
important advances in naval technology. The gunboat CSS

GEORGIA

Confederate Naval Museum, continued

Chattahoochee was a far more conventional wooden-hulled, steam and sail powered vessel that Confederate troops scuttled near the end of the war. Both ships were salvaged from the bottom of the Chattachoochee River in the early 1960s. In addition to the two ships, the museum contains many exhibits and relics from the history of Confederate naval operations.

FORT FREDERICA NATIONAL MONUMENT

Visitor Information: Located on St. Simons Island off the Georgia coast. From US-17 take the St. Simons Causeway to Frederica Road to the monument. Mailing Address: Route 9, Box 286C, St. Simons Island, Georgia 31522. Telephone: (912) 638-3639. Hours: 9:00 am to 5:00 pm daily. Admission: $1.00 per person over age 16.

Items on Display: Uniforms, Field Equipment, Edged Weapons, Shoulder Arms, Ordnance, Coast-Defense Artillery, Historic Structure (ruins of fort).

An active military and civilian community for a relatively brief, but politically significant, period of time, Fort Frederica served as the focal point for a military confrontation that had lasting repercussions on the development of Georgia as a European colony.

The dispute between England and Spain over the territory between the Carolinas and Florida was effectively settled in England's favor in 1742 when an outnumbered force of British regulars and Indian allies repulsed a Spanish attack on Fort Frederica, then ambushed a second column of Spaniards later the same day in what came to be known as the Battle of Bloody Marsh. The battered and demoralized Spanish troops retreated to their stronghold in St. Augustine, thus assuring British colonial dominance of Georgia in the years to come.

The Fort Frederica visitor center houses military and household artifacts excavated from the site. The fort's ruins and the foundations of a number of community structures are visible.

FORT McALLISTER STATE HISTORIC PARK

Visitor Information: Located off I-95 south of Savannah. From I-95 take GA-144 to Richmond Hill, cross US-17 and drive six miles to the GA-144 spur to the park. Mailing Address: Route 2, Box 394-A, Richmond Hill, Georgia 31324. Telephone: (912) 727-2339. Hours: 9:00 am to 5:00 pm Monday through Saturday, 2:00 pm to 5:30 pm

GEORGIA
Fort McAllister State Historic Park, continued

Sunday. Closed Thanksgiving and Christmas. Admission: $1.50 per adult, $0.75 per child.

Items on Display: Uniforms, Field Equipment, Personal Documents, Maps, Photographs, Paintings/Drawings, Flags, Edged Weapons, Side Arms, Shoulder Arms, Field Artillery, Coast-Defense Artillery, Scale Models (ships/boats), Historic Structure (reconstructed earthwork fort).

Fort MacAllister is one of the finest examples of Confederate earthwork fortifications in existence. In 1863 it was the site of several engagements that tested the strength and usefulness of earthwork-versus-conventional fortifications in the face of heavy naval bombardment. The earthworks proved impregnable against the assaults of Union ironclads. Fort MacAllister remained a Confederate stronghold until Union General Sherman's troops stormed and seized control of the fort in December of 1864. A museum at the fort houses artifacts and memorabilia from the site and from the Confederate blockade-runner *Nashville*, destroyed by Union gunfire in the Ogeechee River in 1863.

GEORGIA VETERANS' MEMORIAL STATE PARK & MUSEUM

Visitor Information: Take I-75 south from Macon or north from Valdosta to US-280 east for ten miles to the park on the left. Mailing Address: Route 3, Box 382, Cordele, Georgia 31015. Telephone: (912) 273-2190. Hours: 9:00 am to 4:30 pm daily. Admission: free.

Items on Display: Uniforms, Unit Patches, Field Equipment, Personal Documents, Official Documents, Maps, Photographs, Paintings/Drawings, Flags, Medals, Edged Weapons, Side Arms, Shoulder Arms, Machine Guns, Ordnance, Field Artillery, Aircraft (fixed wing), Amphibious Landing Craft, Tracked Vehicles.

The Georgia Veterans' Memorial State Park and Museum was founded to honor all Georgia veterans who have participated in U.S. wars. Indoor displays date from the Civil War through the Vietnam era. Artifacts on the museum grounds include artillery pieces, tanks and four aircraft, one of which is the B-29 Superfortress long-range bomber.

GEORGIA

KENNESAW MOUNTAIN NATIONAL BATTLEFIELD PARK

Visitor Information: Between I-75 and I-20 northwest of Atlanta. Mailing Address: c/o National Park Service, Box 1167, Marietta, Georgia 30061. Telephone: (404) 427-4686. Hours: 8:30 am to 5:00 pm daily. Closed Christmas and New Year's Day. Admission: free. From I-75 take exit 116 and and follow signs.

Items on Display: Uniforms, Field Equipment, Personal Documents, Official Documents, Paintings/Drawings, Flags, Edged Weapons, Side Arms, Shoulder Arms, Field Artillery, Medical Equipment.

The Kennesaw Mountain National Battlefield Park commemorates one of the last great campaigns of the Civil War, the Union Army's relentless march into the heart of the Confederacy and its destruction of Atlanta late in the summer of 1864. One of several key battles in the campaign was fought at Kennesaw Mountain. An overlook near the summit of the mountain affords a birds-eye view of the battlefield where General Sherman's Union forces met the Confederate Armies of General Joseph E. Johnston. A visitor center houses artifacts and displays relating to the Atlanta campaign.

MUSEUM OF AVIATION

Visitor Information: Located 18 miles southeast of Macon at Robins Air Force Base. From I-75 take exit 45 east to Robins Air Force Base. Turn right and drive three miles to the sign and the museum. Mailing Address: P. O. Box 2469, Warner Robins, Georgia 31099. Telephone: (912) 926-4242/6870. Hours: 10:00 am to 5:00 pm Tuesday through Sunday. Admission: free.

Items on Display: Uniforms, Unit Patches, Field Equipment, Personal Documents, Official Documents, Maps, Photographs, Paintings/Drawings, Flags, Medals, Edged Weapons, Side Arms, Shoulder Arms, Machine Guns, Ordnance, Missiles, Aircraft (fixed wing, rotary wing), Navigational Equipment, Communications Equipment, Scale Models (aircraft, ships/boats).

Over 50 aircraft and missiles from the history of military aviation are on outdoor display at the Robins AFB Museum of Aviation. Highlights include President Lyndon Johnson's VC-140 Lockheed Jetstar, Robert F. Kennedy's CH-21B helicopter and the experimental Benson X-25A Gyrocopter. The large indoor display facility houses an already significant, but still growing, collection of aviation equipment

GEORGIA
Museum of Aviation, continued

and memorabilia from World War I to the present. An original Norden bombsight is on display, as is state-of-the-art avionics equipment, an extensive gun collection, German Luftwaffe items and memorabilia from the career of Brigadier General Robert L. Scott, an ace with the Flying Tigers in World War II and a widely-read author of fourteen books, including the bestselling "God Is My Co-pilot."

NATIONAL INFANTRY MUSEUM

Visitor Information: Located on Baltzell Avenue on Fort Benning, adjacent to the city of Columbus. Take I-185 south into Columbus. At the end of I-185, turn right onto Dixie Road. Drive for approximately one mile then turn right onto First Division Road. Drive another mile, then turn right onto Baltzell Avenue. The museum is on Baltzell. Mailing Address: Building 396, ATTN: ATZB-DPT-MUS, Fort Benning, Georgia 31905-5273. Telephone: (404) 545-2958/4762. Hours: 10:00 am to 4:30 pm Tuesday through Friday, 12:30 pm to 4:30 pm weekends. Admission: free.

Items on Display: Uniforms, Unit Patches, Field Equipment, Personal Documents, Official Documents, Maps, Photographs, Paintings/Drawings, Dioramas, Flags, Battle Streamers, Medals, Edged Weapons, Side Arms, Shoulder Arms, Machine Guns, Flame Throwers, Mines, Ordnance, Nuclear Weapons Displays, Chemical/Biological Weapons Displays, Field Artillery, Air-Defense Artillery, Missiles, Aircraft (fixed wing), Amphibious Landing Craft, Medical Equipment, Tracked Vehicles, Wheeled Vehicles.

The National Infantry Museum is the only museum in the Army museum system devoted exclusively to the roles and contributions of the infantry soldier. As the list above demonstrates, the National Infantry Museum's collection of military artifacts is extensive and varied, with weapons and equipment from the Revolutionary War to the present on display. Test models of various shoulder arms; chemical/biological protection equipment from World Wars I and II; the Davy Crockett, the country's smallest atomic weapon; anti-tank missiles; Civil War and World World II Japanese medical equipment are only a few of the many items on exhibit.

NAVY SUPPLY CORPS MUSEUM

Visitor Information: Located at the U.S. Navy Supply Corps School, Athens, Georgia 30606-5000. From I-85 take exit 441/24 south to Athens Bypass west. Exit onto Prince Avenue east to the Supply

Navy Supply Corps Museum, continued

Corps School. Telephone: (404) 353-7349. Hours: 8:00 am to 4:30 pm Monday through Friday. Closed federal holidays. Admission: free.

Items on Display: Uniforms, Field Equipment, Personal Documents, Official Documents, Photographs, Paintings/Drawings, Flags, Medals, Edged Weapons, Shoulder Arms, Ordnance, Navigational Equipment, Scale Models (ships/boats).

Artifacts and memorabilia pertaining to the history of the Navy Supply Corps are on display at the Supply Corps Museum. Selected exhibits examine the evolution of the Supply Corps' role in the provision of supplies and materiel to land- and sea-based Naval units. Other exhibits focus on specific individuals and explain their contributions to the historical development of the Supply Corps.

OLD FORT JACKSON

Visitor Information: Located off US-80 three miles east of Savannah at 1 Fort Jackson Road, Savannah, Georgia 31404. Telephone: (912) 232-3945. Hours: 9:00 am to 5:00 pm Tuesday through Sunday from March through November, weekends only from December through February. Admission: $1.50 per adult, $0.75 for seniors, military and students.

Items on Display: Uniforms (replicas), Shoulder Arms, Ordnance, Field Artillery, Coast-Defense Artillery, Communications Equipment, Historic Structure (fort).

The oldest original fortification in Georgia, Fort Jackson, largely because of its key location on the Savannah River downstream from the city, played a significant role in the military history of the region beginning with the War of 1812. In 1861, the Governor of Georgia ordered Georgia militia to wrest the fort from Union control. After the fall of Fort Pulaski, Fort Jackson stood as the one line of Confederate defense against an assault by Union forces along the Savannah River. Three long years later, Confederate troops were ordered to abandon Fort Jackson as Union General Sherman's military juggernaut approached from the southwest. Once more in Union hands, the fort was modified over the years until it was finally abandoned in 1905. The fort was open to the public for a brief time in the early '70s, then re-opened in 1976 under the auspices of the Coastal Heritage Society, which maintains the fort to this day as a living history site and attraction.

GEORGIA

24TH INFANTRY DIVISION & FORT STEWART MUSEUM

Visitor Information: Located at the corner of Utility Street and Wilson Avenue on Fort Stewart, 35 miles southwest of Savannah. Accessible from I-95 or US-17. Mailing Address: AFZP-GTM, Fort Stewart, Georgia 31314-5000. Telephone: (912) 767-7885. Hours: 12 noon to 4:00 pm Tuesday, Wednesday and Friday; 1:00 pm to 5:00 pm Saturday and Sunday. Admission: free.

Items on Display: Uniforms, Unit Patches, Field Equipment, Official Documents, Maps, Photographs, Paintings/Drawings, Flags, Medals, Edged Weapons, Side Arms, Shoulder Arms, Machine Guns, Mines, Ordnance, Field Artillery, Air-Defense Artillery, Rockets/Rocket Launchers, Aircraft (rotary wing), Communications Equipment, Medical Equipment, Tracked Vehicles, Wheeled Vehicles.

The 24th Infantry Division was formed in 1941 from elements of the Hawaiian Division and first saw combat at Pearl Harbor. During World War II, the Division engaged the enemy at Hollandia, Leyte, Mindoro, Mindinao, Luzon, and Corregidor. It served as part of the occupying force in Japan at the close of hostilities in the Pacific Theatre and later saw more combat in Korea.

Deactivated in 1970, the Division was reactivated in 1974 and redesignated the 24th Infantry Division (Mechanized) in 1979. In 1980, it became a part of the nation's vital Rapid Deployment Force. Exhibits at the 24th I.D. (M) & Fort Stewart Museum interpret the history of the Division and of Fort Stewart. The outdoor armor and artillery park includes an M24 Light Tank, an M47 Medium Tank, an M74 Recovery Vehicle, an M4A3 Sherman Tank, and a World War II-era 3/4 ton ambulance. A UH-1 helicopter gunship and an OH-13 observation helicopter are also on display, in addition to numerous other items. The museum maintains a branch exhibit at nearby Hunter Army Airfield devoted to the career of Major General Frank Hunter, a military aviation pioneer. A World War II-era 8th Air Force ready room is part of the Hunter AAF exhibit.

U.S. ARMY SIGNAL CORPS MUSEUM

Visitor Information: Located in Building 36305 at Fort Gordon, 12 miles southwest of Augusta. From I-20, take I-520 south to Deans Bridge Road (US-1). Go south on Deans Bridge for five miles to gate 5. The museum is on the left hand side of the road two miles inside of gate 5 at 37th Street. Mailing Address: ATTN: ATZH-DPM,

GEORGIA

U.S. Army Signal Corps Museum, continued

Building 36305, Fort Gordon, Georgia 30905-5020. Hours: 8:00 am to 4:00 pm Monday through Friday, 12:00 noon to 5:00 pm weekends and holidays. Closed Easter, Independence Day, Thanksgiving, Christmas and New Year's Day. Admission: free.

Items on Display: Uniforms, Unit Patches, Field Equipment, Photographs, Paintings/Drawings, Flags, Medals, Edged Weapons, Shoulder Arms, Machine Guns, Field Artillery, Air-Defense Artillery, Satellites/Satellite Communications Displays, Communications Equipment, Tracked Vehicles.

The Signal Corps Museum houses artifacts and memorabilia from the history of Army communications sytems, beginning with the establishment of the Signal Corps in 1860. Permanent displays feature some of the earliest telephone devices made by Alexander Graham Bell and prototypical wireless equipment made by the Italian inventor Marconi, in addition to items belonging to Albert J. Meyer, founder of the U.S. Army Signal Service.

Other exhibits at the museum depict the history of the 10th Armored Division, with particular emphasis on its activities during World War II. Outdoor displays include heavy guns and tracked vehicles.

Other Military Museums, Historic Sites & Exhibits in Georgia

Blue-Gray Museum, Municipal Building, Fitzgerald, Georgia 31750. Telephone: (912) 423-5375.

Civil War Museum, 800 Cherokee Avenue SE, Atlanta, Georgia 30315. Telephone: (404) 658-7625.

Confederate Museum, Alexander Street, Crawfordville, Georgia 30631. Telephone: (404) 456-2221.

81st ARCOM Wildcat Museum, 1514 East Cleveland Avenue, East Point, Georgia 30344. Telephone: (404) 559-5440.

Fort King George Historic Site, P. O. Box 711, Darien, Georgia 31305. Telephone: (912) 437-4770.

Fort Pulaski National Monument, Box 98, Tybee, Georgia 31328. Telephone: (912) 786-5787.

GEORGIA
Other Military Museums in Georgia, continued

Fort Screven, 32 Meddin Street, P. O. Box 366, Tybee Island, Georgia 31328. Telephone: (912) 786-5801.

Mercer Air Museum, c/o Mercer Marine Transport, Box 368, Calhoun, Georgia 30701. Telephone: (404) 629-7371.

Officer Candidate School Hall of Fame, Wigle Hall, 3rd Battalion, (OCS) 11th Infantry, Building 2769, Fort Benning, Georgia 31905-5570. Telephone: (404) 545-4711.

Sunbury Historic Site and Museum, Route 1, Box 236, Midway, Georgia 31320. Telephone: (912) 884-5837.

HAWAII

PACIFIC SUBMARINE MUSEUM

Visitor Information: Located adjacent to the Arizona Memorial Visitor Center at 11 Arizona Memorial Drive, Honolulu, Hawaii 96818. Take the Arizona Memorial exit off the H-1 Freeway. Follow the signs to the visitor center located off Kamehameha Highway. Telephone: (808) 423-1341. Hours: 8:00 am to 4:30 pm daily. Admission: $4.00 per adult, $1.00 per child 6-12, under 6 admitted free.

Items on Display: Uniforms, Unit Patches, Field Equipment, Personal Documents, Official Documents, Maps, Photographs, Paintings/Drawings, Flags, Battle Streamers, Medals, Edged Weapons, Ordnance, Coast-Defense Artillery, Air-Defense Artillery, Missiles, Submarines/Submersible Vehicles, Submarine Equipment Displays, Navigational Equipment, Scale Models (submarines).

Submarine artifacts and submarine-service memorabilia from World War I through the post-World War II era are on display at the Pacific Submarine Museum. Moored nearby is the USS *Bowfin*, one of World War II's most distinguished submarines. Self-guided tours of the *Bowfin* are offered daily.

TROPIC LIGHTNING MUSEUM

Visitor Information: Located on Schofield Barracks, 20 miles northwest of Honolulu. Follow signs from HI-1 to the Schofield Barracks entrance. Security personnel will direct you to the museum. Mailing Address: HQ 25th Infantry Division (Light), c/o AC of S, G5, Schofield Barracks, Hawaii 96857-6008. Telephone: (808) 655-0438/0445. Hours: 10:00 am to 4:00 pm Monday through Friday. Admission: free.

Items on Display: Uniforms, Unit Patches, Field Equipment, Maps, Photographs, Paintings/Drawings, Flags, Battle Streamers, Medals, Edged Weapons, Side Arms, Shoulder Arms, Machine Guns, Flame Throwers, Ordnance, Field Artillery, Rockets/Rocket Launchers, Communications Equipment, Medical Equipment, Tracked Vehicles, Scale Models (aircraft).

Artifacts and displays at the Tropic Lightning Museum focus upon the history of Schofield Barracks and the 25th Infantry Division. Relics from each of the nation's major armed conflicts in the 20th century are on display, with the emphasis on World War II and

HAWAII
Tropic Lightning Museum, continued

subsequent conflicts.

U.S. ARMY MUSEUM OF HAWAII

Visitor Information: Located in Building 32 On Fort DeRussy, on Waikiki Beach between Ala Moana Boulevard, Kalakaua Avenue and Saratoga Road. Mailing Address: P. O. Box 8064, Honolulu, Hawaii 96830-0064. Telephone: (808) 438-2821. Hours: 10:00 am to 4:30 pm Tuesday through Sunday. Admission: free.

Items on Display: Uniforms, Field Equipment, Photographs, Dioramas, Flags, Medals, Edged Weapons, Side Arms, Shoulder Arms, Machine Guns, Ordnance, Field Artillery, Coast-Defense Artillery, Air-Defense Artillery, Aircraft (rotary wing), Tracked Vehicles, Scale Models (aircraft), Historic Structure (reinforced-concrete battery).

Artifacts and exhibits at the Army Museum of Hawaii trace the military history of Hawaii from 1775 to the present, with a special emphasis on the Army in the Pacific and on coast-defense artillery in Hawaii from 1898 to the present. Of special interest is Battery Randolph, a vintage 1909 reinforced-concrete disappearing-gun emplacement. Portions of the battery have been restored and others reconstructed.

USS *ARIZONA* MEMORIAL

Visitor Information: Located at 1 Arizona Memorial Place, Honolulu, Hawaii 96818. Take the Arizona Memorial exit off the H-1 Freeway. Follow the signs to the visitor center located off Kamehameha Highway. Telephone: (808) 422-2771. Hours: 7:30 am to 5:00 pm daily. Boat tours to the memorial operate from 8:00 am to 3:00 pm. Admission: free.

Items on Display: Maps, Photographs, Paintings/Drawings.

The USS *Arizona* Memorial lies over the hull of the battleship *Arizona*, sunk during the Japanese surprise attack on Pearl Harbor on December 7, 1941. The memorial was erected to commemorate the many Americans who died during the Japanese air assault that propelled their country into the Second World War. The names of the 1177 Navy and Marine personnel who died on board the *Arizona* are engraved on a wall of marble in the memorial's shrine chamber. A visitor center on shore offers an interpretive program that includes a

HAWAII

USS *Arizona* Memorial, continued

presentation by a National Park Service Ranger and a film about the Pearl Harbor attack.

Other Military Museums, Historic Sites & Exhibits in Hawaii

USS *Bowfin* Pacific Fleet Submarine Memorial, 11 Arizona Memorial Drive, Honolulu, Hawaii 96818. Telephone: (808) 422-2772.

IDAHO

FORT SHERMAN MUSEUM

General Information: The Fort Sherman branch of the Museum of North Idaho is located on the campus of North Idaho College. Take I-90 east or west to the Coeur d'Alene exit. Follow signs to the college. The museum is off College Drive on the shores of Lake Coeur d'Alene. Mailing Address: P. O. Box 812, Coeur d'Alene, Idaho 83814. Telephone: (208) 664-3448. Hours: 11:00 am to 5:00 pm Tuesday through Saturday from April 1 to October 31; 1:00 pm to 5:00 pm Tuesday through Saturday from May 1 to September 30. Admission: free.

Items on Display: Uniforms, Edged Weapons, Shoulder Arms, Historic Structures (powder magazine, officers' quarters, post chapel).

Originally called Camp Coeur d'Alene, Fort Sherman served as an Army outpost from 1878 until it was abandoned in 1901 after the majority of its troops had departed to fight in the Spanish-American War. The fort's old powder magazine houses the museum, which interprets the history of Fort Sherman with artifacts and memorabilia from the period. One officers' quarters building and the original post chapel, along with the powder magazine, are all that remain of the 52 post buildings standing when the fort closed.

ILLINOIS

CHANUTE AIR FORCE BASE AIR PARK & VISITOR CENTER

Visitor Information: Located 120 miles south of Chicago on Chanute Air Force Base. Take I-57 north or south to US-136 east and follow signs to the base. Visitors should sign in at the North Gate Reception Area. Mailing Address: CTTC/PA, Chanute Air Force Base, Illinois 61868-5000. Telephone: (217) 495-4200 (visitor center); (217) 495-4566 (group tours). Hours: 24 hours daily (air park); 10:00 am to 3:00 pm Tuesday through Thursday, 9:00 am to 5:00 pm weekends (display center). Admission: free.

Items on Display: Uniforms, Unit Patches, Dioramas, Aircraft (fixed wing), Scale Models (aircraft).

Chanute Air Force Base, the third oldest in the nation, is home to the oldest Technical Training Center in the Air Force. Nearly 40 aircraft can be viewed at the base, with 19 at the Thunderbird Air Park, where jet fighters used throughout the history of the Air Force's aerial demonstration teams are on display. Dioramas about Chanute's vital role as a Technical Training Center, aviation uniforms dating from World War I and a large collection of unit patches are on display at the Chanute Visitor Center, as well as scale models of military aircraft.

FIRST DIVISION MUSEUM

Visitor Information: Located due west of downtown Chicago at Cantigny, 1 South 151 Winfield Road, Wheaton, Illinois 60187. From the Chicago Loop, go west on the Eisenhower and East-West Tollway for 30 miles to Naperville Road, turn north for one half mile to Warrenville Road, then turn west for three miles to Winfield Road. Go north on Winfield for two miles to Cantigny. Telephone: (312) 668-5185. Hours: 10:00 am to 5:00 pm Tuesday through Sunday from Memorial Day to Labor Day; 10:00 am to 4:00 pm Tuesday through Sunday for the rest of the year. Admission: free.

Items on Display: Uniforms, Unit Patches, Field Equipment, Personal Documents, Official Documents, Maps, Photographs, Paintings/Drawings, Dioramas, Flags, Battle Streamers, Medals, Edged Weapons, Side Arms, Shoulder Arms, Machine Guns, Flame Throwers, Mines, Ordnance, Field Artillery, Amphibious Landing Craft, Communications Equipment, Medical Equipment, Tracked Vehicles, Scale Models (tracked vehicles).

ILLINOIS
First Division Museum, continued

Artifacts, dioramas, exhibits and recordings at the First Division Museum trace the history of the Army's famous First Division from World War I to Vietnam. The museum is located on the grounds of the 500-acre estate that once served as a country home to Joseph Medill, editor of the Chicago Tribune, and later to his grandson, Robert R. McCormick, who commanded a first division artillery battalion in World War I. McCormick named the estate Cantigny after the French village where America's first offensive in Europe in World War I occurred. Six tanks from World War II, Korea and Vietnam stand outside the museum, along with a DUKW amphibious landing craft and a French 75mm field gun.

FORT SHERIDAN MUSEUM

Visitor Information: Located in Building 33 on Fort Sheridan, 28 miles north of Chicago. Take US-41 north from the Chicago area to the Old Elm Road exit. Go east on Old Elm to the fort. Mailing Address: Building 33, Fort Sheridan, Illinois 60037-5000. Telephone: (312) 926-2173. Hours: 10:00 am to 4:00 pm daily. Admission: free.

Items on Display: Uniforms, Field Equipment, Official Documents, Maps, Photographs, Paintings/Drawings, Flags, Edged Weapons, Side Arms, Shoulder Arms, Machine Guns, Field Artillery, Rockets/Rocket Launchers, Medical Equipment.

The building which houses the Fort Sheridan Museum was built in 1890 and served as the post's stockade for a number of years. Exhibits at the museum focus on the history of the fort and on U.S. Army activities from the latter half of the 19th century to the present. The coach in which General Sheridan rode on his single visit to the post named in his honor is one of the museum's most notable artifacts. Foreign as well as American military artifacts are on display.

GRAND ARMY OF THE REPUBLIC MEMORIAL & VETERANS MILITARY MUSEUM

Visitor Information: Located in downtown Aurora at 23 Downer Place. From I-5 take IL-31 south to the downtown area. Mailing Address: P. O. Box 1043, Aurora, Illinois 60507. Telephone: (312) 897-7221. Hours: 12:00 noon to 4:00 pm Monday, Wednesday and Saturday. Open other hours by arrangement. Admission: free.

ILLINOIS

Grand Army of the Republic Memorial, continued

Items on Display: Uniforms, Field Equipment, Personal Documents, Official Documents, Maps, Paintings/Drawings, Edged Weapons, Side Arms, Shoulder Arms, Machine Guns, Ordnance, Field Artillery, Historic Structure (G.A.R. Memorial).

Dedicated on July 4, 1877, the G.A.R. Memorial served as headquarters for G.A.R. Post 20 for over 65 years, during which time it was visited by many illustrious figures from the Civil War era, including Generals Grant and Sherman. In 1939, the post's surviving Civil War veterans organized the G.A.R. Memorial Association, which to this day manages the memorial and the museum housed within it. The Memorial Association's mission is twofold: to maintain and preserve the memorial as a tribute to veterans of all wars and to collect, preserve and display artifacts and memorabilia pertaining to the nation's military history. The museum's collection consists largely of items from the Civil War and World Wars I and II.

ILLINOIS STATE MILITARY MUSEUM & HALL OF FLAGS

Visitor Information: The museum is located at the corner of North Grand and North MacArthur Boulevard at Camp Lincoln. The Hall of Flags is in the Centennial Building at the corner of 2nd and Edwards Streets in the State Capitol Complex. Take I-72 west or I-55 north or south to Springfield. Mailing Address: Military & Naval Department of Illinois, ATTN: Public Affairs Department, 1301 North MacArthur Boulevard, Springfield, Illinois 62702-2399. Telephone: (217) 782-9365 (museum). Hours: 8:00 am to 4:30 pm Monday through Wednesday. Open Thursday and Friday by appointment. The Hall of Flags is open 8:00 am to 4:30 pm daily.

Items on Display: Uniforms, Field Equipment, Flags, Battle Streamers, Edged Weapons, Side Arms, Shoulder Arms, Tracked Vehicles.

More than 450 Illinois-unit battle flags and streamers from the Illinois State Military Museum's collection are on display in the Centennial Building Hall of Flags at the State Capitol Complex near Camp Lincoln. Many of the battle flags and streamers on display were carried into combat in the Mexican War, the Civil War, the Spanish-American War and World War I. Over 500 other flags, including all those from World War II, are currently in storage along with the majority of the museum's historical holding; however, small, select displays of military artifacts are available for viewing in the

ILLINOIS
Illinois State Military Museum & Hall of Flags, continued

museum building itself at Camp Lincoln and in several other buildings on post.

ROCK ISLAND ARSENAL MUSEUM

Visitor Information: Located on Arsenal Island in the Mississippi River. From I-74, take the 7th Avenue exit west in Moline, Illinois. Follow signs to the Rock Island Arsenal. Mailing Address: ATTN: SMCRI-PCA-M, Rock Island Arsenal, Rock Island, Illinois 61299-5000. Telephone: (309) 782-5021. Hours: 10:00 am to 4:00 pm daily. Closed Thanksgiving, Christmas and New Year's Day. Admission: free.

Items on Display: Uniforms, Field Equipment, Photographs, Side Arms, Shoulder Arms, Machine Guns, Field Artillery, Tracked Vehicles, Scale Models (tracked vehicles).

Established in 1905, the Rock Island Arsenal Museum is the second oldest Army museum in the nation. Located on historic Arsenal Island in the Mississippi River, the museum interprets the history of the island from the construction of Fort Armstrong in 1816 to the present, with key exhibits about the establishment of the Arsenal as a major ordnance- and equipment-manufacturing site in 1862 and about the Confederate prison camp located on the island from 1863 until 1865. Over 1300 examples of military firearms and many other artifacts are on display at the museum.

U-505 GERMAN SUBMARINE

Visitor Information: Located at the Museum of Science & Industry, 57th & Lake Shore Drive, Chicago, Illinois 60637. Take I-55 east to Lake Shore Drive (US-41) south to the museum. Telephone: (312) 684-1414. Hours: 9:30 am to 4:00 pm daily during the winter; 9:30 am to 5:30 pm from Memorial Day to Labor Day and on all holidays. Admission: free.

Items on Display: Official Documents, Photographs, Dioramas, Ships/Boats, Scale Models (ships/boats).

Built in Hamburg and commissioned in August of 1941, the U-505 is a class IX-C German submarine. Captain Daniel V. Gallery, commander of the USS *Guadalcanal*, led the task group that captured the submarine off the coast of North Africa on June 4, 1944. A number of related items are on display near the submarine

ILLINOIS

U-505 German Submarine, continued

itself, including log books, personal items belonging to the German crew, scale models of ships, dioramas and photographs of the submarine's journey from Bermuda to the shores of Lake Michigan. Visitors may also view a short film about the U-505's capture.

Other Military Museums, Historic Sites & Exhibits in Illinois

Daughters of Union Veterans of the Civil War National Headquarters and Museum, Springfield, Illinois 62701. Telephone: (217) 544-0616.

Fort de Chartres State Historic Site, Prairie Du Rocher, Illinois 62277. Telephone: (618) 284-7230.

Fort Massac State Park and Historic Site Complex, Box 708, Metropolis, Illinois 62960. Telephone: (618) 524-9321.

U.S. Coast Guard Patrol Craft *McLaine*, c/o Marine Navigation and Training Association, 2333 North Newcastle Avenue, Chicago, Illinois 60635. Telephone: information not available at press time.

Vietnam Museum, 5002 North Broadway, Chicago, Illinois 60640. Telephone: (312) 728-6111.

INDIANA

GRISSOM AIR MUSEUM

Visitor Information: Located 70 miles north of Indianapolis on Grissom Air Force Base. Take US-31 north from Indianapolis to the base. Mailing Address: 305 AREFS/DOO, Grissom Air Force Base, Indiana. Telephone: (317) 689-2900. Hours: 9:00 am to 4:00 pm daily. Admission: free.

Items on Display: Uniforms, Aircraft (fixed wing).

More than fifteen aircraft from World War II, the Korean War and Vietnam are on display at Grissom's air park. The B-17G and B-25J bombers and the C-47 on display are of World War II vintage. Jet fighters from the Korean War period include the F-84F and the F-86H. Vietnam-era planes include the F-100C, the F-104 and the F-4C.

INDIANA WAR MEMORIAL MILITARY MUSEUM

Visitor Information: Located at 431 North Meridian Street, Indianapolis, Indiana 46204. Take I-65 north or south or I-70 east or west to the Meridian Street exit. The museum is four blocks north of Monument Circle near the center of town. Telephone: (317) 232-7615. Hours: 8:00 am to 4:30 pm daily. Closed Thanksgiving, Christmas and New Year's Day.

Items on Display: Maps, Photographs, Paintings/Drawings, Dioramas, Flags, Field Artillery.

Located in the lower level of the Indiana War Memorial building, the Indiana War Memorial Military Museum interprets the military history of Indiana beginning with the Battle of Tippecanoe. Museum exhibits focus upon the contributions of Indiana veterans in all of the nation's major armed conflicts. The War Memorial itself, a shrine to the principles of patriotism and national loyalty, commemorates Indiana veterans of all wars.

TIPPECANOE BATTLEFIELD & MUSEUM

Visitor Information: Located northwest of Indianapolis off I-65 near the city of Lafayette. Take I-65 to US-43 south to Prophet's Road. Take Prophet's Road to a left on Railroad Street to the battlefield. Mailing Address: P. O. Box 225, Battle Ground, Indiana 47920.

Tippecanoe Battlefield & Museum, continued

Telephone: (317) 567-2147/2148. Hours: 10:00 am to 6:00 pm daily except in January. Admission: $1.50 per adult, $0.75 per child for the museum. Admission to the battlefield is free of charge.

Items on Display: Uniforms, Field Equipment, Maps, Paintings/Drawings, Dioramas, Flags, Edged Weapons, Shoulder Arms, Field Artillery.

The Battle of Tippecanoe pitted Army troops led by William Henry Harrison against an Indian force led by Shawnee warrior Tenskwatawa, brother of Tecumseh. Harrison's decisive victory over the Indians on November 7, 1811, did much to influence the course and speed of westward expansion by European settlers. Exhibits at the battlefield museum place the Battle of Tippecanoe in its historical context and interpret its impact on the lives of both Native Americans and non-natives alike.

U.S. ARMY FINANCE CORPS MUSEUM

Visitor Information: Located on Fort Benjamin Harrison on the northeast side of Indianapolis. Take I-465 (Indianapolis Beltway) to exit 40 east to the fort. Mailing Address: U.S. Army Finance and Accounting Center, Fort Benjamin Harrison, Indiana 46249-0400. Telephone: (317) 542-2169. Hours: call for hours. Admission: free.

Items on Display: Currency and Coins, Personal Documents, Official Documents, Maps, Photographs, Paintings/Drawings.

Military scrip from the Revolutionary War to the present, examples of real and counterfeit currency from a number of foreign countries and many items related to Army Finance Corps activities are on display at the Finance Corps Museum.

Other Military Museums, Historic Sites & Exhibits in Indiana

Civil War Soldiers Monument, Washington and Main Streets, Winchester, Indiana 47394. Telephone: (317) 584-7070.

Fort Knox II Historical Park, P. O. Box 215, Vincennes, Indiana 47591. Telephone: (317) 232-1882.

INDIANA
Other Military Museums in Indiana, continued

Fort Vallonia, Main Street, Vallonia, Indiana 47281. Telephone: (812) 358-3137.

General Lewis B. Hershey Museum, P. O. Box 307, Angola, Indiana 46703. Telephone: (219) 665-3141.

George Rogers Clark National Historical Park, 401 South Second Street, Vincennes, Indiana 47591. Telephone: (812) 882-1776.

Historic Fort Wayne, 107 South Clinton Street, Fort Wayne, Indiana 46802. Telephone: (219) 424-3476.

Soldiers and Sailors Monument, Monument Circle, Indianapolis, Indiana 46204. Telephone: (317) 631-6735.

IOWA

FORT ATKINSON MONUMENT STATE PRESERVE & MUSEUM

Visitor Information: Located several blocks west of Cedar Falls off IA-24. From I-20 in Cedar Falls, Iowa, take US-63 north to IA-24 east toward Fort Atkinson. Mailing Address: Volga River State Recreation Area, Rural Route #1, Fayette, Iowa 52142. Telephone: (319) 425-4161. Hours: grounds open daylight hours daily, museum open by appointment. Admission: free.

Items on Display: Uniforms, Unit Patches, Field Equipment, Personal Documents, Official Documents, Maps, Photographs, Paintings/Drawings, Flags, Battle Streamers, Medals, Edged Weapons, Side Arms, Shoulder Arms, Field Artillery, Historic Structures (fort foundations/buildings).

The relatively brief history of Fort Atkinson parallels the history of the Winnebago Indians in Iowa. When the Army escorted the Winnebagos from Wisconsin to Iowa in 1840, Fort Atkinson was constructed as a base of operations for troops who would be responsible for maintaining order among the Winnebagos, other Indian tribes and white settlers. When the Winnebagos were moved again in 1849, the need for an Army post in the area left with them.

Foundations of original fort buildings are intermixed with several buildings that have survived intact, including a powder magazine and two cannon houses. The Fort Atkinson Museum houses period artifacts excavated at the site and exhibits about the history of Fort Atkinson.

FORT DODGE MUSEUM & FRONTIER VILLAGE

Visitor Information: Located at the junction of US-20 and US-169 in Fort Dodge. Mailing Address: P. O. Box 1798, Fort Dodge, Iowa 50501. Telephone: (515) 573-4231. Hours: 9:00 am to 6:00 pm Monday through Saturday, 12:00 noon to 6:00 pm Sunday from May through mid-October. Admission: $3.00 per adult, $1.00 per child ages 6-18.

Items on Display: Uniforms, Field Equipment, Maps, Photographs, Paintings/Drawings, Medals, Edged Weapons, Side Arms, Shoulder Arms, Machine Guns, Historic Structure (reconstructed fort).

IOWA
Fort Dodge Museum & Frontier Village, continued

Fort Dodge has been reconstructed to appear as it did when originally garrisoned in 1862. The fort museum houses artifacts from the Civil War period through World War II and exhibits relating to the fort's mission as a peace-keeping outpost on the western frontier. The fort is part of a historical complex that includes numerous replicas of shops and stores and community buildings typical of a 19th-century frontier town.

Other Military Museums, Historic Sites & Exhibits in Iowa

Iowa National Guard Museum, Camp Dodge, 7700 N.W. Beaver Drive, Johnston, Iowa 50131-1902. Telephone: (515) 242-5313.

KANSAS

COMBAT AIR MUSEUM

Visitor Information: Located in Hangars 602 and 604 on Forbes Field, Kansas. Take I-70 to US-75 south from Topeka to the Forbes Field exit and follow signs. Mailing Address: Box 19142, Topeka, Kansas 66619. Telephone: (913) 862-3303. Hours: 9:30 am to 4:00 pm Monday through Saturday, 12:30 pm to 4:00 pm Sunday. Admission: $2.50 per adult, $1.00 per student and senior citizen. Uniformed military personnel admitted free.

Items on Display: Uniforms, Unit Patches, Field Equipment, Personal Documents, Official Documents, Maps, Photographs, Paintings/Drawings, Dioramas, Flags, Medals, Edged Weapons, Side Arms, Shoulder Arms, Machine Guns, Flame Throwers, Ordnance, Field Artillery, Rockets/Rocket Launchers, Missiles, Aircraft (fixed wing), Communications Equipment, Tracked Vehicles, Scale Models (aircraft, ships/boats).

In the words of museum officials, the Combat Air Museum is dedicated to "finding, restoring, preserving, displaying and flying aircraft and artifacts associated with American wars." Two hangars, one of which was used during the World War II era for B-17s and B-24s, house the many displays. One also serves as the restoration area. Among the more than 20 aircraft on display are a J-1 "Jenny" from 1917, an F-9F Panther from 1949, an F-84 Thunderstreak from 1954 and a replica of an MC-G-10 Messerschmitt, the German Air Force's most formidable fighter plane during the Second World War. Bombs, missiles, aircraft engines, tracked vehicles and many other items complete the Combat Air Museum's collection.

FORT HARKER MUSEUM

Visitor Information: Located off I-70 west of Salina. From I-70, turn south on KS-156, then take KS-111 east to Kanapolis. Or drive south from Salina on I-135 to KS-140 west to Kanapolis. Mailing Address: c/o President, Ellsworth County Historical Society, 306 Forest Drive, Ellsworth, Kansas 67439. Telephone: (913) 472-3885/4579. Hours: 9:00 am to 12:00 noon and 1:00 pm to 4:00 pm Tuesday through Saturday, 1:00 pm to 5:00 pm Sunday from May 1 to October 1; 9:00 am to 12:00 noon and 1:00 pm to 5:00 pm Saturday, 1:00 pm to 5:00 pm Sunday from October 1 to May 1. Admission: free.

KANSAS
Fort Harker Museum, continued

Items on Display: Uniforms, Unit Patches, Field Equipment, Maps, Photographs, Paintings/Drawings, Flags, Medals, Shoulder Arms, Medical Equipment, Civil War Ambulance, Historic Structure (guardhouse).

Established in 1866 and abandoned in 1872, Fort Harker was a short-lived military outpost, even by frontier standards. Yet many illustrious names were associated with the fort during its brief period of existence, including Colonel George Armstrong Custer and the men of the 7th Cavalry, General Sheridan, "Wild Bill" Hickok and William "Buffalo Bill" Cody.

Exhibits at the Fort Harker Museum interpret the fort's history and the mission of its garrison on the Kansas frontier. Artifacts dating from the Civil War through World War II are on display, notable among which is a Civil War-era ambulance of the kind used to transport wounded soldiers and civilians on the western frontier. The museum is located in the original fort guardhouse. Three other fort buildings, now used as private residences, are located nearby.

FORT LARNED NATIONAL HISTORIC SITE

Visitor Information: From I-70 in Hays, Kansas, take US-183 south for approximately 60 miles to KS-156. Drive east on KS-156 for six miles to the fort. Mailing Address: Route 3, Larned, Kansas 67550. Telephone: (316) 285-6911. Hours: 8:00 am to 5:00 pm daily. Admission: free.

Items on Display: Uniforms, Field Equipment, Personal Documents, Photographs, Paintings/Drawings, Battle Streamers, Edged Weapons, Side Arms, Shoulder Arms, Ordnance, Field Artillery, Medical Equipment, Historic Structure (fort).

From 1822 until the early 1880s, the Santa Fe Trail carried vital commercial traffic between Independence, Missouri, and Santa Fe, New Mexico. Fort Larned, strategically located near the trail on the banks of the Pawnee River, served as an important base of operations for military personnel assigned the arduous tasks of keeping the trail safe for travelers and maintaining peaceful relations between settlers and the Native American inhabitants of the region. Fort Larned also served as an Indian Bureau Agency between 1861 and 1868. As such it became a gathering place for Plains Indian tribes who were given food staples and other items in exchange for their promise not to make war on the white man. As the

KANSAS
Fort Larned National Historic Site, continued

transcontinental railroad system became operational, the importance of the Santa Fe Trail diminished. This, in conjunction with the forced relocation of many Indian tribes to reservations in the Oklahoma Territory, greatly reduced the need for a full complement of troops at Fort Larned. The fort was largely abandoned in 1878.

Original and restored fort structures at the site include several officers' quarters, the quartermaster storehouse, the commissary, the blockhouse and two barracks buildings, one of which houses the visitor center where period artifacts and exhibits interpreting the fort's history are on display.

FORT SCOTT NATIONAL HISTORIC SITE

Visitor Information: Located 90 miles south of Kansas City in the city of Fort Scott, two blocks west of the intersection of US-69 and US-54. Mailing Address: Old Fort Boulevard, Fort Scott, Kansas 66701. Telephone: (316) 223-0310. Hours: 8:00 am to 5:00 pm daily during the fall, winter and spring; 8:00 am to 5:00 pm from June 4 through Labor Day. Closed Thanksgiving, Christmas and New Year's Day. Admission: $1.00 per person over age 12.

Items on Display: Uniforms, Personal Documents, Official Documents, Maps, Photographs, Paintings/Drawings, Edged Weapons, Side Arms, Shoulder Arms, Medical Equipment, Historic Structure (restored/reconstructed fort).

Garrisoned between 1842 and 1853, Fort Scott was one of many peace-keeping forts built on the western frontier in the years preceding the Civil War. Two companies of colorfully uniformed dragoons arrived in 1842 and began constructing the fort, which lay between Fort Leavenworth to the north and Fort Gibson to the south. Because of a lack of hostile Indian activity in the fort's vicinity, troops spent much, if not most, of their time guarding wagon trains and mail coaches on the Santa Fe Trail. As the frontier moved farther west, Fort Scott's location became less strategic in the military's overall plan of defense against hostile activities by Indians. The garrison moved to Fort Leavenworth in 1853.

The fort's buildings have been restored or reconstructed and contain 36 rooms furnished as they were during the fort's years of active service. The restored hospital building houses the visitor center. A museum containing period artifacts and exhibits about the fort and frontier life is housed in the infantry barracks.

KANSAS

FRONTIER ARMY MUSEUM

Visitor Information: Located on Fort Leavenworth, north of Leavenworth off US-73. From I-70 take US-73 north to the fort. Mailing Address: ATTN: ATZL-GOP-MU, Fort Leavenworth, Kansas 66027-5072. Telephone: (913) 684-3191. Hours: 10:00 am to 4:00 pm Monday through Saturday, 12:00 noon to 4:00 pm Sundays and holidays. Closed Easter, Thanksgiving, Christmas and New Year's Day. Admission: free.

Items on Display: Uniforms, Field Equipment, Official Documents, Maps, Photographs, Paintings/Drawings, Dioramas, Flags, Edged Weapons, Side Arms, Shoulder Arms, Field Artillery, Historic Structures (many historic buildings on post).

Established by Colonel Henry Leavenworth on May 8, 1827, Fort Leavenworth became one of the Army's most important frontier outposts during the 1800s. It served as a base of operations for troops guarding the Santa Fe and Oregon Trails, as a major Army headquarters during the Mexican War, and continues to serve as the site of the U.S. Army Command and General Staff College, from which over 80,000 U.S. and allied officers have graduated.

Exhibits, films and multi-media presentations depict the fort's rich and colorful history. Artifacts at the museum date from the early 1800s to the Spanish-American War. A portrait of Colonel Leavenworth by George Catlin, Leavenworth's uniform and sword, many period uniforms and weapons, a genuine prairie schooner and a carriage used by Abraham Lincoln in 1859 are in the museum's collection.

Visitors to the fort may also tour the United States Disciplinary Barracks; the "Rookery," the oldest continuously occupied house in Kansas; the Sutler's Home, built in 1841; and the National Cemetery, where Tom Custer, George Armstrong Custer's brother and the first man ever to win two Medals of Honor, is buried.

HISTORIC FORT HAYS

Visitor Information: Located four miles south of I-70 on the south side of Hays. Mailing Address: Route 2, Box 338, Hays, Kansas 67601. Telephone: (913) 625-6812. Hours: 9:00 am to 6:00 pm Tuesday through Saturday, 1:00 pm to 5:00 pm Sunday and Monday (Memorial Day through Labor Day); 9:00 am to 5:00 pm Tuesday through Saturday, 1:00 pm to 5:00 pm Sunday and Monday (Labor Day through Memorial Day). Admission: free.

Historic Fort Hays, continued

Items on Display: Uniforms, Field Equipment, Photographs, Edged Weapons, Side Arms, Shoulder Arms, Ordnance, Field Artillery, Medical Equipment, Historic Structures (fort buildings).

An active Army post between 1867 and 1889, Fort Hays was one of many frontier Army forts established after the Civil War to keep peace between settlers and Native American inhabitants in the territories west of the Mississippi. Generals Sheridan and Custer were both associated with the fort at different times during their illustrious careers. The famous frontiersman impresario "Wild Bill" Hickok once marshalled in the county where Fort Hays and nearby Hays City were located. He resigned his position after brawling with soldiers from the fort. Mrs. Custer, writing about Hays City, a town with more than its share of saloons, dance halls and trouble, said that "there was enough desperate history in that little town in one summer to make a whole library of dime novels."

Several of the fort's original structures still stand, including the blockhouse, the guardhouse and two officers' quarters. The guardhouse and a visitor center contain a number of artifacts from the Indian Wars period and exhibits that interpret the history of Fort Hays and its predecessor in the area, Fort Fletcher.

U.S. CAVALRY MUSEUM

Visitor Information: Located in Building 205 on Fort Riley, five miles northeast of Junction City. Take I-70 to KS-18 north to the fort. Mailing Address: P. O. Box 2160, Fort Riley, Kansas 66442-5000. Telephone: (913) 239-2743/2737. Hours: 9:00 am to 4:30 pm Monday through Saturday, 12:00 noon to 4:30 pm Sunday. Admission: free.

Items on Display: Uniforms, Unit Patches, Field Equipment, Personal Documents, Official Documents, Photographs, Paintings/Drawings, Dioramas, Flags, Medals, Edged Weapons, Side Arms, Shoulder Arms, Machine Guns, Communications Equipment, Tracked Vehicles, Historic Structure (museum building is an original post building dating from 1853).

Artifacts and exhibits at the U.S. Cavalry Museum interpret the history of Fort Riley and of the United States Cavalry from the Revolution to the post-World War II era. One of the many artifacts from the storied history of the U.S. Cavalry on display is a gas mask designed for the cavalry soldier's best friend—his horse!

KENTUCKY

COLUMBUS-BELMONT BATTLEFIELD STATE PARK

Visitor Information: Located near the junction of KY-58 and KY-123 overlooking the Mississippi River, 36 miles southwest of Paducah. Take US-62 west from Paducah to US-51 south to KY-80 west. Mailing Address: Box 8, Columbus, Kentucky 42031. Telephone: (502) 677-2327. Hours: 9:00 am to 5:00 pm daily May through Labor Day, weekends only after Labor Day. Admission: $0.50 per adult, $0.25 per child.

Items on Display: Uniforms, Personal Documents, Photographs, Paintings/Drawings, Dioramas, Edged Weapons, Shoulder Arms, Ordnance, Medical Equipment, Historic Structure (Infirmary).

The Civil War Museum at the Columbus-Belmont Battlefield State Park is housed in a building that served as an infirmary for soldiers wounded in the Battle of Belmont, a skirmish between Northern and Southern forces that occurred early in the North's western campaign in November of 1861. Displays and an audio-visual program interpret the battle and its consequences for both sides as the war progressed. Artifacts from the battle site on display include a massive anchor and chain that Confederate forces stretched across the Mississippi River to halt the progress of Union boats along the vital waterway.

DON F. PRATT MUSEUM

Visitor Information: Located on Fort Campbell, which straddles the Kentucky-Tennessee state line south of Hopkinsville, Kentucky. Take I-24 to US-41 south to Gate 4 at Fort Campbell. Mailing Address: Fort Campbell, Kentucky 42223-5000. Telephone: (502) 798-3215. Hours: 12:30 pm to 4:30 pm Monday through Friday, 10:00 am to 4:30 pm Saturday, and 12:00 noon to 4:30 pm Sunday. Admission: free.

Items on Display: Uniforms, Unit Patches, Field Equipment, Personal Documents, Official Documents, Maps, Photographs, Paintings/Drawings, Dioramas, Flags, Battle Streamers, Medals, Edged Weapons, Side Arms, Shoulder Arms, Machine Guns, Flame Throwers, Mines, Ordnance, Field Artillery, Air-Defense Artillery, Rockets/Rocket Launchers, Aircraft (rotary wing), Medical Equipment.

Displays and artifacts at the Don F. Pratt Museum focus upon the history and exploits of the 101st Airborne Division. The collection includes one of only three gliders displayed in the U.S. that was used

Don F. Pratt Museum, continued

in World War II, Soviet and American flame throwers, a Vietnam-era Huey helicopter, Vietnam-era medical equipment and displays about the history of Fort Campbell.

KENTUCKY MILITARY HISTORY MUSEUM

Visitor Information: Located in downtown Frankfort. Take I-64 to US-60 north. The museum is at the corner of US-60 (East Main Street) and Capitol Avenue. Mailing Address: c/o Kentucky Historical Society, P. O. Box H, Main Street, Frankfort, Kentucky 40601. Telephone: (502) 564-3265. Hours: 8:30 am to 4:00 pm Monday through Saturday, 1:00 pm to 5:00 pm Sunday. Closed Easter, Thanksgiving, Christmas and New Year's Day. Admission: free.

Items on Display: Uniforms, Unit Patches, Field Equipment, Personal Documents, Official Documents, Maps, Photographs, Paintings/Drawings, Dioramas, Flags, Battle Streamers, Medals, Edged Weapons, Side Arms, Shoulder Arms, Machine Guns, Flame Throwers, Mines, Ordnance, Field Artillery, Rockets/Rocket Launchers.

Chronologically arranged displays at the Kentucky Military History Museum emphasize the participation of native Kentuckians in the military history of Kentucky and that of the nation, beginning with Kentucky's settlement and pioneer days in the mid-1700s and continuing on through the Vietnam War. Items on display include a British flag carried by warring Indians under the leadership of the famous Indian chief Tecumseh during the War of 1812; the plaque removed from Adolph Hitler's cell in Landsberg Prison; a German BMW motorcycle and sidecar bearing S.S. markings; one of only four remaining Williams rapid-fire guns; and a Burnside Type II carbine presented to J. J. Crittenden by President Abraham Lincoln in February of 1862.

PATTON MUSEUM OF CAVALRY & ARMOR

Visitor Information: Located in Building 4554 on the Fort Knox Military Reservation. Take I-65 to US-31W to the Chaffee Avenue exit to Fort Knox. Mailing Address: P. O. Box 208, Fort Knox, Kentucky 40121-0208. Telephone: (502) 624-3812/6350. Hours: 9:00 am to 4:30 pm weekdays year round; 10:00 am to 6:00 pm holidays and weekends from May 1 to September 30; 10:00 am to 4:30 pm holidays and weekends from October 1 to April 30. Closed Christmas Eve and Day and New Year's Eve and Day. Admission: free.

KENTUCKY
Patton Museum of Cavalry & Armor, continued

Items on Display: Uniforms, Field Equipment, Side Arms, Medals, Field Artillery, Tracked Vehicles.

During World War II, a number of armored vehicles captured from the Axis powers were shipped to Fort Knox for testing and evaluation. Since many of the vehicles originated in the area where General George S. Patton's Third Army was operating, the armored vehicles became unofficially known as the Patton collection. In 1949, those vehicles and other items became the Patton Museum of Cavalry and Armor, which features artifacts from the history of the U.S. Cavalry beginning with the American Revolution and continuing on to the mechanized and armored cavalry regiments of today.

A U.S. Sherman tank, a Soviet T34 tank and a British Mark V tank (the world's first combined infantry and tank vehicle) are only a few of the many examples of American and foreign armored vehicles in the museum's collection. Nineteenth-2century cavalry uniforms, field and anti-tank artillery pieces, a Vietnam-era helicopter gunship and a prototype of the Cobra attack helicopter are also on display. The Patton Gallery contains artifacts and memorabilia from the life and career of General Patton, including his famous ivory-handled revolvers. Other exhibits in the museum focus on the history of Fort Knox.

PERRYVILLE BATTLEFIELD STATE HISTORIC SITE

Visitor Information: Located ten miles west of Danville off US-68 or US-150. Mailing Address: Box 296 (Mackville Road), Perryville, Kentucky 40468. Telephone: (606) 332-8631. Hours: 9:00 am to 5:00 pm daily from April 1 to October 31, other times by appointment for the museum. The grounds are open daily year round from 9:00 am to 5:00 pm. Admission: $1.50 per adult, $0.75 per child for the museum. Admission to the grounds is free.

Items on Display: Uniforms, Field Equipment, Personal Documents, Official Documents, Maps, Photographs, Paintings/Drawings, Dioramas, Flags, Medals, Edged Weapons, Side Arms, Shoulder Arms, Ordnance, Field Artillery, Medical Equipment, Scale Models (cannon).

On October 8, 1862, the most important Civil War battle fought in Kentucky took place in the Perryville area, as the South made one last attempt to wrest control of Kentucky from Union forces. The failure of the South to attain its military goal was a major,

Perryville Battlefield State Historic Site, continued

ultimately disastrous setback for the Confederate cause. The museum displays artifacts from the battle and offers an interpretive audiovisual program.

Other Military Museums, Historic Sites & Exhibits in Kentucky

Blue Licks Battlefield State Park, Mount Olivet, Kentucky 41064. Telephone: (606) 289-5507.

Jefferson Davis Monument State Historic Site, P. O. Box 10, Fairview, Kentucky 42221. Telephone: (502) 886-1765.

Old Fort Harrod State Park, P. O. Box 156, Harrodsburg, Kentucky 40330. Telephone: (606) 734-3314.

LOUISIANA

CHALMETTE NATIONAL HISTORICAL PARK

Visitor Information: Located at 8606 West St. Bernard Highway, Chalmette, Louisiana 70043. From I-10 in New Orleans, take the Chalmette exit (LA-47) south to St. Bernard Highway and turn right. Telephone: (504) 589-4428. Hours: 8:00 am to 5:00 pm daily. Closed Mardi Gras, Christmas and New Year's Day. Admission: free.

Items on Display: Uniforms, Field Equipment, Personal Documents, Official Documents, Maps, Paintings/Drawings, Dioramas, Flags, Medals, Edged Weapons, Side Arms, Shoulder Arms, Ordnance, Historic Structures (batteries).

Chalmette National Historical Park, a unit of the Jean Lafitte National Historical Park, was established to preserve the battlefield where American forces, led by Major General Andrew Jackson, defeated the British in the Battle of New Orleans in January of 1815. The visitor center at the site is located in the Beauregard House, where artifacts from the War of 1812 and exhibits placing the Battle of New Orleans in its historical context can be viewed. Though several artillery batteries from the time of the battle are now submerged in the Mississippi River, others have been reconstructed near the "mud rampart," a main part of the American line of defense built before the battle. The Chalmette National Cemetery, established in 1864, is located adjacent to the park.

CONFEDERATE MUSEUM

Visitor Information: Located off I-10 near the French Quarter between 929 Camp Street, New Orleans, Louisiana 70130. Telephone: (504) 523-4522. Hours: 10:00 am to 4:00 pm Monday through Saturday. Closed national holidays and Mardi Gras. Admission: $2.00 per adult, $1.00 per senior citizen and student, $0.50 per child under age 12.

Items on Display: Uniforms, Field Equipment, Personal Documents, Official Documents, Maps, Photographs, Paintings/Drawings, Flags, Battle Streamers, Medals, Edged Weapons, Side Arms, Shoulder Arms, Ordnance, Field Artillery, Coast-Defense Artillery, Medical Equipment.

The oldest museum in Louisiana, Confederate Memorial Hall was opened in 1891 as a repository for Civil War relics, records and memorabilia. The museum's Jefferson Davis collection was donated by

Confederate Museum, continued

Davis' widow. Other items donated by New Orleans residents include bloodstained Confederate battle flags, uniforms, edged weapons, medical instruments and the silver service used in camp by General Robert E. Lee.

FORT POLK MILITARY MUSEUM

Visitor Information: Located on Fort Polk, off US-171, which runs north-south between I-20 and I-10, ten miles south of Leesville at LA-10. Mailing Address: P. O. Drawer R, Fort Polk, Louisiana 71459-5000. Telephone: (318) 535-4840. Hours: 10:00 am to 2:00 pm Wednesday through Friday, 9:00 am to 4:00 pm weekends. Closed Thanksgiving, Christmas and New Year's Day. Admission: free.

Items on Display: Uniforms, Unit Patches, Field Equipment, Personal Documents, Official Documents, Maps, Photographs, Dioramas, Flags, Battle Streamers, Medals, Edged Weapons, Side Arms, Shoulder Arms, Machine Guns, Flame Throwers, Mines, Ordnance, Field Artillery, Air-Defense Artillery, Rockets/Rocket Launchers, Aircraft (rotary wing), Tracked Vehicles.

Indoor and outdoor exhibits at the Fort Polk Military Museum focus on the 12 divisions stationed at the fort since 1941, with an emphasis on the 5th Infantry Division (Mechanized), stationed at Fort Polk since 1974. The extensive outdoor display includes artillery pieces, rocket launchers, tanks, helicopters and other examples of military equipment. Artifacts on exhibit indoors range from Revolutionary War-era uniforms to Vietnam-era shoulder arms.

LOUISIANA MILITARY HISTORY & STATE WEAPONS MUSEUM

Visitor Information: Located three miles south of the central New Orleans business district at 6400 St. Claude Avenue, New Orleans, Louisiana 70146-0330. Telephone: (504) 278-6242. Hours: 8:00 am to 4:00 pm Monday through Friday. Closed weekends and holidays. Admission: free.

Items on Display: Uniforms, Unit Patches, Field Equipment, Personal Documents, Official Documents, Maps, Photographs, Paintings/Drawings, Dioramas, Flags, Battle Streamers, Edged Weapons, Side Arms, Shoulder Arms, Machine Guns, Flame Throwers, Mines, Ordnance, Field Artillery, Air-Defense Artillery,

LOUISIANA
Louisiana Military History Museum, continued

Missiles, Aircraft (fixed wing, rotary wing), Amphibious Landing Craft, Communications Equipment, Tracked Vehicles, Scale Models (tracked/wheeled vehicles), Historic Structure (Jackson Barracks).

The Louisiana Military History and State Weapons Museum is the official National Guard Museum for the state of Louisiana. The museum's extensive collection of military artifacts is housed in and around the Jackson Barracks Powder Magazine. Constructed in 1837 as a munitions storage depot, the magazine also served as a prison for captured soldiers from Germany's Afrika Corps and as an indoor rifle range for Louisiana National Guardsmen.

Jackson Barracks itself was built between 1833-1835 and has remained an active military reservation since that time. Today the historic barracks houses many active National Guard units. Louisiana's Army and Air National Guard HQs are located here.

Both American and captured foreign military weapons and other military artifacts are on display in the magazine and on the grounds outside. Many are arranged by time period and conflict beginning with the American Revolution and continuing on through Vietnam. Of particular interest is a copy of the official transcript from the Nürnberg war trials; a 1917 U.S. Army type-55 Cadillac touring car assigned to the American Expeditionary Force in France in 1918; a rare twenty-eight star United States flag carried during the Mexican War of 1846-1848; and a rare 24-pounder bronze "Coehorn" mortar used during the Civil War. The museum also has a "hands-on" section where visitors may handle and familiarize themselves with a variety of different weapons.

Exterior displays include tanks; personnel carriers; French, Soviet and American artillery pieces; and many other items, including several types of fighter aircraft and one Korean War-era observation helicopter.

LOUISIANA NAVAL WAR MEMORIAL/USS *KIDD*

Visitor Information: Located at 305 South River Road, Baton Rouge, Louisiana 70802. Take the Government Street exit west off I-10 to the memorial. Mailing Address: Louisiana Naval War Memorial Foundation, P. O. Box 44242, Baton Rouge, Louisiana 70804. Telephone: (504) 342-1942. Hours: 9:00 am to 5:00 pm daily. Admission: $3.50 per adult, $2.00 per child ages 6-12, under age 6 admitted free (ship); $1.00 per adult, $0.50 per child ages 6-12, under

LOUISIANA

Louisiana Naval War Memorial/USS *Kidd*

age 6 admitted free (museum). Admission to the ship includes price of admission to the museum.

Items on Display: Uniforms, Unit Patches, Personal Documents, Photographs, Paintings/Drawings, Medals, Aircraft (fixed wing), Ships/Boats, Scale Models (aircraft).

Declared a National Historic Landmark by the U.S. Department of the Interior in January of 1986, the USS *Kidd* is the only surviving Fletcher class destroyer not modernized by the U.S. Navy. Launched on February 28, 1943, the *Kidd* earned four battle stars in the Pacific Theater during World War II and four more during the Korean War. The *Kidd's* exemplary service to the nation came to an end in 1964.

Permanently docked in the Mississippi River, the *Kidd's* hull is completely exposed between August and November when the river reaches its low stage, allowing visitors to examine the *Kidd's* propellers, rudder, stabilizer fins, sonardome and the bow-shearing blade used in anti-submarine warfare.

The visitor center/museum complex on shore contains artifacts and exhibits about America's maritime history, including an excellent collection of ship models, knot-tying displays and lighthouse lights. Also on hand is a genuine P-40 Flying Tiger fighter plane from World War II, the centerpiece of the museum's General Chennault collection. A Louisiana native, General Chennault commanded the Flying Tigers in China.

The Louisiana War Memorial, which stands outside the visitor center/museum, is a black granite monument bearing the names of over 7,000 Louisiana citizens who died in the service of their country from the Revolution to Lebanon.

Other Military Museums, Historic Sites & Exhibits in Louisiana

Barksdale Air Force Base Museum, 2 BMW/PACM, Barksdale, Louisiana 71110-5000. Telephone: (318) 456-3067.

CSS *Pioneer*, c/o Louisiana State Museum, P. O. Box 2458, New Orleans, Louisiana 70716. Telephone: (504) 568-6968.

LOUISIANA
Other Military Museums in Louisiana, continued

Fort Jesup State Commemorative Area, Many, Louisiana 71449. Telephone: (318) 256-5480.

Fort Pike State Commemorative Area, Route 6, Box 194, New Orleans, Louisiana 70129. Telephone: (504) 662-5703.

Fort St. Jean Baptiste State Commemorative Area, P. O. Box 1127, Natchitoches, Louisiana 71457-1127. Telephone: (318) 357-0001.

Mansfield Battle Park Museum, Mansfield State Commemorative Area, Mansfield, Louisiana 71052. Telephone: (318) 872-1474.

Pentagon Barracks Museum, c/o Foundation for Historical Louisiana, 900 North Boulevard, Baton Rouge, Louisiana 70802. Telephone: (504) 342-1866.

MAINE

FORT KNOX STATE HISTORIC SITE

Visitor Information: Located approximately 25 miles south of Bangor off ME-174 in Prospect. Driving north on US-1 in Prospect, turn left on ME-174 before reaching the suspension bridge. The site is on the right hand side of the road. Signs point the way. Mailing Address: R.F.D. #1, Box 1316, Stockton Springs, Maine 04981. Telephone: (207) 469-7719. Hours: 9:00 am to dusk daily from May 1 to November 1. The grounds are open all year. Admission: $1.00 per person from May 15 to October 8. Persons under age 12 or over 65 admitted free.

Items on Display: Ordnance, Coast-Defense Artillery, Historic Structure (fort).

Work began on the massive granite walls of Fort Knox in 1844. The need for a fort strategically located on the banks of the Penobscot River between Castine and Bangor seemed clear. Twice in recent history, during the Revolution and again during the War of 1812, British warships had sailed up the river unhindered and seized the city of Bangor. In 1839, when tensions rose between Britain and the U.S. over border disputes in the North, military planners vowed that history would not be allowed to repeat itself. If open warfare developed again between the two powers, Bangor would be defended, no matter what the cost.

By 1869, when construction activities at the fort ceased with the fort not yet finished, the total cost of construction stood at approximately one million dollars. The tensions that had prompted the fort's construction had long since resolved themselves without bloodshed. Troops who garrisoned the fort during the Civil War, and later during the Spanish-American War, waited without incident for enemy ships that never appeared on the Penobscot. The fort's cannon never fired a shot in anger.

Fort Knox is the largest fort of any kind ever built in Maine. Original walls, earthworks and many of the fort's original buildings still stand, in remarkably good condition given the fort's limited upkeep over the years. Several Rodman cannon remain in place in the fort's gun batteries. An interpretive center is located within the fort's walls.

MAINE

FORT McCLARY STATE HISTORIC PARK

Visitor Information: Located a short distance northeast of Portsmouth, New Hampshire, on the banks of the Piscataqua River. Take ME-103 east off I-95 at Kittery, Maine, to the fort. Mailing Address: c/o General Delivery, Kittery Point, Maine 03905. Telephone: (207) 439-2845. Hours: 9:00 am to 8:00 pm daily from May through October. Admission: free.

Items on Display: Paintings/Drawings, Historic Structure (fort).

For almost 275 years Fort McClary stood guard against enemy ships attempting to navigate up the Piscataqua River. Troops manned the fort's barricades through five wars: the American Revolution, the War of 1812, the Civil War, the Spanish-American War and World War I. As with many forts in the far northeast, however, Fort McClary saw little in the way of armed confrontation during its years as an active post. Original post structures at the site all date from the early to mid-1800s and include the blockhouse, the rifleman's house, the fort's granite walls and caponiers, the granite powder magazine, earthworks and the magazine, which dates from 1808 and is the oldest structure at the site.

FORT WESTERN MUSEUM ON THE KENNEBEC

Visitor Information: Located at the City Center Plaza, 16 Cony Street, Augusta, Maine 04330. Take ME-27 south from I-95 to downtown Augusta. Turn left and cross the Kennebec River on the Father Curran Bridge to the museum. Parking is available behind the museum at City Hall on the right. Telephone: (207) 626-2385. Hours: 10:00 am to 5:00 pm Monday through Saturday, 1:00 pm to 5:00 pm Sunday from mid-June through Labor Day. Admission: $2.50 per adult, $1.50 per person ages 7-12.

Items on Display: Field Equipment, Maps, Flags, Edged Weapons, Shoulder Arms, Ordnance, Field Artillery, Historic Structure (fort).

Fort Western was an important storehouse in the system of forts on the (Kennebec) river during the French and Indian War. Artifacts from the French and Indian War period are on display in the fort museum, along with exhibits that interpret military activities at the fort and in the surrounding region. The fort's original barrack-and-storehouse building, constructed in 1754, still stands, along with reconstructed blockhouses, watchboxes, and other structures.

MAINE

Other Military Museums, Historic Sites & Exhibits in Maine

Barracks Museum of the Border Historical Society (Fort Sullivan), 1 Capen Avenue, Eastport, Maine 04631. Telephone: None.

Joshua L. Chamberlain Civil War Museum, 226 Maine Street, Brunswick, Maine 04011. Telephone: (207) 729-6606 (Pejepscot Historical Society).

Fort Baldwin, c/o Popham Beach State Park, Star Route 3, Phippsburg, Maine 04562. Telephone: (207) 389-1335.

Fort Edgecomb, Rural Route 1, Box 18A, North Edgecomb, Maine 04556. Telephone: (207) 882-7777.

Fort George (Earthworks), c/o Caretaker, 1235 Central Drive, Presque Isle, Maine 04769. Telephone: (207) 764-2041.

Fort Halifax Blockhouse, c/o Caretaker, Box 523, Wilton, Maine 04294. Telephone: (207) 645-4217.

Fort Kent State Historic Site, Page Avenue, Fort Kent, Maine 04743. Telephone: (207) 764-2033.

Fort O'Brien (Fort Machias), c/o Caretaker, 1235 Central Drive, Presque Isle, Maine 04769. Telephone: (207) 764-2041.

Fort Popham, c/o Popham Beach State Park, Star Route 3, Phippsburg, Maine 04562. Telephone: (207) 389-1335.

Fort Pownall, c/o Caretaker, 301 Park Street, Suite 102, Rockland, Maine 04841. Telephone: (207) 596-2253.

Fort William Henry, c/o Colonial Pemaquid, P. O. Box 117, New Harbor, Maine 04550. Telephone: (207) 677-2423.

Maine National Guard Museum, Military Bureau, Camp Keyes, Augusta, Maine 70146-0330. Telephone: (207) 626-4320/4314.

Owls Head Transportation Museum, P. O. Box 277, Owls Head, Maine 04854. Telephone: (207) 594-4418.

USS Bowdoin, c/o Schooner Bowdoin Association, Inc., P. O. Box 1117, Rockland, Maine 04841. Telephone: (207) 594-2301.

MARYLAND

AIRMEN MEMORIAL MUSEUM

Visitor Information: Located a short distance southeast of Washington, D.C., at 5211 Auth Road, Suitland, Maryland 20746. From I-95 (Capital Beltway) take exit 7B north (Branch Avenue-Silver Hill) toward Suitland. Auth Road is the first street on the right. The museum will be on the right three blocks down. Telephone: (301) 899-3500. Hours: 8:00 am to 5:00 pm Monday through Friday. Admission: free.

Items on Display: Uniforms, Field Equipment, Personal Documents, Photographs, Paintings/Drawings, Flags, Medals.

When work is completed at the Airmen Memorial Museum in 1990, it will become, according to museum officials, "the first all-electronic museum" in the Air Force museum system, with "participatory computer exhibits" that use "interactive video disc, compact disc, digital sound, computer graphics, holography and laser technologies" to chronicle the history and contributions of Air Force enlisted personnel. The museum will also use archival materials to portray the life, duties and responsibilities of the enlisted corps." The museum will contain three galleries with at least 18 separate exhibits. One exhibit, a recreated orderly room of the 1940s, will feature a large video screen upon which friends and family members will be able to display the service histories of honorably discharged enlisted personnel. The museum opened in 1986. As of the summer of 1989, a small selection of Air Force artifacts, including paintings, field equipment and uniforms, was on display.

ANTIETAM NATIONAL BATTLEFIELD

Visitor Information: Located 11 miles south of I-70 and one mile north of Sharpsburg. Take the Hagerstown/Sharpsburg exit (exit 29 south) off I-70 onto MD-65 to the battlefield visitor center. Mailing Address: Box 158, Sharpsburg, Maryland 21782. Telephone: (301) 432-5124. Hours: 8:30 am to 5:00 pm daily from Labor Day through Memorial Day, 8:00 am to 6:00 pm daily during the summer (visitor center); park is open dawn to dusk daily year round. Admission: $1.00 per person. Under age 18 and over 62 are admitted free.

Items on Display: Uniforms, Field Equipment, Personal Documents, Official Documents, Maps, Photographs, Paintings/Drawings, Dioramas, Edged Weapons, Side Arms, Shoulder Arms, Field Artillery, Historic Structure (reconstructed Dunker Church, restored

Antietam National Battlefield, continued

Burnside Bridge).

On September 17, 1862, near the town of Sharpsburg, 40,000 Confederate troops led by General Robert E. Lee clashed with 87,000, troops led by General George B. McClellan in the Civil War's bloodiest day of fighting. The battle, which claimed more than 23,000 casualties, ended the first of General Lee's two unsuccessful attempts to carry the war into the North. Pamphlets available at the site's visitor center explain the battle in detail. Period artifacts, including some excavated at the site, are on display.

BRIGADIER GENERAL LEONARD J. RILEY MEMORIAL HOLDING

Visitor Information: Located on Fort Ritchie, 16 miles northeast of Hagerstown. From I-70 in Frederick take US-15 north to Thurmont. In Thurmont take MD-550 west up the mountain for nine miles to the Fort Ritchie main gate. Mailing Address: Fort Ritchie, Maryland 21719-5010. Telephone: (301) 878-5128. Hours: 10:00 am to 2:00 pm Tuesday, Thursday and the first Saturday of each month. Admission: free.

Items on Display: Uniforms, Photographs, Field Artillery, Communications Equipment.

Fort Ritchie's collection of historical artifacts may be rather small by comparison to other military museums, but if you're in the area it's well worth a visit. Key exhibits focus upon the construction of the fort, World War I, World War II, the Seventh Signal Command and the restoration of democracy to the Republic of Grenada (courtesy of U.S. Armed Forces personnel). The Grenada display features part of a Cuban uniform used by a Grenada policeman. Visitors may also thumb through photo albums filled with pictures of World War II activities at the fort.

FORT GEORGE G. MEADE MUSEUM

Visitor Information: Located in Building 4674 on Griffin Avenue on Fort George G. Meade, 30 miles northeast of Washington, D.C. From I-295 (Baltimore-Washington Parkway) take the MD-198 exit and follow signs to the "Main Post." Turn right at the first stoplight on post and stay on Mapes Road to Griffin Avenue. Turn right on Griffin to the museum. Mailing Address: ATTN: AFZI-PTS-MU, Fort

MARYLAND
Fort George G. Meade Museum, continued

George G. Meade, Maryland 20755-5115. Telephone: (301) 677-6966/7054. Hours: 11:00 am to 4:00 pm Wednesday through Saturday, 1:00 pm to 4:00 pm Sunday (subject to change). Admission: free.

Items on Display: Uniforms, Unit Patches, Field Equipment, Official Documents, Photographs, Paintings/Drawings, Dioramas, Battle Streamers, Medals, Edged Weapons, Side Arms, Shoulder Arms, Machine Guns, Mines, Ordnance, Field Artillery, Missiles, Communications Equipment, Medical Equipment, Tracked Vehicles, Wheeled Vehicles, Scale Models (ships/boats).

Exhibits in one gallery at the Fort Meade Museum chronicle the military history of the area surrounding Fort Meade beginning with the American Revolution and continuing on to the establishment of Camp Meade, its transition to a permanent post as Fort Meade, World War II training activities at the fort and the influence of the Vietnam War. Another gallery focuses upon the history and exploits of the 1st U.S. Army from 1918 to the present. Artifacts in the 1st Army gallery include portions of the famous Bridge at Remagen and a large, appropriately bullet-riddled bust of Adolph Hitler that was "liberated" by U.S. service personnel after the fall of Berlin.

Two of the more than ten tracked and wheeled vehicles that stand outside are unique to the Fort Meade Museum. One is the only unaltered Mark VIII tank in the U.S. The other is the FT-17 Renault that was brought back to the U.S. to serve as the memorial to the tank crews of World War I.

FORT McHENRY NATIONAL MONUMENT & HISTORIC SHRINE

Visitor Information: Located at the end of East Fort Avenue in Baltimore. From I-95 take exit 55 and follow the Key Highway to Lawrence Street. Turn left on Lawrence to a left on Fort Avenue and proceed to the park. Mailing Address: End of East Fort Avenue, Baltimore, Maryland 21230-5393. Telephone: (301) 962-4290. Hours: 8:00 am to 5:00 pm daily, open till 8:00 pm mid-June through Labor Day. Admission: $1.00 per person ages 17-61.

Items on Display: Uniforms, Field Equipment, Personal Documents, Official Documents, Maps, Photographs, Paintings/Drawings, Dioramas, Flags, Medals, Edged Weapons, Side Arms, Shoulder Arms, Ordnance, Field Artillery, Coast-Defense Artillery, Rocket,

Medical Equipment, Historic Structure (fort).

Best known as the birthplace of America's national anthem, Fort McHenry was built between 1798 and 1803 to guard the city of Baltimore from hostile ships. Another fort, Fort Whetstone, was built on the same site in 1776, and for the same reasons, though it never came under fire. The same cannot be said for Fort McHenry. During the War of 1812, in September of 1814, Fort McHenry came under heavy bombardment from British ships who sought to neutralize the fort and thus leave Baltimore defenseless. The British attack spanned 25 hours with an estimated 1,500 to 1,800 rounds expended. When the cannonade ended, only four soldiers within the fort's walls had perished and the city of Baltimore remained secure. Pamphlets available at the fort's visitor center tell the Fort McHenry story in detail. Numerous period artifacts are on display in the center and in various original fort buildings.

FORT WASHINGTON

Visitor Information: Located on the Potomac River in Oxon Hill. Take exit 3A south from I-95 (Capital Beltway) for approximately four miles, then turn right onto Fort Washington Road. The fort is at the end of the road. Mailing Address: c/o Headquarters, Fort Washington Park, 1900 Anacostia Drive, S.E., Washington, D.C. 20020. Telephone: (301) 763-4600. Hours: 9:00 am to 5:00 pm daily (fort); 10:00 am to 4:30 pm (visitor center). Admission: $3.00 per vehicle.

Items on Display: Maps, Photographs, Paintings/Drawings, Ordnance, Historic Structures (fort, concrete batteries).

Fort Washington is the second of two forts built at the site. Work was completed at the first fort, Fort Warburton, in 1809. On August 27, 1814, the fort's commander ordered Warburton destroyed to keep it from falling into British hands. Twelve days later, Acting Secretary of War James Monroe ordered that a new fort be built. The urgency associated with Monroe's order subsided when the British fleet sailed for Jamaica later the same year. Work did not begin on the new fort until 1815 and was not completed until 1824.

Fort Washington is a brick-and-masonry fortification surrounded by a dry moat that was originally equipped with a drawbridge. An officers' quarters, a soldiers' barracks and a magazine are adjacent to the parade grounds. A guardroom and the commanding officer's office are

MARYLAND
Fort Washington, continued

a part of the structure surrounding the fort's sally port, or main gateway. Eight concrete batteries were built in the fort's vicinity between 1896-1921 when the fort served as headquarters for the Defenses of the Potomac. Batteries Decatur and White can be seen from the fort today. Battery White is open to the public.

The visitor center contains a small selection of 19-century artifacts and exhibits associated with Fort Washington's history.

NAVAL AIR TEST & EVALUATION MUSEUM

Visitor Information: Located just inside Patuxent Naval Air Station's north gate at the intersection of MD-235 and Shangri-la Drive in Lexington Park. From US-301 take MD-5 south to MD-235 south to the Naval Air Station. Mailing Address: P. O. Box 407, Naval Air Test Center, Patuxent River, Maryland 20670-5000. Telephone: (301) 863-7418. Hours: 10:00 am to 5:00 pm Tuesday through Saturday and 12:00 noon to 5:00 pm Sunday from July through September; 11:00 am to 5:00 pm Tuesday through Saturday and 12:00 noon to 5:00 pm Sunday October through June. Admission: free.

Items on Display: A specific list was not available at press time; however, aircraft, aircraft engines, systems and components are known to be a part of the museum's collection.

The Naval Air Test and Evaluation Museum is the only museum in the country with exhibits about the testing and evaluation of Naval aircraft. Audio-visual and hands-on displays examine the processes involved in testing Naval aircraft, aircraft systems and components. Historic Naval aircraft are on outdoor display.

NOAA'S NATIONAL OCEAN SURVEY DISPLAY CENTER

Visitor Information: Located on the second floor at 6001 Executive Boulevard in Rockville. From I-270, take the Montrose Road exit east to a right onto Executive Boulevard. The National Oceanic and Atmospheric Administration offices in Building 6001 are located behind Building 6005 on the left. Ample parking is available in the shopping center parking lot in the next block on the left. Mailing Address: U.S. Department of Commerce, National Oceanic and Atmospheric Administration, 2nd Floor, 6001 Executive Boulevard,

MARYLAND
NOAA's National Ocean Survey Display Center, continued

Rockville, Maryland 20852. Telephone: (301) 443-8509. Hours: 8:00 am to 4:00 pm Monday through Friday. Admission: free:

Items on Display: Uniforms, Official Documents, Maps, Photographs, Paintings/Drawings, Flags, Medals, Navigational Equipment, Surveying Equipment, Scale Models (ships/boats).

Many people, especially life-long civilians, don't know that the United States has seven, not six, uniformed services. Everyone has heard of the Army, Navy, Marine Corps, Air Force and Coast Guard. Most have heard of the U.S. Public Health Service Corps, too, thanks in large part to the high visibility of a recent Surgeon General of the U.S., who frequently appeared on television and in newspapers wearing his Admiral's uniform. The seventh service, the one many have never heard of, is the National Oceanic and Atmospheric Administration (NOAA) Corps, a small, scientifically elite group of commissioned officers who serve in a broad variety of technical fields. NOAA Corps officers engage in scientific research, command ships, pilot aircraft and, in times of national emergency, serve under the direction of the Department of Defense as members of the Armed Forces. The National Ocean Survey Display Center in Rockville contains artifacts from Corps history and from the history of its predecessors, the U.S. Coast Survey and the Coast and Geodetic Survey.

Old surveying instruments, NOAA Corps uniforms, scale models of NOAA ships and other items are on display. Of special interest: the original manuscript of the first topographic survey produced by the U.S. Coast and Geodetic Survey in 1834 and a mock-up of the bridge of the NOAA ship *Pierce*, with a radar unit, pilot stand, split throttle control console and a brief audio-visual presentation depicting NOAA activities at sea.

U.S. ARMY ORDNANCE MUSEUM

Visitor Information: Located on Aberdeen Proving Ground, mid-way between Baltimore and Washington, D.C. Take exit 85 off I-95 to MD-22 and follow signs to the Aberdeen Proving Ground Military Police Gate. Mailing Address: U.S. Army Ordnance Center and School, Aberdeen Proving Ground, Maryland 21005-5201. Telephone: (301) 278-3602/2396/7472/7473. Hours: 12:00 noon to 4:45 pm Tuesday through Friday, 10:00 am to 4:45 pm weekends (museum); 9:00 am to sundown daily (grounds). Admission: free.

MARYLAND
U.S. Army Ordnance Museum, continued

Items on Display: Uniforms, Field Equipment, Photographs, Paintings/Drawings, Flags, Edged Weapons, Side Arms, Shoulder Arms, Machine Guns, Flame Throwers, Mines, Ordnance, Chemical/Biological Weapons Displays, Field Artillery, Coast-Defense Artillery, Air-Defense Artillery, Rockets/Rocket Launchers, Missiles, Amphibious Landing Craft, Tracked Vehicles.

Museum officials proudly declare that the U.S. Army Ordnance Museum has "the most complete collection of weapons in the world." Exhibits and artifacts both indoors and out provide a walking tour through the evolution and development of numerous types of weapons including tanks, bazookas, artillery pieces, side arms and machine guns. Among the many notable artifacts on outdoor display: a 280mm atomic cannon that weighs 166,638 pounds; the massive, 43,600-pound T-12 general purpose bomb, designed to penetrate German submarine pens reinforced by as many as 50 feet of concrete; and the famous German Leopold Railway Cannon, nicknamed "Anzio Annie" by Allied troops at Anzio, the only German railroad gun known to have survived World War II.

U.S. NAVAL ACADEMY MUSEUM

Visitor Information: Located on the grounds of the U.S. Naval Academy in Annapolis. Exit from US-50/301 in Annapolis onto Rowe Boulevard and proceed through three traffic lights. Turn left in front of the Maryland State House onto College Avenue. Drive two blocks then turn right at the traffic light onto King George Street. Proceed straight ahead for three blocks to gate 1 at the Naval Academy. Parking is available near the Halsey Field House. The museum is a three-block walk away. Civilians are not allowed on the grounds until after 9:00 am. Mailing Address: Annapolis, Maryland 21402-5034. Telephone: (301) 267-2108. Hours: 9:00 am to 5:00 pm Monday through Saturday, 11:00 am to 5:00 Sunday. Closed Thanksgiving, Christmas and New Year's Day. Admission: free.

Items on Display: Uniforms, Personal Documents, Official Documents, Photographs, Paintings/Drawings, Dioramas, Flags, Medals, Edged Weapons, Side Arms, Shoulder Arms, Machine Guns, Ordnance, Naval Artillery, Coast-Defense Artillery, Aircraft (fixed wing), Space Exploration Displays, Ships/Boats, Submarines/Submersible Vehicles, Navigational Equipment, Scale Models (aircraft, ships/boats, submarines/submersible vehicles).

U.S. Naval Academy Museum, continued

MARYLAND

The Naval Academy Museum, in the words of museum officials, "serves as an educational and inspirational resource for the Brigade of Midshipmen at the United States Naval Academy, for other students of American naval history, and for thousands of visitors each year. Through its collections and exhibits the museum contributes to the recognition of history as a basic source of knowledge in advancing the theory and practice of sea power." Through the use of "three dimensional and graphic materials, the museum demonstrates the Navy's role, in war and in peace, in defending and preserving the ideals of our country and mankind." Artifacts from the entire history of the U.S. Navy are on display. Permanent exhibits include outstanding collections of ship and boat models, naval battle prints and naval medals. The U.S. Navy Trophy Flag Collection contains over 600 examples of historic American flags and captured foreign ensigns. The space exploration display focuses upon the 28 astronauts who graduated from the Academy.

The Naval Academy itself is a National Historic Landmark and a walking tour of the grounds is highly recommended. The buildings designed by architect Ernest Flagg and built in the Beaux Art style between 1899-1908 are of special interest, as is the chapel which contains the crypt of John Paul Jones.

USS *TORSK*

Visitor Information: Located in Baltimore's Inner Harbor. The Torsk is moored at Pier III alongside the National Aquarium. From I-95, follow signs to the Inner Harbor. Mailing Address: c/o Baltimore Maritime Museum, Pier IV, Pratt Street, Baltimore, Maryland 21202. Telephone: (301) 396-3854/5528. Hours: 9:30 am to 4:30 pm daily from October through May, 9:30 am to 7:00 pm June through September. Admission: $2.50 per adult, $1.00 per child under age 12.

Items on Display: Ships/Boats, Submarines/Submersible Vehicles.

Commissioned in December, 1944, the USS *Torsk* earned the distinction of firing the last torpedoes and sinking the last Japanese combatant ships of World War II when she sank two Japanese coast defense vessels on August 14, 1945. In later years, she participated in the blockade of Cuba and served as a training vessel for U.S. Naval Reserve personnel. In 1972, when the *Torsk* was transferred to the state of Maryland after nearly three decades of service, she held the world record for the greatest number of dives, a record that will probably never be broken. Veteran submariners are often on hand

MARYLAND
USS Torsk, continued

topside to answer questions about the submarine's history and exploits. Visitors to the Inner Harbor may also tour the U.S. Coast Guard Lightship *Chesapeake* and the U.S. Coast Guard Cutter *Taney*. The admissions fee above includes admission to all three vessels.

Other Military Museums, Historic Sites & Exhibits in Maryland

Armory Wargaming Museum, 4145 Amos Avenue, Baltimore, Maryland 21215. Telephone: (301) 764-8100.

Fifth Regiment Armory Museum, Huffman and Preston Streets, Baltimore, Maryland. Telephone: (301) 576-6000.

Fort Frederick State Park and Museum, P. O. Box 177, Big Pool, Maryland 21711. Telephone: (301) 842-2155.

Gathland Museum, 900 Arnoldstown Road, Jefferson, Maryland 21755. Telephone: (301) 293-2420.

NASA/Goddard Space Flight Center, Visitor Center, Code 130, Greenbelt, Maryland 20771. Telephone: (301) 286-8981.

Point Lookout State Park and Visitor Center, Star Route Box 48, Scotland, Maryland 20687. Telephone: (301) 872-5688.

Star-Spangled Banner Flag House and 1812 Museum, 844 East Pratt Street, Baltimore, Maryland 21202. Telephone: (301) 837-1793.

U.S. Coast Guard Cutter *Taney*, c/o Baltimore Maritime Museum, Pier IV, Pratt Street, Baltimore, Maryland 21202. Telephone: (301) 396-3854/5528.

U.S. Coast Guard Lightship *Chesapeake*, c/o The Baltimore Maritime Museum, Pier IV, Pratt Street, Baltimore, Maryland 21202. Telephone: (301) 396-3854/5528.

US Frigate *Constellation*, Constellation Dock, Baltimore, Maryland 21202. Telephone: (301) 539-4018/1797.

MASSACHUSETTS

ANCIENT & HONORABLE ARTILLERY COMPANY

Visitor Information: Located in downtown Boston in Faneuil Hall. From I-93 north or south take the Court Street exit west to New Congress Street. Turn right (north) on New Congress to a right on South Market Street. Faneuil Hall is on the left. Mailing Address: Faneuil Hall, Boston, Massachusetts 02109. Telephone: (617) 227-1638. Hours: 10:00 am to 4:00 pm Monday through Friday. Admission: free.

Items on Display: Uniforms, Unit Patches, Field Equipment, Personal Documents, Official Documents, Maps, Photographs, Paintings/Drawings, Flags, Battle Streamers, Medals, Edged Weapons, Side Arms, Shoulder Arms, Machine Guns, Ordnance, Field Artillery, Coast-Defense Artillery, Aircraft (fixed wing).

Artifacts from the Revolutionary War to World War II are on display at the museum in Faneuil Hall, which was donated to the city of Boston by merchant Peter Faneuil in 1742. The hall's first floor has always served as a market place. The its second floor serves as a meeting hall and has been called the "Cradle of Liberty" because of the historic protests that colonists made here against British policies in the New World.

BATTLESHIP COVE

Visitor Information: Located in Fall River off I-195 between Bedford and Providence, Rhode Island. Take exit 5 off I-195 into Fall River and follow signs. Mailing Address: Fall River, Massachusetts 02721. Telephone: (508) 678-1100. Hours: 9:00 am to 5:00 pm daily (open till 6:00 pm from June 1 through August 31). Admission: $6.00 per adult, $3.00 per child ages 6-13.

Items on Display: Uniforms, Unit Patches, Field Equipment, Personal Documents, Officials Documents, Maps, Photographs, Paintings/Drawings, Flags, Medals, Edged Weapons, Side Arms, Shoulder Arms, Machine Guns, Mines, Ordnance, Air-Defense Artillery, Rockets/Rocket Launchers, Aircraft (fixed wing), Ships/Boats, Amphibious Landing Craft, Submarine/Submersible Vehicles, Submarine Equipment, Navigational Equipment, Communications Equipment, Medical Equipment, Scale Models (aircraft, amphibious landing craft, tracked vehicles).

MASSACHUSETTS
Battleship Cove, continued

Along with Patriot's Point Naval and Maritime Museum in South Carolina and the Naval and Serviceman's Park in New York, Battleship Cove has one of the finest collections of historic naval vessels and related artifacts and displays in the country.

All nine decks of the battleship *Massachusetts* are open for self-guided tours. Longer than two football fields and weighing 35,000 tons, the *Massachusetts* participated in 35 battles during World War II without the loss of a single crewmember. Massachusetts' World War II Memorial is on the battleship. The USS *Joseph P. Kennedy, Jr.*, a Gearing-class destroyer named for President John Kennedy's older brother, served in Korea and Vietnam and houses Massachusetts' official Korean and Vietnam War Memorial. The Admiral Arleigh Burke National Destroyermen's Museum on board the Kennedy chronicles the history of the destroyer and offers insight into the day-to-day lives of its crewmembers. Visitors may also tour a World War II attack sub, the USS *Lionfish*. Every part of the sub is open, from the conning tower and control room to the crew's living quarters. An amphibious landing craft is also on display, along with the only two P.T. boats from World War II on display anywhere. (The P.T. Boat Museum is listed separately in this book.)

The visitor center on shore contains numerous exhibits and artifacts.

BOSTON NATIONAL HISTORICAL PARK

Visitor Information: Located in downtown Boston and adjacent Charlestown. One visitor center is located at 15 State Street across from the Old State House in downtown Boston. Another is located at the Charlestown Navy Yard. The park is accessible via I-93. Signs are posted. Mailing Addresses: Charlestown Navy Yard, Charlestown, Massachusetts 02129; Superintendent, 15 State Street, Boston, Massachusetts 02109. Telephone: (617) 242-5641. Hours: varies according to site. Admission: free.

Items on Display: A specific list was not available at press time. The USS *Constitution* Museum at the Charlestown Navy Yard, however, contains military and naval artifacts dating back to the Revolution. Two historic warships are on display near the museum. The USS *Constitution* and Museum and the USS *Cassin Young* are listed separately in this book.

The Boston National Historical Park consists of a number of historic sites, including the Charlestown Navy Yard, the Bunker Hill

Boston National Historical Park, continued

MASSACHUSETTS

Monument, Dorcester Heights National Historic Site, the Paul Revere House and Faneuil Hall (listed separately in this book as the Ancient and Honorable Artillery Company). Most of the sites are connected by the Freedom Trail, a three-mile-long trail that provides visitors with a walking tour of 16 historic sites and structures in downtown Boston and Charlestown. Park officials suggest that visitors who want to visit all the sites along the trail should plan to spend the entire day.

FORT DEVENS MUSEUM

Visitor Information: Located 35 miles northwest of Boston on Fort Devens in Building P-5, Antietam Street. Take MA-2 to the Fort Devens exit onto Jackson Road. Proceed on Jackson Road to the stop sign at Givry Street and turn left. Then turn right onto Sherman Avenue and drive past the post's HQ to Antietam. Turn right onto Antietam and follows signs to the museum. Mailing Address: ATTN: AFZD-PTMS-H, Fort Devens, Massachusetts 01433-5090. Telephone: (508) 796-3163. Hours: 10:00 am to 4:00 pm Monday through Saturday. Admission: free.

Items on Display: Uniforms, Unit Patches, Field Equipment, Photographs, Medals, Edged Weapons, Side Arms, Shoulder Arms, Machine Guns, Mines, Ordnance, Field Artillery, Wheeled Vehicles.

Exhibits at the Fort Devens Museum chronicle the history of the fort from its beginnings as Camp Devens in 1917. American, German and Japanese artifacts from the two world wars are on display and include a ceremonial Nazi dagger, a 3-inch model 1902 field gun, an 81mm mortar bomb, a German anti-tank mine, a training kit used to familiarize troops with Japanese mines and American posters from the two world wars.

P.T. BOAT MUSEUM & LIBRARY

Visitor Information: Located on board the USS *Massachusetts* at Battleship Cove in Fall River, Massachusetts (see the Battleship Cove listing for driving directions). Mailing Address: P. O. Box 109, Memphis, Tennessee 38101. Telephone: (901) 272-9980. Hours: 9:00 am to 5:00 pm daily (open till 6:00 pm from June 1 through August 31). Admission: $6.00 per adult, $3.00 per child ages 6-13.

Items on Display: Uniforms, Unit Patches, Field Equipment, Personal Documents, Official Documents, Maps, Photographs,

MASSACHUSETTS
P.T. Boat Museum & Library, continued

Paintings/Drawings, Dioramas, Flags, Coast-Defense Artillery, Air-Defense Artillery, Ships/Boats, Submarines/Submersible Vehicles, Navigational Equipment, Scale Models (ships/boats, submarines/submersible vehicles).

The P.T. Boat Museum and Library on board the USS *Massachusetts* is dedicated to the preservation of artifacts and memorabilia from the famed P.T. Boat squadrons of World War II. Displays at the museum focus upon the 43 commissioned squadrons that operated during World War II, the 21 Tenders (or mother ships) that supported P.T. Boat operations and the far-flung bases out of which the P.T. Boat squadrons operated.

An authentic World War II Quonset Hut beside the battleship houses two restored P.T. Boats, an 80' Elco Patrol Torpedo Boat (PT 619) and a 78' Higgins (PT 796). The Higgins is the only wooden World War II P.T. Boat on display anywhere and was used in President John F. Kennedy's inaugural parade, with PT-796 temporarily changed to PT-109. Among the P.T. Boat models on display are some that were used in the making of the Otto Preminger film "In Harm's Way," which starred John Wayne and Kirk Douglas. Other items on display: a one-man Japanese suicide submarine and other captured Japanese and German artifacts including propaganda leaflets and binoculars.

SPRINGFIELD ARMORY NATIONAL HISTORIC SITE

Visitor Information: Located off I-91 in the city of Springfield at One Armory Square, Springfield, Massachusetts 01105. Take I-91 to State Street in Springfield. From State Street turn left onto Federal Street, then left again onto the grounds of the Springfield Technical Community College and follow signs to the armory. Telephone: (413) 734-6477. Hours: 8:00 am to 4:30 pm daily. Closed Thanksgiving, Christmas and New Year's Day. Admission: free.

Items on Display: Side Arms, Shoulder Arms, Ordnance, Historic Structures (arsenal building, master armorer's house, CO's quarters).

Established in 1777 by order of General George Washington, the Springfield Armory was the nation's first arsenal. Originally a safe, centrally located storage facility for weapons and ammunition, the armory ultimately became one of the key facilities for the design, development and production of military small arms in the world.

MASSACHUSETTS
Springfield Armory National Historic Site, continued

The main arsenal building dates from 1847 and houses one of the world's largest collections of small arms, many of which were designed and manufactured at Springfield. The Model 1903 bolt-action rifle developed at Springfield is reputedly one of the most accurate rifles ever made. The army adopted the famous M-1 Garand, developed at the armory by John C. Garand, in 1936 and the Marines followed suit in 1940. General Patton called the M-1 "the greatest weapon ever made." The armory's last small arm was the M-14, so effective that it alone replaced four other military rifles.

USS *CONSTITUTION* MUSEUM

Visitor Information: Located in Building 22 at the Charlestown Navy Yard in downtown Boston. Accessible via I-93. Follow the brown and white signs. Mailing Address: P. O. Box 1812, Boston, Massachusetts 02129. Telephone: (617) 242-0543 or 426-1812. Hours: 9:00 am to 6:00 pm daily during the summer, 9:00 am to 5:00 pm daily during spring and fall, 10:00 am to 4:00 pm Monday through Friday and 9:00 am to 5:00 pm weekends during the winter. Admission: $2.00 per adult, $1.50 per senior citizen, $0.50 per student.

Items on Display: Uniforms, Field Equipment, Personal Documents, Official Documents, Maps, Paintings/Drawings, Flags, Medals, Edged Weapons, Side Arms, Shoulder Arms, Ordnance, Ships/Boats, Navigational Equipment, Medical Equipment, Scale Models (ships/boats), Historic Structure (1832 pump house).

Exhibits at the USS *Constitution* Museum focus on the history of the world's oldest commissioned warship, the USS *Constitution*. Commissioned in 1797 and named by George Washington for the document she would defend at sea, the USS *Constitution's* greatest victories occurred during the War of 1812, when she proved invincible against a numerically far superior British fleet. According to legend, the Constitution acquired her famous nickname, "Old Ironsides," during her battle against the HMS *Guerriere* in August of 1812. The story says that shots from the *Guerriere*, a 38-gun British frigate, made no impression on the ship's planking and fell into the sea. Seeing this, a British sailor shouted, "Her sides are made of iron!" The *Constitution's* victory over the *Guerriere* became a celebrated event, strengthened American resolve and renewed a young nation's belief in its equally young Navy. Pamphlets available at the museum chronicle the ship's entire history in detail. The ship itself is berthed outside the museum and is open for tours.

MASSACHUSETTS
USS *Constitution* Museum, continued

One of the museum's most popular exhibits is a computer game that simulates the *Constitution's* crossing of the Atlantic in 1803. Visitors are invited to make key decisions that confronted the ship's captain on the long voyage to Europe. Other exhibits focus on the sailor's life, the ship's more notable captains and efforts undertaken over the last two centuries to preserve the ship. Numerous naval artifacts, many dating from the War of 1812, are on display.

Visitors to the Navy Yard may also tour the USS *Cassin Young*, one of 174 Fletcher-class destroyers built during World War II. While serving the Pacific Theater, the *Cassin Young* participated in the invasions of Saipan, Guam, Tinian, the Philippines, Leyte, Luzon and Iwo Jima. The ship earned the Navy Unit Commendation medal and four battle stars during the war.

Other Military Museums, Historic Sites & Exhibits in Massachusetts

Drummer Boy Museum, Route 6A, Brewster, Massachusetts 02631. Telephone: (508) 896-3823.

Fort Sewall, c/o Marblehead Recreation and Parks Department, 10 School Street, Marblehead, Massachusetts 01945. Telephone: (617) 631-2868.

General Sylvanus Thayer Birthplace, 786 Washington Street, Braintree, Massachusetts. Telephone: (617) 848-1640.

Higgins Armory Museum, 100 Barber Avenue, Worcester, Massachusetts 01606. Telephone: (508) 853-6015.

Minuteman National Historical Park, P. O. Box 160, Concord, Massachusetts 01742. Telephone: (508) 369-6944.

MICHIGAN

KALAMAZOO AVIATION HISTORY MUSEUM

Visitor Information: Located at 3101 East Milham Road, Kalamazoo, Michigan 49002. From I-94 take exit 78 south onto Portage Road past the Kalamazoo County Airport entrance to Milham Road. Turn left on Milham and drive one quarter mile to the museum entrance. Telephone: (616) 382-6555. Hours: 10:00 am to 5:00 pm Monday through Saturday, 1:00 pm to 5:00 pm Sunday. Admission: fee charged.

Items on Display: Uniforms, Flight Equipment, Photographs, Dioramas, Flags, Ordnance, Aircraft (fixed wing), Navigational Equipment, Scale Models (aircraft).

One of the finest World War II-era aviation museums in the country, the Kalamazoo Aviation History Museum houses artifacts, exhibits and historic aircraft that chronicle the contributions made by Allied air power to the defeat of the Axis forces. Visitors may watch as museum personnel restore old aircraft to airworthy status in the restoration section of the museum's hangar. Static and airworthy fighter, bomber and trainer aircraft on display in the hangar give visitors an up-close look at many of the most famous aircraft of the World War II era. The museum's Grumman XF8F-1D Bearcat, Grumman F6F-5N Hellcat, Goodyear FG-1D Corsair, and its splendid Curtiss P-40N-35CU Warhawk, one of the famous "Flying Tigers," are all airworthy craft, as are many others in the museum's growing collection.

SELFRIDGE MILITARY AIR MUSEUM

Visitor Information: Located on Selfridge Air National Guard Base, 25 miles northeast of Detroit. From I-94 eastbound take exit 240 left onto Hall Road and proceed for one and a half miles and turn right at the base's main gate. Turn right on the perimeter road and drive one quarter mile to the museum. Mailing Address: 127 TFW/MU, Box 43, Selfridge Air National Guard Base, Michigan 48045. Telephone: (313) 466-5035. Hours: 1:00 pm to 5:00 pm Sunday from April 1 through October 31. Weekday visits by groups of 20 or more may be arranged in advance. Admission: free.

Items on Display: Uniforms, Field Equipment, Photographs, Paintings/Drawings, Edged Weapons, Machine Guns, Ordnance, Aircraft (fixed wing), Scale Models (aircraft).

MICHIGAN
Selfridge Military Air Museum, continued

Exhibits at the Selfridge Military Air Museum chronicle the history of Selfridge from its establishment as Selfridge Field in 1917 and depict the missions and activities of units stationed here. Indoor displays include aircraft engines, some cut-away for a look at the inner workings of the engines; scale models of aircraft flown by units at Selfridge; and memorabilia from the different services that have had units stationed here. Currently, Selfridge is the only reserve forces base with permanently assigned units from five of the nation's seven uniformed services. Aircraft on outdoor display include the Convair C-131D Samaritan (under restoration), the Goodyear FG-1D Corsair I, a North American F-86A Sabre and nearly 15 other aircraft.

USS *SILVERSIDES*

Visitor Information: Located in the channel between Lake Michigan and Muskegon Lake in Muskegon, approximately 40 miles northeast of Grand Rapids. Take I-96 east from Grand Rapids to MI-31 north to Muskegon. Call for specific driving directions in Muskegon. Mailing Address: c/o Great Lakes Naval and Maritime Museum, P. O. Box 1692, Muskegon, Michigan 49443. Telephone: (616) 755-1230 (ticket booth) or (616) 722-3751 (Chamber of Commerce). Hours: 10:00 am to 6:00 pm daily from May 1 through September 30, weekends in April and October. Admission: $2.50 per adult, $1.50 per senior and child ages 5-11.

Items on Display: Submarines/Submersible Vehicles.

Winner of four Presidential Unit Citations—the highest award Navy ships can win—and 12 battle stars, the USS *Silversides* is the nation's most successful surviving World War II-era submarine. Only two submarines scored more kills than the Silversides' 23. Only four other subs destroyed more enemy cargo. None of the other subs exists today.

One of the most publicized surgical procedures of World War II took place on the *Silversides* when a Pharmacist's Mate removed a crewman's gangrenous appendix. Though the Pharmacist's Mate had no prior surgical experience, his efforts proved so successful that just six days later the crewman was standing watch. The operation was dramatized in the movie "Destination Tokyo."

After the war, the *Silversides* served as a reserve training submarine until it was decommissioned in 1969. Restoration work on the

USS *Silversides,* continued

submarine began in 1972. Her diesel engines and most of her systems now operate as they did during World War II.

Other Military Museums, Historic Sites & Exhibits in Michigan

Fort de Baude Museum, 334 North State Street, Saint Ignace, Michigan 49781. Telephone: (906) 648-8686.

Fort Machilimackinic, Mackinaw City, Michigan 49702. Telephone: (616) 436-5563.

Fort Mackinac Museum, Mackinac Island, Michigan 49757. Telephone: (906) 847-3328.

Fort Saint Joseph Museum, 508 East Main Street, Niles, Michigan 49120. Telephone: (616) 683-4702, extension 236/212.

Fort Wilkens Historic Complex, Copper Harbor, Michigan 49918. Telephone: (906) 289-4215.

Historic Fort Wayne, 6325 West Jefferson Avenue, Detroit, Michigan 48209. Telephone: (313)297-9360.

Michigan Space Center, 2111 Emmons Road, Jackson, Michigan 49201. Telephone: (517) 787-4425.

Michigan's Own—Military and Space Museum, 245 South Main, Frankenmuth, Michigan 48734. Telephone: (517) 652-8005.

Revolutionary War Sloop *Welcome,* P. O. Box 873, Mackinaw City, Michigan 49701. Telephone: (616) 436-5563.

Saginaw Gig Boat, c/o Saginaw County Historical Museum, 500 Federal Avenue, Saginaw, Michigan 48609. Telephone: (517) 752-2861.

YP 587 Patrol Craft, c/o Naval Sea Cadets Corps, 26400 W. Eleven Mile, Southfield, Michigan 40834. Telephone: (313) 352-6630.

MINNESOTA

HISTORIC FORT SNELLING

Visitor Information: Located one mile east of the Twin Cities International Airport in St. Paul. Take the Fort Snelling exits off MN-5 and MN-55. Mailing Address: Fort Snelling History Center, St. Paul, Minnesota 55111. Telephone: (612) 726-1171. Hours: 10:00 am to 5:00 pm daily from May through October. Admission: $2.00 per adult, $1.00 per senior citizen and child.

Items on Display: Uniforms, Field Equipment, Dioramas, Edged Weapons, Shoulder Arms, Field Artillery, Historic Structure (reconstructed and restored fort.)

Built by the 5th Regiment of Infantry at the junction of the Mississippi and Minnesota Rivers between 1819 and 1825, Fort Snelling was one of a chain of forts that stretched from Lake Michigan to the Missouri River. The troops that garrisioned these remote outposts had similar missions: ending British control of the lucrative fur trade, winning Indian support and cooperation away from the British, enforcing American laws, apprehending law breakers and protecting travelers and traders. Fort Snelling, as the northernmost fort in the chain, quickly became the central location for trade and commercial activities in the Upper Mississippi Valley. By the mid-1800s, however, the establishment of forts further west lessened Fort Snelling's importance and it became a supply depot in 1851. Reactivated as a training center during the Civil War, Fort Snelling remained an active post, fulfilling recruiting and training missions, until final deactivation in 1946.

Today the old fort has been restored and reconstructed to its 1820's appearance. Living history demonstrations occur daily, with staff members in period garb marching on the parade ground, tending the blacksmith shop or talking to visitors about pioneer life.

MINNESOTA AIR GUARD MUSEUM

Visitor Information: Located on the Air National Guard Base at the Minneapolis-St. Paul International Airport in downtown Minneapolis. Drive south from the intersection of Crosstown Highway 62 and Hiawatha Avenue (MN-55) to the airport/base. Mailing Address: P. O. Box 11598, St. Paul, Minnesota 55111. Telephone: (612) 725-5609. Hours: 10:00 am to 4:00 pm Saturday and 12:00 noon to 4:00 pm Sunday from mid-April through mid-October. Admission: free.

Minnesota Air Guard Museum, continued

Items on Display: Uniforms, Unit Patches, Official Documents, Photographs, Aircraft (fixed wing).

Chronologically arranged displays of artifacts, photographs, personal memorabilia and other items trace the history of the Minnesota Air Guard from the 1920s to the present. Historic aircraft used by Air Guard personnel on display outdoors include an F-94A all-weather jet interceptor, a C-131 transport plane, an O-47A observation plane and a BC-1A trainer.

MINNESOTA MILITARY MUSEUM

Visitor Information: Located on Camp Ripley north of Little Falls, a short distance northeast of US-10. Drive east on MN-115 from US-10 or west on MN-115 from MN-371 to Camp Ripley. Mailing Address: Camp Ripley, Little Falls, Minnesota 56345. Telephone: (612) 632-6631, extension 374. Hours: 11:00 am to 7:00 Tuesday through Sunday from Memorial Day weekend to Labor Day weekend. Open other times of the year by special request. Admission: free.

Items on Display: Uniforms, Unit Patches, Field Equipment, Personal Documents, Official Documents, Maps, Photographs, Paintings/Drawings, Flags, Medals, Edged Weapons, Side Arms, Shoulder Arms, Machine Guns, Flame Throwers, Ordnance, Field Artillery, Coast-Defense Artillery, Air-Defense Artillery, Aircraft (fixed wing, rotary wing), Amphibious Landing Craft, Tracked Vehicles, Scale Models (fort).

Formerly known as the Camp Ripley Interpretive Center, the Minnesota Military Museum is the official museum for the Minnesota Army National Guard. The museum's mission is twofold: to preserve artifacts from the history of Minnesota's militia and National Guard units and to interpret military history as experienced by citizens of the state. Special exhibits focus on the experiences of Minnesota citizens in the nation's wars since 1858, Minnesota militia and National Guard units since 1856, Minnesota's frontier forts and the roles they played and Minnesota Medal of Honor recipients. Another exhibit, "The Footlocker," contains memorabilia and war souvenirs collected by Minnesotans during their service overseas.

PLANES OF FAME AIR MUSEUM

Visitor Information: Located at the northwest corner of the Flying Cloud Field in Eden Prairie, a suburb of Minneapolis. From I-494,

MINNESOTA
Planes of Fame Air Museum, continued

take highway 169 south to county road 1 (Pioneer Trail). Turn west and drive to the northwest corner of the field. Signs are posted. Mailing Address: 14771 Pioneer Trail, Eden Prairie, Minnesota 55344. Telephone: (612) 941-2633. Hours: 11:00 am to 5:00 pm weekends from Memorial Day through Labor Day. Admission: $5.00 per adult, $2.00 per child ages 9-17.

Items on Display: Uniforms, Unit Patches, Photographs, Paintings/Drawings, Flags, Medals, Air-Defense Artillery, Aircraft (fixed wing), Scale Models (aircraft).

In the words of museum officials, the Planes of Fame Air Museum "is dedicated to preserving our precious American aviation history and to educating the public about the contribution air power made to the Allies' victory during World War II." Exhibits about World War II air power and artifacts from World War II-era aviation are on hand in the museum building, where aerial combat films may be viewed. The museum's main attraction, though, is the significant number of authentically restored and air-worthy World War II aircraft in its collection, including the FG-1D Corsair, the F6F-5 Hellcat, the F8F Bearcat, a B-25J Mitchell bomber, a Russian YAK-11 Trainer and others. Many of these planes are flown on a regular basis.

Other Military Museums, Historic Sites & Exhibits in Minnesota

Fort Belmont, Highway 71 South, Jackson, Minnesota 56143. Telephone: (507) 847-3261.

Fort Ridgely and Fort Ridgely Interpretive Center, Fort Ridgely State Park, Highway 4 (Route 1, Box 29), Fairfax, Minnesota 55332. Telephone: (507) 426-7888.

MISSISSIPPI

BEAUVOIR—THE JEFFERSON DAVIS SHRINE

Visitor Information: Located on the Gulf Coast just west of Biloxi. From I-10, exit onto I-110 south to US-90 west for approximately five miles to the shrine on the right. Signs are posted. Mailing Address: Box 200, West Beach Boulevard, Biloxi, Mississippi 39531. Telephone: (601) 388-1313. Hours: 9:00 am to 5:00 pm daily. Closed Christmas. Admission: $4.00 per adult, $3.00 per senior citizen and active duty military, $2.00 per child ages 6-16.

Items on Display: Uniforms, Field Equipment, Personal Documents, Official Documents, Maps, Photographs, Paintings/Drawings, Dioramas, Flags, Medals, Edged Weapons, Side Arms, Shoulder Arms, Ordnance, Medical Equipment, Historic Structure (last home of Jefferson Davis).

Beauvoir—French for "beautiful view"—is the elegant, ante-bellum mansion in which Jefferson Davis, President of the Confederate States of America, spent the last years of his life. Here he wrote his famous memoir of the Civil War years, *The Rise and Fall of the Confederate Government*. Here he is said to have regained the peace of mind and serenity that the war years and his subsequent imprisonment at Fort Monroe had taken from him.

The first floor of the mansion is a Davis family museum, containing personal mementos and period furnishings, many of which belonged to Jefferson Davis and his wife and daughter, who lived here with him.

The old hospital building on the grounds now houses a Confederate Museum, with numerous period artifacts and displays about the war. The Tomb of the Unknown Soldier of the Confederate States of America is located in the Confederate Cemetery a short walk from the mansion, where more than 700 former Confederate soldiers and family members are buried, all of whom lived in the home between 1904 and 1957 when it served as the Jefferson Davis Memorial Home for Confederate Soldiers and Sailors.

GRAND GULF MILITARY MONUMENT PARK

Visitor Information: Located ten miles northwest of Port Gibson off MS-61. Drive south from Vicksburg or north from Port Gibson on MS-61 to the Grand Gulf exit and proceed seven miles to the park. Mailing Address: Route 2, Box 389, Fort Gibson, Mississippi 39150.

MISSISSIPPI
Grand Gulf Military Monument Park, continued

Telephone: (601) 437-5911. Hours: 8:00 am to 12:00 noon and 1:00 pm to 5:00 pm Monday through Saturday, 10:00 am to 6:00 pm Sunday. Admission: $1.00 per adult, $0.50 per accompanied child.

Items on Display: Uniforms, Field Equipment, Personal Documents, Maps, Photographs, Paintings/Drawings, Dioramas, Flags, Medals, Edged Weapons, Side Arms, Shoulder Arms, Ordnance, Field Artillery, Medical Equipment, Scale Models (ships/boats), Historic Structures (forts).

Grand Gulf began as a small, French settlement on the Mississippi River in the early 1700s. By the mid-1800s, the cotton industry's use of Grand Gulf as a major port for the shipment of cotton to northern factories had transformed the town into a prosperous, thriving community with nearly 1,000 residents, a hospital, two newspapers and numerous other businesses. Its prosperity, however, ended when the unpredictable currents of the Mississippi shifted and leveled the town's business district. The Civil War completed what nature had begun.

Twice occupied by Union troops, who burned what few buildings remained before their second withdrawal from the area, Grand Gulf remained largely abandoned until General Ulysses S. Grant's plans for the conquest of Vicksburg to the north once again brought Grand Gulf onto center stage. Grant realized that in order to divide the Confederate forces along the Mississippi, he would need to capture all Confederate installations along the river's banks. After Flag Officer David Farragut's naval forces captured Baton Rouge and Natchez, only Vicksburg remained to be won. When direct assaults on Vicksburg proved unsuccessful and costly, Grant retreated downriver and sought to land at Grand Gulf, hoping to mount an assault from the east on Vicksburg. But Confederate General John Pemberton outguessed Grant by ordering his troops to garrison Forts Cobun and Wade at Grand Gulf and repulse any Union attempts to cross the river. The Confederate defenses proved adequate to the task and forced Grant even further down the west bank of the river, where he finally managed to cross at Bruinsburg with little resistance. Soon thereafter, he took the town of Port Gibson, which left the Confederate troops at Grand Gulf, fortified for a western assault, outflanked and outnumbered. The Confederates abandoned the town, Grant marched north toward Vicksburg and the history of Grand Gulf came to an end.

Today the museum at the Grand Gulf Military Monument Park houses numerous artifacts from the Civil War era. Several buildings

Grand Gulf Military Monument Park, continued

from Grand Gulf's heyday as a busy port town have been reconstructed, including a church, a watermill, a carriage house and a pavilion.

VICKSBURG NATIONAL MILITARY PARK/ USS *CAIRO* MUSEUM

Visitor Information: Located in the northeastern section of the city of Vicksburg. The park entrance and visitor center are located on Clay Street (US-80), one mile off I-20. Mailing Address: Vicksburg National Military Park (USS *Cairo* Museum), 3201 Clay Street, Vicksburg, Mississippi 39180. Telephone: (601) 636-2199. Hours: 9:00 am to 5:00 pm daily. Closed Christmas. Admission: $3.00 per vehicle to the park; no admission fee for the museum.

Items on Display: Field Equipment, Photographs, Paintings/Drawings, Edged Weapons, Side Arms, Shoulder Arms, Field Artillery, Ordnance, Ships/Boats, Scale Models (ships/boats), Medical Equipment.

After his victories at Port Gibson and Grand Gulf, General Ulysses S. Grant marched along the route of the Southern Railroad of Mississippi, ultimately destined for Vicksburg, the last remaining Confederate stronghold along the banks of the Mississippi River. After defeating Confederate forces at the battles of Champion Hill and Big Black River, Grant prepared for a quick assault on Vicksburg from the east. But after both his first and second assaults failed to breach Vicksburg's formidable defenses, Grant realized that only a siege would bring it down. He ordered Union gunboats to bombard the city from the river and set up batteries of artillery to pound the city from the east. The Confederate commander soon saw the hopeless position he now occupied and after negotiating with the Union general agreed to surrender. The visitor center at the park contains artifacts from the battle for Vicksburg and displays that interpret the significance of its capture by the Union.

The USS *Cairo* Museum, between tour stops seven and eight, houses artifacts found on board the first vessel ever sunk by an electronically detonated mine. On December 12, 1862, the Union ironclad *Cairo* was proceeding up the Mississippi toward Vicksburg when mines tore two holes in its hull. Though it sank within minutes, no lives were lost. Rediscovered in 1956 and finally lifted, in three pieces, from the muddy waters of the Mississippi in 1964, the *Cairo* offered historians a unique opportunity to gain insight into the

MISSISSIPPI
Vicksburg National Military Park, continued

lives of Civil War-era sailors. Numerous artifacts were recovered from the Cairo, many of them personal items owned by those who lived on board, including shaving gear, pipes, toothbrushes, tobacco, soap and a domino set. Many types of military gear were found on board as well and are on display. The *Cairo* itself rests outside the museum on a concrete foundation, where restoration work is largely completed.

Other Military Museums, Historic Sites & Exhibits in Mississippi

Battlefield Park, c/o Jackson Convention and Visitors Bureau, Box 1450, Jackson, Mississippi 39205. Telephone: (601) 960-1891.

Brices Cross Roads Museum, Box 100, Baldwyn, Mississippi 38824. Telephone: (601) 365-9371.

Brices Cross Roads National Battlefield Site, c/o Natchez Trace Parkway, Rural Route 1, NT-143, Tupelo, Mississippi 38801. Telephone: (601) 842-1572.

Fort Massachusetts, c/o Gulf Islands National Seashore, 3500 Park Road, Ocean Springs, Mississippi 39564. Telephone: (602) 875-0821.

Mississippi Military Museum, P. O. Box 627, (120 N. State Street), Jackson, Mississippi 39205. Telephone: (601) 354-7555.

NASA/John C. Stennis Space Center, Visitor Center, John C. Stennis Space Center, Mississippi 39529. Telephone: (601) 688-3341.

Northeast Mississippi Museum, Box 993, Corinth, Mississippi 38834. Telephone: (601) 286-6403.

Tupelo National Battlefield, c/o Natchez Trace Parkway, Rural Route 1, NT-143, Tupelo, Mississippi 38801. Telephone: (601) 842-1572.

MISSOURI

CIVIL WAR MUSEUM OF JACKSON COUNTY

Visitor Information: Located off US-50 in Lone Jack, 15 miles southeast of Independence. Take US-50 to the Lone Jack exit and drive exit block south on Highway 150 to the museum. Mailing Address: Route 1, Lone Jack, Missouri 64070. Telephone: (816) 566-2272. Hours: 9:00 am to 5:00 pm Wednesday through Sunday from April 15 to October 15. Admission: $1.00 per adult, $0.50 per child.

Items on Display: Uniforms, Field Equipment, Personal Documents, Official Documents, Maps, Photographs, Paintings/Drawings, Dioramas, Edged Weapons, Shoulder Arms, Ordnance, Medical Equipment.

Exhibits about the Battle of Lone Jack, the Battle of Westport and other significant Civil War engagements in the Jackson County area are on display in the Civil War Museum of Jackson County, along with original artifacts used at the Battle of Lone Jack and other items from the time period. A nine-and-a-half minute audio-visual program acquaints visitors with Jackson County's Civil War legacy. Living history interpretations of Civil War camp life and the conditions under which the ordinary soldier lived and fought occur on selected weekends during the summer.

FORT LEONARD WOOD MUSEUM

Visitor Information: Located on Fort Leonard Wood, 85 miles northeast of Springfield. Take the Fort Leonard Wood exit off I-44 and follow signs to the museum. Mailing Address: ATTN: ATZT-PTM-OM, Fort Leonard Wood, Missouri 65473-5165. Telephone: (314) 368-4249. Hours: 10:00 am to 4:00 pm Monday through Saturday. Admission: free.

Items on Display: Uniforms, Unit Patches, Field Equipment, Personal Documents, Official Documents, Flags, Battle Streamers, Medals, Edged Weapons, Side Arms, Shoulder Arms, Machine Guns, Flame Throwers, Mines, Field Artillery, Rockets/Rocket Launchers, Ships/Boats, Tracked Vehicles, Wheeled Vehicles.

The Fort Leonard Wood Museum's collection focuses upon the histories of Major General Leonard Wood, of Pulaski County, of the fort itself and of the Corps of Engineers. Museum personnel say that they plan to open a "historical vehicle park" in the near future, which will contain more than 20 tracked and wheeled vehicles.

MISSOURI
Fort Leonard Wood Museum, continued

Another on-going project involves the "complete restoration of a World War II training area, to include barracks, officer's quarters, mess halls and dayrooms."

LIBERTY MEMORIAL MUSEUM

Visitor Information: Located at 100 West 26th Street, Kansas City, Missouri 64108. Take I-35 south to the 27th/Broadway exit. Turn left at the stop sign to the museum entrance. Telephone: (816) 221-1918. Hours: 9:30 am to 4:30 pm Tuesday through Sunday. Closed Thanksgiving, Christmas and New Year's Day. Admission: free to the exhibit areas. Admission to the museum's tower, with its view of the city, is $0.50 per adult and $0.25 per child.

Items on Display: Uniforms, Unit Patches, Field Equipment, Personal Documents, Official Documents, Maps, Photographs, Paintings/Drawings, Flags, Battle Streamers, Medals, Edged Weapons, Side Arms, Shoulder Arms, Machine Guns, Ordnance, Field Artillery, Air-Defense Artillery, Submarine Equipment, Communications Equipment, Scale Models (aircraft, tracked vehicles).

Liberty Memorial Museum officials say that their museum is "the only military museum in the United States specializing in the First World War period." Period artifacts and exhibits that interpret the history of the war are on display. Selected exhibits focus upon women in the service, field artillery, equipment carried by a field soldier, the air service and other subjects.

SOLDIERS' MEMORIAL MILITARY MUSEUM

Visitor Information: Located in downtown St. Louis at 1315 Chestnut Street, St. Louis, Missouri 63103. Take I-70 to the Market Street exit west to 14th Street. Turn right on 14th and go one block to Chestnut Street and turn right again to the museum. Telephone: (314) 622-4550. Hours: 9:00 am to 4:30 pm daily. Closed Thanksgiving, Christmas and New Year's Day. Admission: free.

Items on Display: Uniforms, Unit Patches, Personal Documents, Official Documents, Photographs, Paintings/Drawings, Flags, Medals, Edged Weapons, Side Arms, Shoulder Arms, Machine Guns, Mines, Ordnance, Field Artillery, Medical Equipment, Scale Models (ships/boats, tracked vehicles).

Soldiers' Memorial Military Museum, continued

Dedicated in 1936 to honor St. Louis' veterans and war dead, the Soldier's Memorial Military Museum contains artifacts and exhibits "depicting St. Louis' patriotic and active military involvement from 1800 through the present," according to museum officials. Artifacts on display include a 12 gauge percussion shot gun and letter given to Buffalo Bill by Kit Carson in 1865, the pilot wheel and bell from the USS *St. Louis*, the flight jacket worn by Lt. General James H. Doolittle when he commanded the 8th Air Force, original drawings by German Field Marshall Edwin Rommel and many other items.

USS *INAUGURAL*

Visitor Information: Located at 300 North Lenore K. Sullivan Boulevard, on the riverfront in downtown St. Louis at the north leg of the Arch. Take I-70 into downtown St. Louis and follow signs to the Arch. Mailing Address: St. Louis Concessions, Inc., 2241 Edwards Street, St. Louis, Missouri 63110. Telephone: (314) 771-9911. Hours: 10:00 am to dusk daily from April through October. Admission: $1.75 per adult, $1.25 per child over age four.

Items on Display: Ships/Boats.

A World War II-era minesweeper, the USS *Inaugural* participated in the battle for Okinawa and performed patrol and mine-sweeping operations between Hawaii and the Western Pacific Islands and off the coasts of Japan and Korea. Before she was decommissioned in 1946, the *Inaugural* cleared 82 mines from the Pacific Ocean and earned two battle stars. Now a National Historic Landmark, the *Inaugural* is open for self-guided tours.

WILSON'S CREEK NATIONAL BATTLEFIELD

Visitor Information: Located approximately ten miles southwest of Springfield at the intersection of MO-ZZ and Farm Road 182. From I-44 exit south onto MO-MM to US-60. Cross US-60 onto the M Highway. Turn south onto MO-ZZ to Farm Road 182, turn left, then turn right into the park. Mailing Address: Postal Drawer C, Republic, Missouri 65738. Telephone: (417) 732-2662. Hours: 8:00 am to 5:00 pm daily (winter); 8:00 am to 6:00 pm daily (spring and fall); 8:00 am to 8:00 pm daily (summer). Closed Christmas and New Year's Day. Admission: a moderate fee is charged.

Items on Display: Field Equipment, Official Documents, Maps, Paintings/Drawings, Dioramas, Edged Weapons, Side Arms, Shoulder

MISSOURI
Wilson's Creek National Battlefield, continued

Arms, Ordnance, Field Artillery, Medical Equipment.

Exhibits at the Wilson's Creek National Battlefield visitor center interpret the events surrounding the Civil War engagement that occurred at Wilson's Creek. Among the period artifacts on display in the visitor center is the presentation sword that belonged to General Nathaniel Lyon, the first Union general killed in battle during the Civil War.

Other Military Museums, Historic Sites & Exhibits in Missouri

Battle of Lexington Historic Site, P. O. Box 6, Lexington, Missouri 64067. Telephone: (816) 259-2112.

Confederate Memorial, Route 1, Box 221A, Higginsville, Missouri 64037. Telephone: (816) 584-2853.

Fort Osage, 4th and Osage Streets, Sibley, Missouri 64015. Telephone: (816) 795-8200.

General John J. Pershing Boyhood Home, P. O. Box 141, Laclede, Missouri 64651. Telephone: (816) 963-2525.

Jefferson Barracks Historic County Park, Grant Road and Kingston, St. Louis, Missouri 63155. Telephone: (314) 544-4154.

South River Fort and Museum, 4805 McMasters Avenue, Hannibal, Missouri. Telephone: (314) 221-1440.

MONTANA

BIG HOLE NATIONAL BATTLEFIELD

Visitor Center: Located 12 miles west of Wisdom. Take I-15 southwest from Butte or north from Dillon to the Divide exit onto MT-43 through Wisdom to the battlefield. Or take US-93 south from Missoula to MT-43 west for 16 miles to the battlefield. Mailing Address: P. O. Box 237, Wisdom, Montana 59761. Telephone: (406) 689-3155. Hours: 8:00 am to 8:00 pm daily during the summer season, 8:30 am to 5:00 pm daily during the winter season. Admission: $3.00 per car May through September.

Items on Display: Uniforms, Field Equipment, Personal Documents, Photographs, Edged Weapons, Shoulder Arms, Field Artillery.

The Nez Perce War pitted a freedom-seeking, swiftly moving band of 800 non-treaty Nez Perce Indians against Army units bent on confining them to a reservation. A key event in the four-month-long war, the Battle of the Big Hole began on the morning of August 9, 1877, when almost 200 troops led by Colonel John Gibbon of the 7th Infantry mounted a surprise attack on the sleeping Indian encampment. Stunned by the unexpected attack and by the indiscriminate slaughter of their women and children, the Nez Perce warriors still managed to rally and mounted a counterattack that eventually proved decisive. Colonel Gibbon's troops were beseiged by the Indians and pinned down by sniper fire until the evening of August 10, when the last remaining Nez Perce left to join Chief Joseph and the rest of the Indian band as they continued south, their hopes for a permanent and peaceful freedom now more distant than ever.

Indeed, less than two months later at Bear Paw Mountain, Chief Joseph and the last of the non-treaty Nez Perce surrendered. They had traveled 1,700 miles and were stopped just 30 miles short of their goal—the Canadian provinces. In his eloquent statement of surrender, Chief Joseph spoke of the old among his people who were dead, of the young who were freezing to death, of his own children who were missing and possibly dying or dead in the surrounding hills. "From where the sun now stands," he concluded, "I will fight no more forever."

Interpretive exhibits and period artifacts are on display at the battlefield visitor center.

MONTANA

CUSTER BATTLEFIELD NATIONAL MONUMENT

Visitor Information: Located at the intersection of I-90 and MT-212. The memorial can be seen from both roadways. Mailing Address: P. O. Box 39, Crow Agency, Montana 59022. Telephone: (406) 638-2622. Hours: 8:00 am to 4:30 pm daily during fall/winter months, 8:00 am to 7:00 pm daily during spring/summer months. Admission: $3.00 per vehicle, $1.00 per person on commercial bus tours.

Items on Display: Uniforms, Field Equipment, Personal Documents, Official Documents, Maps, Photographs, Paintings/Drawings, Dioramas, Flags, Medals, Edged Weapons, Side Arms, Shoulder Arms.

Exhibits at the Custer Battlefield National Monument visitor center and museum interpret the famous encounter between Custer's 7th Cavalry and a superior force of Native American warriors at the Little Big Horn. Artifacts include Custer's dress coat, West Point album and a suit of buckskins he once wore. A boot cut from the foot of a 7th Cavalry trooper by a victorious warrior, a bugle thought to have been found on the battlefield and rare examples of military uniforms, weapons and equipment are on display as well.

MALMSTROM AIR FORCE BASE MUSEUM & AIR PARK

Visitor Information: Located on Malmstrom Air Force Base, one mile east of the city of Great Falls. From I-15 take the 10th Avenue exit south to the base or take the Malmstrom exit off US-87/89. The museum is just inside the base's main gate at the east end of 2nd Avenue North. Mailing Address: 341 SMW/DO24, Malmstrom Air Force Base, Montana 59402-5000. Telephone: (406) 731-2705 (recording); (406) 731-2408 (group tours). Hours: daylight hours daily (air park); 12:00 noon to 3:00 pm Monday through Saturday in the summer, Monday through Friday in the spring and fall and Monday through Wednesday in the winter. Admission: free.

Items on Display: Uniforms, Unit Patches, Maps, Photographs, Dioramas, Shoulder Arms, Machine Guns, Ordnance, Missiles, Aircraft (fixed wing, rotary wing), Space Craft, Navigational Equipment, Communications Equipment, Wheeled Vehicles, Scale Models (aircraft).

Exhibits at the Malmstrom Air Force Base Museum chronicle the history of the base and of the units stationed there. Selected displays

MONTANA
Malmstrom Air Force Base Museum & Air Park, continued

focus upon the Lewis and Clark expedition of 1805, the World War II era, Malmstrom's Strategic Missile and Air-Defense missions and other base functions. A Minuteman III ICBM stands outside the museum building along with several historic aircraft including the Mitchell B-25J bomber and the F-86A Saber Jet.

Other Military Museums, Historic Sites & Exhibits in Montana

Chief Joseph Battleground of the Bear's Paw State Monument, c/o State of Montana Department of Commerce, 1424 9th Avenue, Helena, Montana 59620-0401. Telephone: (406) 444-3494.

Fort Keogh Officers' Quarters, c/o Range Riders Museum, Miles City, Montana 59301. Telephone: (406) 232-6146.

Historical Museum at Fort Missoula, Building 322, Fort Missoula, Missoula, Montana 59801. Telephone: (406) 728-3476.

Reno-Benteen Battlefield Memorial, c/o State of Montana Department of Commerce, 1424 9th Avenue, Helena, Montana 59620-0401. Telephone: (406) 444-3494.

Rosebud Battlefield, c/o State of Montana Department of Commerce, 1424 9th Avenue, Helena, Montana 59620-0401. Telephone: (406) 444-3494.

NEBRASKA

FORT ATKINSON STATE HISTORICAL PARK

Visitor Information: Located ten miles north of Omaha off US-75, east of the town of Fort Calhoun. Take the US-75 north exit off I-680, then turn east in Fort Calhoun and drive one mile to the park. Signs are posted along I-680 and US-75. Mailing Address: Box 240, Fort Calhoun, Nebraska 68023. Telephone: (402) 468-5611. Hours: 8:00 am to dusk daily (park); 9:00 am to 5:00 pm daily from late May to early September (visitor center). Admission: $2.00 per vehicle.

Items on Display: Uniforms (reproductions), Field Equipment, Official Documents, Paintings/Drawings, Flags, Medals, Edged Weapons, Side Arms, Shoulder Arms, Ordnance, Scale Models (ships/boats), Historic Structure (partially reconstructed fort).

Constructed on the banks of the Missouri River in 1819, Fort Atkinson was the nation's first military outpost west of the Missouri. The fort's garrison of 1,000 men was large by the standards of the time and its two primary missions interrelated: to facilitate the burgeoning fur trade in the region and to enforce peaceful relations between fur traders and Indians. The Army abandoned the fort in 1827 as part of a general realignment of its western forces. During the decades that followed, all traces of the original structures vanished.

Today reconstruction efforts continue, with work on the west and south walls and barracks already completed. A visitor center at the site houses interpretive displays about the fort's history and a number of period artifacts.

FORT KEARNY STATE HISTORICAL PARK

Visitor Information: Located off I-80 near the city of Kearney. From I-80 take NE-10 south for four miles to the 50-A link and drive west for three miles to the park. Signs are posted on I-80. Mailing Address: Route 4, Kearney, Nebraska 68847. Telephone: (308) 234-9513. Hours: 9:00 am to 5:00 pm daily from Memorial Day through the Labor Day weekend. Tours offered year round by appointment. Grounds open year round. Admission: $2.00 per vehicle.

Items on Display: Personal Documents, Official Documents, Maps, Photographs, Paintings/Drawings, Flags, Edged Weapons, Side Arms, Shoulder Arms, Ordnance, Field Artillery, Communications Equipment, Historic Structures (reconstructed fort, earthworks).

NEBRASKA

For Kearny State Historical Park, continued

Constructed in 1848 on the Platte River and garrisoned until 1871, Fort Kearny protected the many travelers who followed the Oregon Trail as they journeyed to the Oregon frontier. A visitor center at the park houses interpretive displays and artifacts from the fort's history. Scale models depict fort activities and a 24-pounder howitzer cannon that is fired on ceremonial occasions. The fort's blacksmith and powder shop, powder magazine and stockade have been reconstructed and are open for self-guided tours.

FORT ROBINSON STATE PARK

Visitor Information: Located in the northwestern corner of the state in Fort Robinson State Park, three miles west of the town of Crawford on US-20. Mailing Address: P. O. Box 304, Crawford, Nebraska 69339. Telephone: (308) 665-2852. Hours: 8:00 am to 5:00 pm daily from Memorial Day through Labor Day; 8:00 am to 5:00 pm Monday through Saturday, 1:30 pm to 5:00 pm Sunday from April 1 to November 1; 8:00 am to 5:00 pm Monday through Friday during the rest of the year. Admission: $1.00 per adult. Accompanied children admitted free.

Items on Display: Uniforms, Field Equipment, Personal Documents, Official Documents, Photographs, Edged Weapons, Side Arms, Shoulder Arms, Ordnance, Field Artillery, Historic Structure (fort).

Established after the Civil War to protect the Indians from the white man, Fort Robinson served through the turbulent Indian War's period into the 20th century and remained an active post until the World War II era. Historically the fort played many roles. It was the site of the infamous Cheyenne Outbreak, was the world's largest Quartermaster Remount Depot, an Olympic equestrian training facility, a field artillery testing facility, a prisoner-of-war camp and much more. Exhibits at the Fort Robinson Museum interpret the fort's entire history in detail. Period artifacts excavated on site are also on display. Many of the fort's original buildings still stand, including the officers' quarters (1887), the guardhouse (1875) and the post adjutant's office (1874).

STATE ARSENAL MUSEUM

Visitor Information: Located at the corner of 17th and Court Streets in downtown Lincoln. From I-80 take I-180 into downtown Lincoln. Turn left on P Street, then left again onto 17th Street. Drive for approximately one mile to the Nebraska State Fair Grounds and

NEBRASKA
State Arsenal Museum, continued

the museum. Mailing Address: 1300 Military Road, Lincoln, Nebraska 68508-1090. Telephone: (402) 471-4182 (during the Nebraska State Fair); (402) 473-1124 (other times). Hours: 8:00 am to 8:00 pm while the Nebraska State Fair is in progress. Other times by appointment only. Admission: fee charged when fair is in progress.

Items on Display: Uniforms, Unit Patches, Field Equipment, Personal Documents, Official Documents, Photographs, Paintings/Drawings, Flags, Battle Streamers, Medals, Edged Weapons, Side Arms, Shoulder Arms, Machine Guns, Mines, Ordnance, Rockets/Rocket Launchers, Communications Equipment, Tracked Vehicles, Scale Models (aircraft).

Artifacts and exhibits from the history of Nebraska's National Guard units are on display in the State Arsenal Museum. World War I displays include examples of trench artwork. The museum's oldest artifact is a Snaphaunce shoulder arm dating from 1620 that was used at Plymouth Plantation by the Pilgrims. Tracked vehicles on display include a Sherman Tank, a Korean War-era M-59 Armored Personnel Carrier and a M-1905 Field Artillery Cannon.

STRATEGIC AIR COMMAND MUSEUM

Visitor Information: Located on Offutt Air Force Base south of Omaha at 2510 Clay Street, Bellevue, Nebraska 68005. If eastbound on I-80, take the NE-370 exit and follow signs. If westbound on I-80, take the US-75 south (Omaha Kennedy Freeway) exit to Harvell Drive and follow signs. From I-29, take the Bellevue exit and follow signs. Telephone: (402) 292-2001. Hours: 8:00 am to 8:00 pm from Memorial Day through Labor Day; 8:00 am to 5:00 pm during the rest of the year. Closed Thanksgiving, Christmas, and New Year's Day. Admission: free. The museum is reached on base through a separate, free-access gate and there are no restrictions.

Items on Display: Uniforms, Unit Patches, Field Equipment, Personal Documents, Official Documents, Maps, Photographs, Paintings/Drawings, Flags, Battle Streamers, Medals, Edged Weapons, Side Arms, Shoulder Arms, Machine Guns, Mines, Ordnance, Nuclear Weapons Displays, Missiles, Aircraft (fixed wing, rotary wing), Military Intelligence/Covert Operations Displays, Communications Equipment, Scale Models (aircraft).

One of the Air Force's finest museums, the Strategic Air Command Museum preserves and displays artifacts about the use of strategic

Strategic Air Command Museum, continued

air power and houses interpretive exhibits that depict the development of the Strategic Air Command itself. Selected exhibits in the museum building focus on the evolution of aircraft engines, the careers and achievements of former SAC commanders, the career of General Curtis LeMay, SAC missiles, World War II's RAF Eagle Squadrons, and the history of Offutt Air Force Base.

Thirty aircraft from World War II-era strategic operations are on display outside the museum. SAC's first B-52, one of only four B-36s in existence, a U-2 spy plane and one of only three RAF Vulcans on display in the U.S. are in the museum's collection. Since Offutt's main runway is close to the outdoor display area, visitors can watch a wide variety of Air Force, Navy, Army and British military aircraft land, take off or do practice touch-and-goes.

Other Military Museums, Historic Sites and Exhibits in Nebraska

Fort Hartstuff State Historical Park, Route 1, Box 37, Burwell, Nebraska 68823. Telephone: (308) 346-4715.

Fort Sidney Complex, 6th and Jackson Streets, Box 596, Sidney, Nebraska 69162. Telephone: (308) 254-2150.

General George Crook House, P. O. Box 11398, Omaha, Nebraska 68111. Telephone: (402) 455-9990.

USS *Marlin* and USS *Hazard*, c/o Greater Omaha Military Historical Society, P. O. Box 9056, Station C, Omaha, Nebraska 68109. Telephone: (402) 345-1959.

NEVADA

FORT CHURCHILL STATE HISTORIC PARK

Visitor Information: Located seven miles south of Silver Springs off US-95A. Signs are posted. Mailing Address: Silver Springs, Nevada 89429. Telephone: (702) 577-2345. Hours: 8:00 am to 4:30 pm daily from Memorial Day through Labor Day. Hours vary during the rest of the year. Admission: free.

Items on Display: Field Equipment, Shoulder Arms, Flag (reproduction), Dioramas, Historic Structure (ruins of fort).

Fort Churchill was built in 1860 in response to escalating hostilities between white settlers and Indian tribes in the Nevada territory. Many punitive missions against the Indians were launched from the fort, whose garrison also protected the Pony Express and other mail routes that ran through the area. Abandoned in 1869, the fort's buildings suffered at the hands of vandals and over the years fell into the ruins that exist today. Markers at the site identify the locations of structures that have completely vanished. The park visitor center contains only a few military artifacts, but several exhibits interpret the fort's history in detail.

THUNDERBIRDS MUSEUM

Visitor Information: Located on Nellis Air Force Base, eight miles northeast of Las Vegas. Take I-15 north from Las Vegas to the base. Mailing Address: P. O. Box 9733, Nellis Air Force Base, Nevada 89191-5000. Telephone: (702) 652-4018. Hours: 2:00 pm to 3:30 pm Tuesday and Thursday. Admission: free.

Items on Display: Unit Patches, Photographs, Paintings/Drawings, Flags, Scale Models (aircraft).

Exhibits at the Thunderbirds Museum interpret the history of the U.S. Air Force's Air Demonstration Squadron. Photographs and scale models of the different aircraft used by the team over the years are on display, in addition to flags from many of the nations visited by the team, team unit patches and works of art presented to the team by U.S. and foreign officials.

NEW HAMPSHIRE

FORT CONSTITUTION

Visitor Information: Located on New Hampshire's Atlantic coast off NH-1B at the Coast Guard Station in Newcastle. Park at the station and follow signs to the fort. Mailing Address: Seacoast Ranger, c/o Wentworth-Coolidge Mansion, Little Harbor Road, Portsmouth, New Hampshire 03801. Telephone: (603) 436-5294/6607. Hours: daylight hours on weekends. Admission: fee charged.

Items on Display: Historic Structure (ruins of fort).

The Fort Constitution site first served a military purpose in 1632, when an earthwork fortification equipped with four heavy guns was constructed. In 1692 the British added more cannon and materiel to the site and named it Fort William and Mary. On December 14, 1774, in one of the first military actions against the Crown, colonists raided the fort and made off with five tons of British gunpowder. The next day, another party of colonists raided and took 16 small cannon. These actions, which took place months before the events at Lexington and Concord, were key elements in the chain of events that lead to the Revolutionary War.

After the war, the fort was repaired and garrisoned by a United States artillery company and given a new name: Fort Constitution. The ruins of this fort are those seen today.

USS *ALBACORE*

Visitor Information: Located in Albacore Park off I-95 in Portsmouth. Take I-95 to the Market Street east exit (exit 7) to Albacore Park. Mailing Address: Port of Portsmouth Maritime Museum and Albacore Park, P. O. Box 4367, Portsmouth, New Hampshire 03801. Telephone: (603) 436-3680. Hours: 9:30 am to 5:30 pm daily (submarine); 7:00 am to 7:00 pm daily (Albacore Park and Memory Garden). Admission: fee charged.

Items on Display: Submarine. Related artifacts and exhibits are in the visitor center.

The world's fastest submarine when commissioned, the USS *Albacore* served from 1953 until 1972 as an experimental vessel. The *Albacore* functioned as a submerged laboratory on which Naval engineers tested dive brakes, sonar systems, escape mechanisms and much more for the first time. The *Albacore's* teardrop hull design became

NEW HAMPSHIRE
USS *Albacore*, continued

the model for the U.S. Navy's nuclear-powered submarine fleet and for submarines all over the world. The submarine is open for self-guided tours.

Other Military Museums, Historic Sites & Exhibits in New Hampshire

Fort Stark, Seacoast Ranger, c/o Wentworth-Coolidge Mansion, Little Harbor Road, Portsmouth, New Hampshire 03801. Telephone: (603) 436-5294/6607.

Odiorne Point State Park (Fort Dearborn), Seacoast Ranger, c/o Wentworth-Coolidge Mansion, Little Harbor Road, Portsmouth, New Hampshire 03801. Telephone: (603) 436-5294/6607.

NEW JERSEY

ARMAMENT RESEARCH, DEVELOPMENT & ENGINEERING CENTER MUSEUM

Visitor Information: Located on Picatinny Arsenal, 30 miles west of Newark. Take exit 34 off I-80 and drive north on NJ-15 for one mile to the arsenal. Mailing Address: SMCAR-MM, Building 2, ARDEC Museum, Picatinny Arsenal, New Jersey 07806-5000. Telephone: (201) 724-3222. Hours: 9:00 am to 3:00 pm Monday through Friday. Admission: free.

Items on Display: Uniforms, Photographs, Shoulder Arms, Mines, Ordnance, Nuclear Weapons Displays, Field Artillery, Air-Defense Artillery, Rockets/Rocket Launchers.

Artifacts from the history of Picatinny Arsenal's weapons research and development activities are on indoor and outdoor display at the ARDEC Museum. Anti-tank and -personnel mines; Davy Crockett, Honest John, Sergeant, Lance and Corporal nuclear weapons; 20th-century field artillery; and numerous other types of explosive devices are in the museum's collection.

FORT DIX MUSEUM

Visitor Information: Located on Fort Dix, 15 miles southeast of Trenton. From the New Jersey Turnpike, take exit 5 (Mount Holly) and turn left on Woodlane Road. Turn left again on NJ-537 at Unionville then turn right at Route 670 at Jobstown, then turn right at NJ-68. Take NJ-68 to the traffic circle, follow circle around and turn right at the third exit. Proceed to the next traffic circle and take the first right onto Delaware Avenue. Look for the museum sign on the right. Mailing Address: ATTN: ATZD-GCD, Fort Dix, New Jersey 08640-5000. Telephone: (609) 562-6983. Hours: 8:30 am to 4:00 pm Monday through Friday. Closed on all federal holidays. Admission: free.

Items on Display: Uniforms, Unit Patches, Field Equipment, Personal Documents, Official Documents, Maps, Photographs, Paintings/Drawings, Flags, Battle Streamers, Medals, Edged Weapons, Side Arms, Shoulder Arms, Machine Guns, Mines, Ordnance, Chemical/Biological Weapons Displays, Field Artillery, Rocket Launchers, Medical Equipment.

Exhibits at the Fort Dix Museum interpret the history of Fort Dix from its beginnings as Camp Dix in 1917 to the present. Selected

NEW JERSEY
Fort Dix Museum, continued

displays focus on the fort's construction, Civilian Conservation Corps' activities at Camp Dix before World War II, G.I. equipment and training, the role of Women in the Army at Fort Dix, tenant unit histories and other subjects.

NEW JERSEY NATIONAL GUARD MILITIA MUSEUM

Visitor Information: Located in Building 66 on the National Guard Training Center at Sea Girt, on the Atlantic Coast in the central part of the state. From the Garden State Parkway, take exit 98 east onto NJ-38 toward Belmar. Turn south at NJ-35 and go to the fourth traffic light. Turn left at the light onto Sea Girt Avenue and proceed east until you cross the railroad tracks. Turn right onto the training center. Mailing Address: Building 66, National Guard Training Center, Box 277, Sea Girt, New Jersey 08750-5000. Telephone: (201) 446-5200 extension 350. Hours: open during the first full weekend of each month and during the last two weeks of June and the first two weeks of July. Admission: free

Items on Display: Uniforms, Unit Patches, Field Equipment, Personal Documents, Official Documents, Maps, Photographs, Paintings/Drawings, Dioramas, Flags, Medals, Edged Weapons, Side Arms, Shoulder Arms, Machine Guns, Field Artillery, Rockets/Rocket Launchers, Medical Equipment, Tracked Vehicles, Scale Models (ships/boats).

Exhibits at New Jersey's National Guard Militia Museum interpret state militia and guard unit activities in New Jersey from Revolutionary times to the present. What may be the only surviving caisson and limber for a 1915 3.8 inch field artillery piece is on display, as is a complete steel caisson and limber for a French 75 mm. artillery piece. The museum also houses two of the first 36 M1857 12-pounder bronze guns manufactured, many examples of pre- and post-World War II field jackets and other types of equipment. A nearly complete osteopathic field chest from the Spanish-American War is also on display.

OLD BARRACKS MUSEUM

Visitor Information: Located just south of and adjacent to the New Jersey State House on Barrack Street, Trenton, New Jersey 08608. From the north, take I-95 to NJ-29 south to the Willow Street (or

NEW JERSEY

Old Barracks Museum, continued

Willow/Barrack) exit. Or take US-1 south to the Capitol Complex exit and follow signs to the State Capitol. From the south, take the New Jersey Turnpike north to exit 7 to US-206 north (South Broad Street) to Lalor Street. Turn left on Lalor and follow signs to NJ-29 north to the Willow Street (or Willow/Barrack) exit. Or take I-295 to US-130 north to US-206 north and proceed as above. From the east, take I-295 west to its end then take the Arena Drive exit to its end. Turn left onto South Olden Avenue, left again onto Greenwood Avenue to its end. Proceed through the first traffic circle and over the bridge then take the last exit off the second circle to Market Street and follow signs to the State Capitol. Or take NJ-33 west to Nottingham Way and bear right at Greenwood Avenue then proceed as above. From the west, take I-95 to exit 1 south in New Jersey to NJ-29 south (along the river) to the Willow Street (or Willow Barrack) exit. Or take US-1 north to the Capitol Complex exit and follow signs to the State Capitol. Telephone: (609) 396-1776. Hours: 10:00 am to 5:00 pm Monday through Saturday, 1:00 pm to 5:00 pm on Sunday. Closed Easter, Thanksgiving, Christmas Eve, Christmas and New Year's Day. Admission: $2.00 per adult, $1.00 per senior citizen and student, $0.50 per child age 12 and under (all prices are suggested donations).

Items on Display: Uniforms (reproductions), Field Equipment, Personal Documents, Maps, Paintings/Drawings, Dioramas, Edged Weapons, Side Arms, Shoulder Arms, Ordnance, Field Artillery, Naval Artillery, Historic Structure (barracks).

The director of the Old Barracks Museum writes that "the museum is located in a historic building originally known as the Trenton Barracks, built in 1758 to house British soldiers fighting in North America during the French and Indian War. It was one of five such barracks, each designed to hold 300 men, that were built at the same time in colonial New Jersey. Only the Trenton Barracks stands today." She also writes that the barracks "is the only British barracks built during the French and Indian War still standing in North America. The building was also used during the American Revolutionary War by American, British, and Hessian soldiers."

The museum is currently undergoing extensive renovation. When renovations are completed, more of the building will be open to the public and the military aspects of the building's history will be emphasized to a greater degree than in the past. Exhibits and artifacts on display generally date from the French and Indian War and the Revolutionary War periods. Items of particular interest in the museum's collection include the only full 'rib' remaining from the

NEW JERSEY
Old Barracks Museum, continued

Triumphal Arch erected in 1789 to welcome George Washington to Trenton (on his journey to take the presidential oath of office in New York), as well as a number of 19th century prints that commemorated the event.

U.S. ARMY CHAPLAIN MUSEUM

Visitor Information: Located on Fort Monmouth, 20 miles southeast of New Brunswick. Take exit 105 off the Garden State Parkway and follow signs to the fort. Mailing Address: USACHCS, ATTN: ATSC-SEC-M, Walters Hall, Building 1207, Fort Monmouth, New Jersey 07703-5000. Telephone: (201) 532-5809/3487. Hours: call for hours as they may change after renovation work is completed. Admission: free.

Items on Display: Uniforms, Personal Documents, Official Documents, Photographs, Dioramas.

Items from the history of the U.S. Army chaplaincy, including chalices, stoles and chaplain uniforms and kits are on display in the Chaplain Museum. Once renovation work has been completed, the museum will include a 180-foot photo montage depicting chaplain history. Selected displays will focus on the chaplain's kit, the ethnic chaplain, chaplains' assistants, the chaplain as a P.O.W. and other related subjects.

U.S. ARMY COMMUNICATIONS-ELECTRONICS MUSEUM

Visitor Information: Located in Building 275 on Fort Monmouth, 20 miles southeast of New Brunswick. Take the Garden State Parkway to exit 105 north and follow signs to the fort. Enter the main gate off NJ-35 and ask security personnel for directions to Building 275 (Kaplan Hall). Mailing Address: Kaplan Hall, Building 275, Fort Monmouth, New Jersey 07703-5000. Telephone: (201) 532-4390. Hours: 12:00 noon to 4:00 pm Monday through Friday, same hours on Saturdays between Memorial Day and Labor Day. Admission: free.

Items on Display: Field Equipment, Space Exploration Displays, Communications Equipment.

Artifacts about the evolution and technological development of Army communications equipment and methods are on display at the

NEW JERSEY
U.S. Army Communications-Electronics Museum, continued

Communications-Electronics Museum. Selected exhibits focus on early airborne radio communications; the career of Edwin Armstrong, a radio pioneer; vacuum tubes; radio research laboratories; the U.S. Army Signal School; radio miniaturization; and other related subjects.

USS *LING* SUBMARINE MEMORIAL & MUSEUM

Visitor Information: Located at Court and River Streets in Hackensack. Driving directions vary greatly depending on the direction from which you are approaching Hackensack. Call for directions. Mailing Address: P. O. Box 395, Hackensack, New Jersey 07602. Telephone: (201) 342-3268. Hours: 10:00 am to 4:00 pm daily. Closed on Mondays and Tuesdays during December and January. Admission: $2.50 per adult, $1.50 per child under age 12.

Items on Display: Photographs, Paintings/Drawings, Mines, Artillery, Missiles, Submarines/Submersible Vehicles, Scale Models (ships/boats, submarines).

The USS *Ling* was commissioned in June, 1945, and made one war patrol during World War II. After the war, the *Ling* served as a training vessel for the New London Group, Atlantic Reserve Fleet and for Naval Reserve Submarine Divisions 2-23 and 3-55. She was decommissioned in 1971. Naval artifacts on display in the museum include a Japanese periscope collection, ship and submarine models and cassette tapes about World War II and the USS *Ling*.

Other Military Museums, Historic Sites and Exhibits in New Jersey

Aviation Hall of Fame of New Jersey, Teterboro Airport, Teterboro, New Jersey 07608. Telephone: (201) 288-6344.

Holland I, Holland II *(Fenian Ram)*, c/o Paterson Museum, 2 Market Street, Paterson, New Jersey 07501. Telephone: (201) 888-3874.

Morristown National Historical Park, Washington Place, Morristown, New Jersey 07960. Telephone: (201) 539-2016.

Thomas Clarke House (Battle of Princeton), 500 Mercer Street, Princeton, New Jersey 08540. Telephone: (609) 921-0074.

NEW MEXICO

ALAMOGORDO SPACE CENTER

Visitor Information: Located at the top of NM-2001 in Alamogordo. From US-54/70, turn east on Indian Wells Road and follow the signs. Mailing Address: P. O. Box 533, Alamogordo, New Mexico 88311-0533. Telephone: (505) 437-2840. Hours: 9:00 am to 6:00 pm daily. Closed Christmas. Admission: fees charged for the theater and the space hall. Combined tickets are available.

Items on Display: Uniforms, Official Documents, Photographs, Paintings/Drawings, Flags, Medals, Rockets/Rocket Launchers, Space Craft, Space Exploration Displays, Satellite Communications Displays, Navigational Equipment, Scale Models (space craft).

One of the world's premier space museums, the Space Center in Alamogordo chronicles the history of space exploration. Four floors of space-related exhibits and artifacts depict different aspects of space exploration, including manned space flight, living and working in space, planetary studies and projects conducted in New Mexico.

Space Shuttle flight coveralls, Apollo and Skylab space suits, samples of space food, miniature flags flown to the moon on a moon-landing mission and others flown on board the shuttle Challenger are among the many items on display, as is a mission patch worn aboard the space shuttle Challenger when it tragically exploded. A full-size mock-up of a Mercury space capsule lets visitors see why none of our early astronauts were six feet four inches tall. Scale models of Gemini, Apollo and Vostok space craft are nearby, along with a Lunar Rover Training Vehicle used by astronauts. Thirteen satellites and informational displays about satellite uses and communications technology are located in the "Satellites Serving Mankind" gallery. One display shows current communications routes between satellites and earth stations around the world. The Space Center is also home to The International Space Hall of Fame, where each September leading figures in the space-exploration field are formally inducted.

CONFEDERATE AIR FORCE MUSEUM—NEW MEXICO WING

Visitor Information: Located at the Hobbs/Lea County Airport outside of Hobbs in the southeastern corner of the state. From Hobbs, take US-62/180 west for four miles to the airport. Mailing Address: P. O. Box 1260, Hobbs, New Mexico 88240. Telephone: (505) 393-7543. Hours: daylight hours daily. Admission: free.

NEW MEXICO
Confederate Air Force Museum—New Mexico Wing, continued

Items on Display: Uniforms, Paintings/Drawings, Photographs, Aircraft (fixed wing), wheeled vehicles.

The CAF Museum's collection includes eight military aircraft, a vintage 1942 German jeep, an aircraft engine display, a link trainer flight simulator and other items of interest.

FORT UNION NATIONAL MONUMENT

Visitor Information: Located off I-25 approximately 25 miles north of Las Vegas. Take I-25 to exit 366 (Watrous) and go west on NM-477 for eight miles to the monument. Mailing Address: Watrous, New Mexico 87753. Telephone: (505) 425-8025. Hours: 8:00 am to 6:00 pm daily from May 28 to September 4, 8:00 am to 4:30 pm from September 5 to May 27. Admission: $1.00 per person or $3.00 per car (whichever is less) during the summer months.

Items on Display: Uniforms, Field Equipment, Personal Documents, Official Documents, Maps, Photographs, Paintings/Drawings, Edged Weapons, Side Arms, Shoulder Arms, Ordnance, Field Artillery, Historic Structures (ruins of fort, earthworks).

The largest military installation on the southwestern frontier once stood at the Fort Union National Monument site. The last of three forts built at the site to guard travelers on the Santa Fe trail, it served as an active Army post from 1863 to 1891. The fort's ruins have now been stabilized and include foundations, walls and chimneys of shops, warehouses, offices, officers' quarters, enlisted barracks, stables, a sutler's store, the post hospital, laundress' quarters and guardhouse. A Civil War-era earthwork, once garrisoned by 600 soldiers, has been preserved as well.

Several exhibits at the Fort Union museum focus upon the activities of infantry, cavalry and artillery units stationed at the fort, with displays of weapons, uniforms and other items used by each. The Fort Union Arsenal contains weapons and ammunition of the types stored and disbursed at the arsenal between 1851, when the first fort was built, and 1891, when the third fort was abandoned.

NATIONAL ATOMIC MUSEUM

Visitor Information: Located on Kirtland Air Force Base in Albuquerque. From I-40 east take the Wyoming Boulevard exit south for two miles to the base. From I-40 West take the Central Avenue

NEW MEXICO
National Atomic Museum, continued

exit onto US-66 west to Wyoming Boulevard. Turn left on Wyoming to the base. Mailing Address: Department of Energy, Albuquerque Operations Office, P. O. Box 5400, Albuquerque, New Mexico 87115. Telephone: (505) 844-8443. Hours: 9:00 am to 5:00 pm daily. Closed Easter, Thanksgiving, Christmas and New Year's Day. Admission: free.

Items on Display: Ordnance, Nuclear Weapons Displays, Field Artillery, Rockets, Missiles, Aircraft (fixed wing).

Artifacts and exhibits at the National Atomic Museum chronicle the evolution of nuclear weapons and weapons-delivery devices from the early 1940s to the present. Interpretive exhibits focus on the development of the first nuclear weapons, early airdrop techniques, modern delivery methods and the H-bomb. A wide variety of unclassified nuclear bomb, missile and shell casings is on display, from the famous Fat Man and Little Boy devices that devastated Hiroshima and Nagasaki and brought an end to the war in the Pacific, to the B-43 thermonuclear bomb, currently in the nation's active nuclear stockpile, which employs a steel pike to penetrate hard targets and hold it in place until detonation. Outdoor exhibits include a Boeing B-52 Stratofortress; the Hound Dog, a long-range, thermonuclear, air-to-ground strategic missile; a 280mm atomic cannon; and an example of the famous Redstone rocket, one of which carried America's first astronaut, Alan Shepard, into space.

WHITE SANDS MISSILE RANGE MISSILE PARK & VISITOR CENTER

Visitor Information: Located 50 miles west of Alamogordo off US-70 on White Sands Missile Range. From I-25 at Las Cruces, take US-70 east for 22 miles to the White Sands exit. Turn right (or south) onto the missile range access road (Owen road) to the Military Police checkpoint (Las Cruces Gate). Valid driver's license and proof of automobile insurance is required. Mailing Address: Public Affairs, Building 122, White Sands Missile Range, New Mexico 88220-5000. Telephone: (505) 678-1134/1135/1700. Hours: 8:00 am to 4:00 pm Monday through Friday. Admission: free.

Items on Display: Photographs, Nuclear Weapons Displays, Rockets/Rocket Launchers, Missiles, Historic Structure (Launch Complex-33).

NEW MEXICO
White Sands Missile Range Missile Park, continued

Scientists detonated the world's first atomic bomb at White Sands Missile Range (then called the White Sands Proving Ground) on July 16, 1945. Twice a year, White Sands personnel conduct tours of the Trinity Site where a brief commemorative program is held. Historic Launch Complex-33, where much of this nations' early missile research was conducted, is also located at White Sands and can be visited on special occasions as announced by White Sands officials. Both the Trinity Site and LC-33 have been designated National Historic Landmarks. The White Sands visitor center houses a small nuclear weapons display and photographs from the history of missile research and development. Outside, the White Sands Missile Park contains a variety of missiles and rockets with informational markers that give pertinent facts about each piece of hardware.

Other Military Museums, Historic Sites & Exhibits in New Mexico

Fort Burgwin Research Center, P. O. Box 314, Ranchos de Taos, New Mexico 87557. Telephone: (505) 758-8322.

Fort Seldon State Monument, P. O. Box 58, Radium Springs, New Mexico 88054. Telephone: (505) 526-8911.

Fort Sumner State Monument. P. O. Box 356, Fort Sumner, New Mexico 88119. Telephone: (505) 355-2573.

General Douglas L. McBride Military Museum, New Mexico Military Institute, Roswell, New Mexico 88201. Telephone: (505) 622-6250.

Old Fort Sumner Museum, c/o Proprietor, Box 1881, Taiban, New Mexico 88134. Telephone: (505) 355-2942.

Rough Riders Memorial and City Museum, 727 Grand Avenue, Las Vegas, New Mexico 87701. Telephone: (505) 454-1401.

NEW YORK

CROWN POINT STATE HISTORIC SITE

Visitor Information: Located 4 1/2 miles east of NY-9N/22 at the Lake Champlain Bridge. From Plattsburg, take I-87 south to NY-9N east which merges with NY-22. Take NY-9N/22 south to the exit east for Crown Point. Mailing Address: R.D. #1, Box 219, Crown Point, New York 12928. Telephone: (518) 597-3666. Hours: 10:00 am to 5:00 pm Wednesday through Saturday, 1:00 pm to 5:00 pm Sunday from May through October. Open other times by appointment. Admission: free.

Items on Display: Uniforms, Field Equipment, Maps, Paintings/Drawings, Dioramas, Edged Weapons, Shoulder Arms, Ordnance, Field Artillery, Historic Structure (ruins of fort).

Crown Point was a key location in the struggle between the French and the British for military and commercial supremacy in the new world in the first half of the 18th century. French soldiers occupied the Crown Point site in 1731. Three years later, work began on the first fortification in the Champlain Valley, Fort St. Frédéric. Until the construction of Carillon (later called Fort Ticonderoga) was completed 24 years later at another site, Fort St. Frédéric gave the French control of the vital Lake Champlain waterway between Montreal and New York. After four unsuccessful attempts, the British, with a combined force of 12,000 troops, finally seized the fort in 1759. They immediately began building their own fort at the site: His Majesty's Fort at Crown Point. Ruins of both forts are visible today.

Artifacts from the Revolutionary War and the French and Indian War eras are on display in the visitor center, where exhibits and pamphlets tell the story of Crown Point in detail.

FORT ONTARIO STATE HISTORIC SITE

Visitor Information: Located at the north end of East 7th Street in Oswego, 35 miles northwest of Syracuse on the shores of Lake Ontario. From the Thruway take exit 36 to Route 81 north, then take exit 29N to Route 481 north to the junction with Route 104. Turn right at Route 104 and follow signs to the site. Mailing Address: P. O. Box 102, Oswego, New York 13126. Telephone: (315) 343-4711. Hours: 10:00 am to 5:00 pm Wednesday through Saturday, 1:00 pm to 5:00 pm Sunday from May 1 to the end of September. Admission: $0.50 per adult, $0.25 per child from Memorial Day to

Fort Ontario State Historic Site, continued

Labor Day.

Items on Display: Uniforms, Field Equipment, Maps, Photographs, Paintings/Drawings, Edged Weapons, Shoulder Arms, Ordnance, Field Artillery, Coast-Defense Artillery, Historic Structure (restored fort).

Strategically located at the mouth of the Oswego River, Fort Ontario was an active military post for almost two centuries. Established by the British in the late 1750s, the fort was not abandoned until the U.S. Army withdrew its personnel in 1946. The fort has now been restored to its 1860's appearance. Exhibits at the site's orientation center chronicle the fort's history in detail from the French and Indian War through World War II. An Officers' Quarters, decorated with 19th-century furnishings and textiles, interprets the period between 1868 and 1872.

FORT STANWIX NATIONAL MONUMENT

Visitor Information: Located at 112 East Park Street, Rome, New York 13440. Take the New York State Thruway (I-90) east from Syracuse to exit 33 onto NY-365 north to Rome and the fort, which is located in the center of town. Follow signs to the parking area. Hours: 9:00 am to 5:00 pm daily from April 1 to December 31. Closed Thanksgiving and Christmas. Admission: $1.00 per adult. Senior citizens and children under 16 admitted free.

Items on Display: Personal Documents, Edged Weapons, Shoulder Arms, Ordnance, Field Artillery (reproductions), Historic Structure (reconstructed fort).

The National Park Service's pamphlet about Fort Stanwix explains that "the modern city of Rome, N.Y., lies astride an ancient water route linking the Great Lakes with the Atlantic Ocean. Except for the short portage across nearly level ground between the Mohawk River east of the city and Wood Creek to the west, a traveler in Colonial times could journey by water all the way from New York City to Canada and back again. Indians used the portage for centuries, calling it the De-O-Wain-Sta. The English called it the Oneida Carry and it became a funnel for commerce, settlement, and military activity.

"The British built Fort Stanwix here in 1758 to replace three smaller forts which protected the portage during the early years of the French and Indian War. Named for its builder, Brig. Gen. John

NEW YORK
Fort Stanwix National Monument, continued

Stanwix, the fort never saw action and was abandoned after the British conquest of Canada in 1763."

Patriot leaders rebuilt the fort in the mid-1760s. In August of 1777, British forces laid siege to the fort, but withdrew after finding the fort's walls impenetrable and its garrison unwilling to surrender under any circumstances. The fort remained an active post until 1781 and by 1830 had been leveled.

The fort has been approximately 80% reconstructed and its casemates and barracks furnished with period reproductions. Eleven reproduction cannon are on the grounds. The visitor center houses Revolutionary War artifacts, one of which is the finest example of an 18th-century Grenadier's matchcase ever excavated in North America.

GENERAL GRANT NATIONAL MEMORIAL

Visitor Information: Located at the junction of 122nd Street and Riverside Drive in New York City. Riverside Drive is accessible from the Henry Hudson Parkway. Mailing Address: 122nd Street and Riverside Drive, New York, New York 10027. Telephone: (212) 666-1640. Hours: 9:00 am to 5:00 pm Monday, Wednesday and Sunday. Closed federal holidays. Admission: free.

Items on Display: Personal Documents, Official Documents, Photographs, Paintings/Drawings, Dioramas.

The largest mausoleum in America, the General Grant National Memorial took six years to build. Out of admiration and respect for the man many credited with having saved the Union, ninety thousand people donated more than $600,000 toward its construction. Exhibits and memorabilia pertaining to the civilian and military careers of Ulysses S. Grant are on display at the memorial. General Grant and Mrs. Grant are interred side-by-side in identical, 8 1/2 ton granite sarcophagi.

HARBOR DEFENSE MUSEUM OF NEW YORK CITY

Visitor Information: Located off I-278 in the southwest section of Brooklyn. Take I-278 to Shore Parkway south and the fort. Mailing Address: c/o Fort Hamilton Historical Society, Fort Hamilton, Brooklyn, New York 11252. Telephone: (718) 630-4349. Hours: 1:00 pm to 4:00 pm Monday, Thursday and Friday, 10:00 am to 5:00 pm Saturday, 1:00 pm to 5:00 pm Sunday. Closed Presidents' Day, Labor

Harbor Defense Museum of New York City, continued

Day, Columbus Day, Martin Luther King's Birthday, Thanksgiving and Christmas week through New Year's Day. Admission: free.

Items on Display: Uniforms, Maps, Photographs, Paintings/Drawings, Side Arms, Shoulder Arms, Machine Guns, Mines, Coast-Defense Artillery, Historic Structure (fort).

Exhibits at the Harbor Defense Museum chronicle various aspects of military history from the 17th century to the present, with special emphasis on coast-defense fortifications, coast-defense artillery and the military history of New York City. The museum is housed in one of Fort Hamilton's original caponiers (1825-1831).

HOMEVILLE MUSEUM

Visitor Information: Located off I-81 approximately 35 miles south of Syracuse in Homer at 49 Clinton Street. From I-81 in Homer take exit 12 (Route 41 north) through the village and across the railroad tracks to the museum on the left. Clinton Street and Route 41 are the same. Mailing Address: 49 Clinton Street, Homer, New York 13077. Telephone: (607) 749-3105. Hours: 7:00 pm to 9:00 pm Thursday from May through October, 1:00 pm to 4:00 pm every second Wednesday and fourth Sunday of every month. Admission: free.

Items on Display: Uniforms, Unit Patches, Field Equipment, Official Documents, Maps, Photographs, Paintings/Drawings, Dioramas, Flags, Medals, Edged Weapons, Side Arms, Shoulder Arms, Tracked Vehicles, Scale Models (aircraft).

The Homeville Museum is privately owned and operated by Ken Eaton, who has collected military memorabilia, model trains and railroad artifacts for over forty years. Military memorabilia from the Civil War through Vietnam are housed upstairs. The downstairs houses what must be one of the largest, privately owned railroad model and artifact collections in the country.

INTREPID SEA-AIR-SPACE MUSEUM

Visitor Information: Located in mid-town Manhattan in the Hudson River at Pier 86, West 46th Street and 12th Avenue. The museum is ten minutes due south of the George Washington Bridge via the Henry Hudson Parkway and 12 minutes due north of the World Trade Center, Holland Tunnel, Brooklyn Battery Tunnel and

NEW YORK
Intrepid **Sea-Air-Space Museum, continued**

the Statue of Liberty via 12th Street. Mailing Address: Pier 86, West 46th Street and 12th Avenue, New York, New York 10036. Telephone: (212) 245-0072. Hours: 10:00 am to 5:00 pm Wednesday through Sunday. Closed all federal holidays in the winter. Admission: $4.75 per adult, $4.00 per senior citizen, $2.50 per child ages 7-13, uniformed military admitted free.

Items on Display: A complete list was unavailable at press time, but the museum's collection does include the following: Uniforms, Official Documents, Maps, Photographs, Paintings/Drawings, Dioramas, Flags, Medals, Rockets/Rocket Launchers, Aircraft (fixed wing, rotary wing), Space Craft, Satellites, Ships/Boats, Scale Models (aircraft, ships/boats).

During World War II, the USS *Intrepid* participated in the battle for the Philippines; the Battle of Leyte Gulf; the invasion of the Marshall Islands, Paulau and Okinawa; the raid on the Truk Fortress and the massive air battle off the coast of Formosa. The *Intrepid* later served three combat tours in Vietnamese waters and was a NASA Prime Recovery Vessel for the Gemini space program. Opened as a museum in 1983, the *Intrepid* now houses one of the most fascinating and extensive collections of military and space-related artifacts and exhibits anywhere, with five major exhibit theme halls. More than 70 historic aircraft, spacecraft, rockets and satellites; multi-media presentations; hundreds of scale models; and the largest Medals of Honor collection in existence are all part of the museum's collection.

NATIONAL WARPLANE MUSEUM

Visitor Information: Located 30 minutes south of Rochester off NY-63 in the Genesee Valley region. Take I-390 south from Rochester to exit 8. Turn west on NY-20A into the village of Geneseo and follow signs to museum. Driving north from Corning on I-390, take exit 7 north on NY-63 to Geneseo and follow signs to museum. Mailing Address: P. O. Box 159, Geneseo, New York 14454. Telephone: (716) 243-0690. Hours: 9:00 am to 5:00 pm Monday through Friday, 10:00 am to 5:00 pm weekends. Admission: $3.00 per adult, $1.00 per child under age 12.

Items on Display: Uniforms, Unit Patches, Personal Documents, Maps, Photographs, Paintings/Drawings, Medals, Ordnance, Aircraft (fixed wing), Scale Models (aircraft).

In the words of museum officials, the National Warplane Museum is

National Warplane Museum, continued

"dedicated to the restoration and maintenance of flying-condition World War II aircraft." The collection currently includes a Boeing B-17 Flying Fortress, a Beachcraft C-45, a PBY-6A Catalina and six other historic, World War II-era aircraft, all in air-worthy condition. Restoration work continues on several others. Static displays of other aircraft may also be viewed.

Would-be visitors should call before visiting, since aircraft in the museum's collection may be attending air shows at other locations, especially during the spring and summer. In mid-August annually, the "1941 Wings of Eagles" air show takes place at the museum, with many World War II-era aircraft participating.

NAVAL & SERVICEMEN'S PARK

Visitor Information: Located in downtown Buffalo at the foot of Pearl Street, behind the Buffalo Memorial Auditorium. Take I-90 (New York State Thruway) north to exit 53 onto I-190 east for Buffalo and Niagara Falls. Drive for approximately five miles to the Church Street exit. Once off the ramp turn right at the first stop sign onto Lower Terrace. From Lower Terrance turn right onto Pearl Street. The parking lot is at the foot of Pearl Street. Mailing Address: 1 Naval Park Cove, Buffalo, New York 14202. Telephone: (716) 847-1773. Hours: 10:00 am to dusk daily from April 1 through October 31, 10:00 am to dusk weekends in November. Admission: $3.50 per adult, $2.50 per senior citizen and child ages 6-16.

Items on Display: Many of the museum's exhibits are rotating exhibits. Items on permanent display include the following: Aircraft (fixed wing), Ships/Boats, Tracked Vehicles, Scale Models (ships/boats).

Two historic warships and one World War II-era submarine are permanently moored in Lake Erie off the shores of the Buffalo and Erie County Naval and Servicemen's Park. The USS *The Sullivans*, a Fletcher-class destroyer commissioned in 1943, participated in a number of major engagements in the Pacific Theater and later served in the Korean War and the blockade of Cuba. She earned nine battle stars in World War II and two in Korea. The USS *Little Rock* was commissioned as a light cruiser in 1945 and converted to a guided missile cruiser in 1960. She served as flagship for the Second and Sixth Fleets and was decommissioned in 1976. Self-guided tours of both ships are keyed to pamphlets available in the museum that explain what different sections of the ships were used for. The

NEW YORK
Naval & Servicemen's Park, continued

submarine USS *Croaker* was moved to the Naval and Servicemen's Park from Groton, Connecticut, in the late 1980s.

Items on display in the museum and on the grounds include a FJ-4B Fury Jet, a PTF-17 patrol torpedo (fast) boat from the Vietnam era, a Korean War-era M-41 tank and the Jim Gillis collection of military artifacts and scale-model ships.

NEW WINDSOR CANTONMENT
STATE HISTORIC SITE

Visitor Information: Located ten miles north of West Point off I-84 and I-87. From I-84 take exit 7 south onto Route 300 for 1 1/2 miles to Temple Hill Road. Turn left on Temple Hill and proceed 1 1/2 miles to the site. Markers are posted on Route 300. Mailing Address: Box 207, Vails Gate, New York 12584. Telephone: (914) 561-1765. Hours: 10:00 am to 5:00 pm Wednesday through Saturday and 1:00 pm to 5:00 pm Sunday from late April to late October. Admission: free.

Items on Display: Field Equipment, Personal Documents, Official Documents, Maps (replicas), Paintings/Drawings, Dioramas, Medals, Edged Weapons, Side Arms, Shoulder Arms, Ordnance, Field Artillery, Historic Structure (reconstructed Temple Building, first Army chapel in America).

The following paragraphs are excerpts from Site Manger E. Jane Townsend's description of the New Windsor Cantonment.

"New Windsor Cantonment State Historic Site commemorates" the last encampment of General George Washington "and of the Continental Army in 1782-1783. Eight thousand troops from New York, New Jersey, Massachusetts, New Hampshire and Maryland encamped at New Windsor, building some 600 log huts on 1600 acres. It was here that the cessation of hostilities was announced to the troops, bringing the eight year long struggle for independence to a successful conclusion.

"Today New Windsor Cantonment State Historic Site is a living history site with military drills and camp-life demonstrations daily (in our season!). Although there is one 18th-century log building and one reconstruction of the Publick Building, also known as the Temple Building and used for religious services, there are no original huts remaining from the encampment.

NEW YORK
New Windsor Cantonment State Historic Site, continued

"A visitor center has two permanent exhibits and one audio-visual show. The orientation exhibit tells the story of the Cantonment using original artifacts...reproductions and copies of illustrative materials. Of greatest significance...is the Badge of Military Merit, the forerunner to today's Purple Heart medal. Of the three that were awarded in the Revolutionary War...this is the only known one."

The visitor center also houses an exhibit about 18th-century artillery, with 15 original British, French and American pieces from the Revolution to the Civil War.

OLD RHINEBECK AERODROME

Visitor Information: Located at 42 Stone Church Road, three miles north of Rhinebeck, 100 miles north of New York City. Take the Taconic Parkway to NY-199 west to US-9 south to a left onto Stone Church Road and the aerodrome. Mailing Address: RD 1, Box 89, Rhinebeck, New York 12572. Telephone: (914) 758-8610. Hours: 10:00 am to 5:00 pm daily from May 15 through October. Admission: $3.00 per adult, $1.00 per child ages 6-10 (Monday through Friday); $7.00 per adult, $3.00 per child ages 6-10 (weekends when the air shows take place).

Items on Display: Uniforms, Official Documents, Maps, Photographs, Paintings/Drawings, Dioramas, Medals, Edged Weapons, Side Arms, Field Artillery, Air-Defense Artillery, Aircraft (fixed wing), Tracked Vehicles, Wheeled Vehicles.

The Old Rhinebeck Aerodrome has one of the country's largest collections of airplanes from the first four decades of aviation history. Many of the planes are in air-worthy condition and participate in air shows on summer weekends after June 15. Among the more than 50 airplanes at the aerodrome: the American Curtiss Jenny trainer, the British Sopwith Camel, the German Fokker Triplane and the French Spad XIII. The museum also houses an extensive engine collection, a World War I Renault Tank and Columbia Ambulance and many other items from the pioneer days of aviation, World War I and the Lindbergh era.

Before and after the weekend air shows, visitors can soar over the surrounding countryside in a vintage 1929, New Standard D-25 open-cockpit biplane. Plane rides last 15 minutes and cost $20.00 per person.

NEW YORK

SACKETS HARBOR BATTLEFIELD STATE HISTORIC SITE

Visitor Information: Located on the west side of Sackets Harbor village on Lake Ontario, one mile from NY-3 and nine miles west of exit 45 off I-81. Take I-81 north from Syracuse to exit 45 west onto NY-3 to the village of Sackets Harbor. Turn right at Main Street or right at Washington Street to the site. Mailing Address: Box 27, West Washington Street, Sackets Harbor, New York 13685. Telephone: (315) 646-3634. Hours: 10:00 am to 5:00 pm Wednesday through Saturday, 1:00 pm to 5:00 pm Sunday from late May to mid-October. The grounds are open year round. Admission: free.

Items on Display: Uniforms, Maps, Paintings/Drawings, Edged Weapons, Side Arms, Shoulder Arms, Field Artillery, Historic Structures [Commandant's House (1850-1861), ruins of Fort Kentucky (1814)].

The brig *Oneida*, the first U.S. warship to ply the waters of the Great Lakes, was stationed at Sackets Harbor with a company of Marines in 1809. Three years later, with the outbreak of the War of 1812, Sackets Harbor rapidly became the center of U.S. naval and military operations for the Upper St. Lawrence Valley and Lake Ontario. A British-Canadian force attacked Sackets Harbor in 1813 in an attempt to destroy the extensive ship-building facilities located there. Though fire destroyed much valuable materiel, the Americans proved victorious and ship-building and supply activities continued though the end of the war. Improved Canadian-American relations ended the need for a base at Sackets Harbor in the 1880s.

The historic Union Hotel (1817-1818) at the site houses interpretive exhibits about the War of 1812 and local history. Fourteen rooms in the old Commandant's House (1850-1861) are open to the public as well.

WASHINGTON'S HEADQUARTERS STATE HISTORIC SITE

Visitor Information: Located at 84 Liberty Street in Newburgh, approximately 15 miles north of West Point. From I-84, take exit 10 onto US-9W south for two miles. Turn left onto NY-17K east for one mile then turn right onto Liberty Street. Take the third left onto Lafayette Street and drive two blocks to the site. Mailing Address: P. O. Box 1783, Newburgh, New York 12550. Telephone: (914) 562-1195. Hours: 10:00 am to 5:00 pm Saturday, 1:00 pm to 5:00 pm Sunday

NEW YORK
Washington's Headquarters State Historic Site, continued

and by appointment from January through March; 10:00 am to 5:00 pm Wednesday through Saturday, 1:00 pm to 5:00 pm Sunday from April through December. Admission: free.

Items on Display: Uniforms, Field Equipment, Personal Documents, Official Documents, Maps, Paintings/Drawings, Medals, Edged Weapons, Side Arms, Shoulder Arms, Ordnance, Field Artillery, Medical Equipment, Scale Models (Hasbrouck House, Washington's Hq).

The Hasbrouck House, built by Colonel Jonathan Hasbrouck between the years 1750-1770, houses six galleries containing artifacts and memorabilia from the Revolutionary War era. General and Mrs. George Washington occupied the house, which served as the general's headquarters, from April of 1782 to August of 1783. Other noteworthy occupants from the same era include Baron von Steuben and Colonel and Mrs. Timothy Pickering. A desk used by Washington at a previous headquarters is on display, as are two discharge certificates signed by Washington; Martha Washington's pocket watch, made in 1753 and given to her by her first husband; engraved powderhorns from the Revolutionary War; and the only extant Revolutionary War-period linen hunting/rifle shirt.

WATERVLIET ARSENAL MUSEUM

Visitor Information: Located off Broadway South in Watervliet, approximately ten miles north of Albany and adjacent to the city of Troy. From I-87 south, take exit 7 onto NY-7 east toward Troy/Cohoes. Exit 7 east at I-787 south toward Albany. Take the Green Island/Watervliet exit off I-787 onto Broadway South to the Arsenal. From I-87 north, take exit 23 onto I-787 north to NY-378 west to NY-32 north to the arsenal. Mailing Address: Watervliet Arsenal (SMCWV-INM), Watervliet, New York 12189-4050. Telephone: (518) 266-5805/5868. Hours: 10:00 am to 3:00 pm Tuesday through Saturday. Closed federal holidays. Admission: free.

Items on Display: Photographs, Paintings/Drawings, Ordnance, Field Artillery, Coast-Defense Artillery, Air-Defense Artillery, Historic Structure [Warehouse (1859)].

For 175 years, the Watervliet Arsenal has produced heavy and light weapons, ordnance and field equipment for the U.S. Armed Forces. Many examples of rare and unique field, coast-defense and air-defense artillery and related ordnance items are in the museum's

NEW YORK
Watervliet Arsenal Museum, continued

collection, some dating from pre-Revolutionary times. Examples of the types of heavy weapons designed and manufactured at the arsenal today are on display as well.

WEST POINT MUSEUM

Visitor Information: Located on the grounds of the United States Military Academy at West Point, 36 miles north of New York City. Accessible via I-87 or US-9W. Directional signs are posted on both highways. Mailing Address: United States Military Academy, West Point, New York 10996. Telephone: (914) 938-3201. Hours: 10:30 am to 4:15 pm daily. Closed Christmas and New Year's Day. Admission: free.

Items on Display: A complete list was unavailable at press time, but the museum is known to contain the following: Uniforms, Unit Patches, Field Equipment, Official Documents, Maps, Photographs, Paintings/Drawings, Flags, Medals, Edged Weapons, Side Arms, Shoulder Arms, Machine Guns, Ordnance.

According to museum officials, the West Point Museum is "the most comprehensive military museum in the United States," with exhibits that "range from prehistoric times to today's conquest of space." The museum fulfills its primary mission of assisting the cadet academic program by providing lectures, classroom displays and research assistance. Museum personnel extend this assistance to collectors and military historians as well, and actively support many post activities.

Nearby, a small interpretive center is located at Fort Putnam, a Revolutionary War fort that was constructed in 1778. The fort has been reconstructed to its 1780s appearance and is open daily from May through November.

Other Military Museums, Historic Sites & Exhibits in New York

Bennington Battlefield, c/o Saratoga-Capital Park Region, Saratoga Springs, New York 12866. Telephone: (518) 584-2000.

Castle Clinton National Monument, c/o 26 Wall Street, Manhattan Sites, New York, New York 10005. Telephone: (212) 344-7220.

NEW YORK
Other Military Museums in New York, continued

Cradle of Aviation Museum, Mitchell Field Naval Support Activity, Garden City, New York 11530-5000. Telephone: (516) 222-1191.

Fort Defiance, c/o Fort Ticonderoga, Box 390, Ticonderoga, New York 12883, Telephone: (518) 585-2821.

Fort Mount Hope, c/o Fort Ticonderoga, Box 390, Ticonderoga, New York 12883. Telephone: (518) 585-2821.

Fort Ticonderoga, Box 390, Ticonderoga, New York 12883. Telephone: (518) 585-2821.

Fort William Henry Museum, Canada Street, Lake George, New York 12845. Telephone: (518) 668-5471.

Lake George Battlefield Park, c/o Lake George Historical Association, Box 472, Lake George, New York 12845. Telephone: (518) 668-5044.

Old Fort Johnson, c/o The Montgomery County Historical Society, Fort Johnson, New York 12070. Telephone: (518) 843-0300.

Old Fort Niagara, c/o Old Fort Niagara Association, P. O. Box 169, Youngstown, New York 14174-0169. Telephone: (716) 745-7611.

Oriskany Battlefield, NY-69, Oriskany, New York 13424. Telephone: (315) 768-7224.

Plattsburgh Air Force Base Museum, 380 BMW/PA, Plattsburgh Air Force Base, New York 12903-5000. Telephone: (518) 565-6165.

Saratoga National Historical Park, RD #2, Box 33, Stillwater, New York 12170-0033. Telephone: (518) 664-9821.

Stony Point Battlefield, P. O. Box 182, Stony Point, New York 10980. Telephone: (914) 786-2521.

NORTH CAROLINA

BENTONVILLE BATTLEGROUND STATE HISTORIC SITE

Visitor Information: Located off US-701 approximately 25 miles southwest of Goldsboro. Take I-95 south from Rocky Mount to exit 90 onto US-701 south for 15 miles to State Road 1008. Turn left on SR-1008. The site is three miles ahead. Take I-95 north from Fayetteville to exit 58 onto US-13 east to US-701. Turn left (north) onto US-701 to a right onto SR-1008 to the site. Mailing Address: P. O. Box 27, Newton Grove, North Carolina 28366. Telephone: (919) 594-0789. Hours: 9:00 am to 5:00 pm Monday through Saturday, 1:00 pm to 5:00 pm Sunday from April 1 through October 31; 10:00 am to 4:00 pm Tuesday through Saturday, 1:00 pm to 4:00 pm Sunday from November 1 through March 31. Admission: free.

Items on Display: Uniforms, Field Equipment, Personal Documents, Official Documents, Maps, Photographs, Paintings/Drawings, Dioramas, Flags, Edged Weapons, Side Arms, Shoulder Arms, Ordnance, Field Artillery, Medical Equipment, Historic Structures (Harper House, original and reconstructed earthworks).

When troops led by Union General Sherman and Confederate General Johnston met in battle at Bentonville in March, 1865, the largest battle ever fought in North Carolina ensued. The battle lasted three days with more than 4,000 men listed as dead, wounded or missing. When the Confederate Army retreated, the last major offensive action of the Civil War by the Confederate Army came to an end. Sherman proceeded to Goldsboro where much-needed supplies awaited his men. One month later, Johnston surrendered to Sherman near Durham and the war in the Carolinas ended. Interpretive exhibits at the visitor center explain the battle in detail. Period artifacts, including many excavated at the site, are on display.

The Harper House, located on the battlefield, served as a hospital for Union XVI Army Corps troops. It is one of the few houses in the country that has been restored as a Civil War-era field hospital. Original Civil War medical equipment is on display.

CASWELL-*NEUSE* STATE HISTORIC SITE

Visitor Information: Located 3/4 of a mile off the US-70 bypass on West Vernon Avenue in Kinston. Take US-70 east from Goldsboro to the US-70 bypass. Signs are posted. Mailing Address: P. O. Box 3043, Kinston, North Carolina 28502-3043. Telephone: (919) 522-2091.

NORTH CAROLINA
Caswell-*Neuse* State Historic Site, continued

Hours: 9:00 am to 5:00 pm Monday through Saturday, 1:00 pm to 5:00 pm Sunday from April through October; 10:00 am to 4:00 pm Tuesday through Saturday, 1:00 pm to 4:00 pm Sunday from November through March. Admission: free.

Items on Display: Uniforms, Field Equipment, Personal Documents, Official Documents, Maps, Photographs, Paintings/Drawings, Flags, Edged Weapons, Shoulder Arms, Ordnance, Ships/Boats, Scale Models (ships/boats).

The two visitor centers at the Caswell-*Neuse* State Historic Site embrace two separate historical periods. The Richard Caswell Memorial and visitor center houses artifacts and exhibits about the political and military careers of Richard Caswell, the first constitutionally elected governor of the state of North Carolina. The Caswell family cemetery at the site dates from the mid-1700s.

The second visitor center focuses on the history of the Confederate ironclad gunboat CSS *Neuse*, the structural remains of which are on display outside the visitor center. *Neuse* artifacts on indoor display include personal belongings of the crew, parts of the ship's iron plating, a scale model of the ship and exhibits and an audio-visual program about the ship's Civil War activities. A functional nautical blacksmith's shop is also located at the site. Demonstrations are given.

82ND AIRBORNE DIVISION
WAR MEMORIAL MUSEUM

Visitor Information: Located at the intersection of Gela Street and Ardennes Street on Fort Bragg, 15 miles northwest of Fayetteville. Take I-95 to NC-24 west to the fort. Signs are posted. Mailing Address: Gela and Ardennes Streets, Fort Bragg, North Carolina 28307-5000. Telephone: (919) 396-5307. Hours: 10:00 am to 4:30 pm Tuesday through Saturday, 11:30 pm to 4:00 pm Sunday. Admission: free.

Items on Display: A complete list was unavailable at press time, but the museum's collection is known to contain the following: Uniforms, Field Equipment, Edged Weapons, Side Arms, Shoulder Arms, Machine Guns, Ordnance, Field Artillery, Aircraft (fixed wing, rotary wing).

NORTH CAROLINA
82nd Airborne Division War Memorial Museum, continued

One of the largest museums in the Army museum system, the 82nd Airborne Division Museum displays weapons and other military artifacts of American, Russian, British, French, German, Italian and North Vietnamese origin. German artifacts include a fine collection of Nazi daggers and the enormous swastika banner that hung at Hilter's retreat in Berchtesgaden, Germany. Uniforms worn by World War I Medal of Honor winner Sergeant Alvin York and Generals Ridgway, Gavin and Westmoreland are on display as well.

Various types of fixed- and rotary-wing aircraft used by the division from World War II through Vietnam are located on the grounds, as are a number of artillery pieces, one of which is a German 150mm captured at Normandy.

GUILFORD COURTHOUSE
NATIONAL MILITARY PARK

Visitor Center: Located at 2332 New Garden Road, six miles northwest of the center of Greensboro off US-220 North. From I-85 take exit 121 (Holden Road) north to Wendover Avenue east. Exit onto Battleground Avenue North. Drive for approximately four miles and turn right onto New Garden Road. Mailing Address: P. O. Box 9806, Greensboro, North Carolina 27429-0806. Telephone: (919) 288-1776. Hours: 8:30 am to 5:00 pm daily. Hours are extended to 6:00 pm during the summer months. Closed Christmas and New Year's Day. Admission: free.

Items on Display: Uniforms, Field Equipment, Personal Documents, Official Documents, Maps, Paintings/Drawings, Dioramas, Flags, Edged Weapons, Side Arms, Shoulder Arms, Field Artillery, Ordnance.

Guildford Courthouse commemorates and preserves the site of a significant engagement between loyalist and patriot forces in 1781. The loyalists were lead by Cornwallis, whose surrender to George Washington at Yorktown later the same year would, for all practical purposes, end the Revolutionary war. The patriot forces were lead by Nathanael Greene, hand-picked by George Washington to be commanding general of the Continental Army's Southern Department. Though Greene chose the site of the engagement, Cornwallis' troops proved victorious when Greene was forced to withdraw from the field, leaving his artillery behind.

NORTH CAROLINA
Guildford Courthouse National Military Park, continued

But the victory, a bitter and costly one for Cornwallis, had consequences that proved mortal to the loyalist cause. Greene's forces had suffered few casualties, while Cornwallis' had suffered an enormous number. Unable to pursue Greene as he made for South Carolina, Cornwallis retreated to Wilmington on the North Carolina coast, intent upon taking Virginia. In the following months, Greene retook South Carolina, while Cornwallis pursued a hopeless campaign that lead to his final surrender. Pamphlets and interpretive exhibits at the site's visitor center tell the story of Guilford Courthouse in detail. Artifacts from the battlefield and other period items are on display.

J.F.K. SPECIAL WARFARE MUSEUM

Visitor Information: Located in Building D-2502 on Fort Bragg, 15 miles northwest of Fayetteville. Take I-95 to NC-24 west to the fort. The J.F.K. Museum is on Marion Road off Gruber Road. Signs are posted. Mailing Address: CMDR, USAJFKSWCS, ATSU-SE-MUS, Fort Bragg, North Carolina 28307-5000. Telephone: (919) 432-4272/1533. Hours: 11:30 am to 4:00 pm Tuesday through Sunday. Admission: free.

Items on Display: Uniforms, Unit Patches, Field Equipment, Maps, Photographs, Paintings/Drawings, Dioramas, Flags, Battle Streamers, Medals, Edged Weapons, Side Arms, Shoulder Arms, Field Artillery, Medical Equipment, Tracked Vehicles.

The J.F.K. Special Warfare Museum chronicles the history of U.S. Army special operations forces. Selected exhibits focus on the Special Forces (Green Berets), U.S. Army Rangers, Psychological Operations (PSYOP) units and Civil Affairs units. Exhibits about earlier special forces units including the Rangers, the First Special Service Force, O.S.S. Detachment 101, the Alamo Scouts and the Airborne Rangers of Korea are on display as well, as are captured German and Japanese weapons from World War II and captured Viet Cong and North Vietnamese weapons, uniforms and booby traps.

MOORES CREEK NATIONAL BATTLEFIELD

Visitor Information: Located 20 miles northwest of Wilmington on NC-210. From Wilmington, take US-421 north to the junction with NC-210. Take NC-210 west for approximately five miles to the battlefield. Mailing Address: P. O. Box 69, Currie, North Carolina 28435. Telephone: (919) 283-5591. Hours: 8:00 am to 5:00 pm Monday

NORTH CAROLINA
Moores Creek National Battlefield, continued

through Friday, 9:00 am to 5:00 pm weekends. Open till 6:00 pm weekends during the summer. Admission: free.

Items on Display: Uniforms, Field Equipment, Personal Documents, Official Documents, Maps, Dioramas, Flags, Edged Weapons, Side Arms, Shoulder Arms, Field Artillery, Historic Structure (reconstructed earthworks).

The Moores Creek National Battlefield commemorates the site of a small but important clash between North Carolina patriots and loyalists. The victory achieved at Moores Creek by the outnumbered patriot force ended British authority in the colony, served to delay a full-scale invasion of the South by British troops and, most importantly, prompted North Carolina authorities to instruct its delegation to the Continental Congress to vote for independence—the first colony to do so. Pamphlets and exhibits interpret the battle and its consequences in detail. Period artifacts are on display.

USS *NORTH CAROLINA* BATTLESHIP MEMORIAL

Visitor Information: Located at the intersection of US-17/74/76/421, three miles from Wilmington. Mailing Address: Eagle Island, P. O. Box 417, Wilmington, North Carolina 28402. Telephone: (919) 762-1829. Hours: 8:00 am to 8:00 pm daily during the summer, 8:00 am to sunset daily during the rest of the year. Outdoor sound-and-light show at 9:00 pm nightly from the first Friday in June through Labor Day. Admission: $4.00 per adult, $2.00 per child ages 6-11.

Items on Display: A complete list of items on display in the visitor center and the on-board museum was unavailable at press time, but the memorial is known to include the following: Photographs, Aircraft (fixed wing), Ships/Boats, Scale Models (ships/boats).

At the time of her commissioning in 1941, the USS *North Carolina* was considered one of the most powerful naval weapons in the world. The ship earned 15 battle stars while participating in every major naval offensive in the Pacific Theater from Guadalcanal to Okinawa. A self-guided tour of the ship includes the pilot house, crew's quarters, galley, sick bay, engine room, the ship's big guns, a museum and an OS2U Vought Kingfisher float plane. The visitor center on shore houses period artifacts and exhibits.

NORTH CAROLINA

Other Military Museums, Historic Sites & Exhibits in North Carolina

Alamance Battleground & Visitor Center, Burlington, North Carolina 27215. Telephone: (919) 227-4785.

Fort Anderson Historic Site, Wilmington, North Carolina 28402. Telephone: (919) 371-6613.

Fort Dobbs State Historic Site, Route 9, Box A-415, Statesville, North Carolina 28677. Telephone: (704) 873-5866.

Fort Fisher State Historic Site, Kure Beach, North Carolina 28449. Telephone: (919) 458-5538.

Fort Macon State Park, P. O. Box 127, Atlantic Beach, North Carolina 28512. Telephone: (919) 726-3775.

Fort Raleigh National Historic Site, Lindsay Warren Visitor Center, Route 1, Box 675, Manteo, North Carolina 27954. Telephone: (919) 473-5772.

General William C. Wallace Museum, 209 West Divine Street, Dunn, North Carolina 28334. Telephone: (919) 892-1497.

New Hanover County Museum (Blockade Runner Museum's collection), 814 Market Street, Wilmington, North Carolina 28401. Telephone: (919) 341-4350.

NORTH DAKOTA

FORT BUFORD STATE HISTORIC SITE

Visitor Information: Located 26 miles southwest of Williston on ND-1804. Mailing Address: Route 3, Box 67, Williston, North Dakota 58801. Telephone: (701) 572-9034. Hours: 9:00 am to 6:00 pm daily from June 1 through September 1. Admission: $0.50 per adult, $0.25 per child over age 6 (museum); camping and picnic areas are free.

Items on Display: Uniforms, Field Equipment, Personal Documents, Maps, Photographs, Medals, Edged Weapons, Side Arms, Shoulder Arms, Scale Models (fort), Historic Structure (officers' quarters).

Located at the confluence of the Yellowstone and Missouri Rivers, the Fort Buford site's museum houses artifacts and memorabilia from the Indian Wars period in the Upper Missouri Valley (approximately 1866-1895). Exhibits interpret the Indian Wars and the Army soldier's role on the frontier. The museum building itself is an officers' quarters built in 1872.

FORT TOTTEN STATE HISTORIC SITE

Visitor Information: Located 14 miles southwest of Devils Lake on ND-57. Take ND-57 to the intersection with BIA road #7. Turn south of BIA for approximately one mile past the Fort Totten community buildings and Catholic Church. The fort is on the east side of the road. Mailing Address: P. O. Box 224, Fort Totten, North Dakota 58335. Telephone: (701) 766-4441. Hours: 8:00 am to 5:00 pm daily from May 16 through September 15, other months by appointment (museum); grounds are open year round. Admission: free.

Items on Display: Uniforms, Unit Patches, Field Equipment, Personal Documents, Flags, Medals, Edged Weapons, Side Arms, Shoulder Arms, Ordnance, Historic Structures (restored fort buildings).

Fort Totten was an active Army post from 1867 until 1890. Its garrison patrolled the nearby International Boundary and protected the residents of the Fort Totten reservation and settlers in the region. Units from Fort Totten's 7th Cavalry also served with Lt. Col. George Armstrong Custer during his disastrous campaign against the Sioux in 1876.

Many of the fort's buildings have been restored, including the officers' quarters, quartermaster storehouse, commissary and chaplains' and

NORTH DAKOTA

Fort Totten State Historic Site, continued

surgeons' quarters. Exhibits and artifacts in the site's interpretive center and in the Pioneer Daughters Museum focus on the Indian Wars period.

Other Military Museums, Historic Sites & Exhibits in North Dakota

Camp Hancock State Historic Site, c/o North Dakota Heritage Center, Capital Grounds, Bismarck, North Dakota 58504. Telephone: (701) 224-2666.

Fort Abercrombie Historic Site, Abercrombie, North Dakota 58001. Telephone: (701) 553-8513.

Fort Abraham Lincoln State Historical Park, Rural Route 2, Box 139, Mandan, North Dakota 58554. Telephone: (701) 663-9571.

Fort Clark Historic Site, HC2, Box 26, Center, North Dakota 58530. Telephone: (701) 794-8832.

Fort Ransom State Park, Box 67, Fort Ransom, North Dakota 58033. Telephone: (701) 973-4331.

Grand Forks Air Force Base Museum, Grand Forks Air Force Base, North Dakota 58205-5000. Telephone: (701) 747-3352.

Minot Air Force Base Museum, 57 AD/CS, Minot Air Force Base, North Dakota 58705-5000. Telephone: (701) 723-3026.

Whitestone Battlefield Historic Site and Museum, Rural Route 1, Box 125, Kulm, North Dakota 58456. Telephone: (701) 396-7731.

OHIO

FORT LAURENS STATE MEMORIAL

Visitor Information: Located off I-77, ten miles south of Canton. Take exit 93 (Bolivar-Zoar exit) off I-77 and drive one half mile southwest on County Road 102 to the memorial. Mailing Address: Route 1, Box 442, Bolivar, Ohio 44612. Telephone: (216) 874-2059. Hours: 9:30 am to 5:00 pm Wednesday through Saturday, 12:00 noon to 5:00 pm Sunday from May 27 through Labor Day; 9:30 am to 5:00 pm Saturday, 12:00 noon to 5:00 pm Sunday from September through October. Open during other months by appointment to groups of 20 or more. Admission: $1.50 per adult, $1.00 per child ages 6-12.

Items on Display: Uniforms, Field Equipment, Paintings/Drawings, Flags (reproductions), Edged Weapons, Shoulder Arms.

Fort Laurens was constructed in 1778 by American militia under the command of General Lachlan McIntosh. McIntosh wanted to drive deep into the Ohio country, but harsh weather conditions and other factors slowed his command's progress to a scant five miles per day. McIntosh reluctantly decided to abandon the campaign and ordered the fort built near the site of present day Bolivar. After the fort was completed, McIntosh and most of the garrison returned to points east. The men left behind endured a nightmarish winter, during which starvation and the threat of attack by British troops or British-lead Indians were constant companions. Exhibits and an audio-visual program at the Fort Laurens Museum interpret the Fort Laurens story in detail. Revolutionary War-period artifacts, including those excavated at the site during the 1970s, are on display.

FORT MEIGS STATE MEMORIAL

Visitor Information: Located at 29100 West River Road in Perrysburg on the south side of Toledo. Take I-75 to I-475 to the OH-25 north exit (Perrysburg). From OH-25 turn left onto OH-65. The memorial is one half mile ahead on the right. Mailing Address: P. O. Box 3, Perrysburg, Ohio 43551. Telephone: (419) 874-4121. Hours: vary with season; call before going. Admission: fee charged.

Items on Display: Uniforms, Field Equipment, Personal Documents, Official Documents, Maps, Paintings/Drawings, Dioramas, Edged Weapons, Side Arms, Shoulder Arms, Field Artillery (reproduction), Historic Structure (reconstructed fort).

Fort Meigs State Memorial, continued

Established in February of 1813, Fort Meigs remained an active Army post for little more than two years. During that brief span of time, however, it became a focal point in the northwest campaign of the War of 1812. A succession of British victories throughout 1812 and into 1813 prompted the establishment of Fort Meigs in the Ohio Territory. At that time, the only northwestern outpost that remained in American hands was Fort Wayne in Indiana Territory. Because of this, General William Henry Harrison, commander of the Northwest Army, felt it was imperative for the Army to make a stand in Ohio. Construction of the fort began in February of 1813. In the spring, as expected, British forces, aided by their Canadian and Indian allies, laid siege to the fort. The bombardment that began on May 1 lasted for five days, when Kentucky militiamen arrived to reinforce the garrison. When the British withdrew four days later, the tide had turned in the northwest campaign.

The British laid siege to the fort again in July, again without success. They moved on to Fort Stevenson, where the pattern was repeated and the British suffered heavy losses. At this time, they retreated back into Canada. A short time later, Commodore Oliver Hazard Perry's naval forces defeated the British Navy on Lake Erie. With the British and their allies now clearly on the run on all fronts in the Northwest, General Harrison ordered most of Fort Meigs' garrison to take the offensive and march into Canada. By the spring of 1815, the war had ended with a decisive American victory, and Fort Meigs was formally abandoned by the Army.

Three of the seven reconstructed blockhouses at the fort house exhibits about the War of 1812, the construction and reconstruction of the fort and the day-to-day lives of the soldiers who garrison the fort. The reconstructed Quartermaster Storehouse houses additional interpretive exhibits and artifacts from the period, some of which were excavated at the site. Living history demonstrations are given during the summer and on weekends during the spring and fall.

FORT RECOVERY STATE MUSEUM

Visitor Information: Located at 1 Fort Site Street in Fort Recovery, three blocks west of the intersection of OH-49 and OH-119, approximately 20 miles northwest of Greenville. Take OH-49 north from Greenville to OH-119 west for three blocks to the museum. Mailing Address: 1741 Union City Road, Fort Recovery, Ohio 45846. Telephone: (419) 375-4649/2311. Hours: 1:00 pm to 5:00 Tuesday through Saturday, 12:00 noon to 5:00 pm Sunday during June, July

OHIO
Fort Recovery State Museum, continued

and August; weekends only in May and September. Admission: $1.00 per adult, $0.50 per child age 12 and under or $2.50 for family, whichever is less.

Items on Display: Uniforms (reproductions), Field Equipment, Maps, Paintings/Drawings, Edged Weapons, Side Arms, Shoulder Arms, Ordnance, Field Artillery, Medical Equipment, Historic Structure (partially reconstructed fort).

Exhibits and artifacts at the Fort Recovery State Museum all relate to the two battles fought in the area during the Indian Wars of the 1790s. One of the most significant victories by a native force over an invading European force occurred in 1791 when Indian warriors defeated St. Clair's army. Anthony Wayne's victory over the Indians three years later opened the way for new settlement in the Northwest Territory. Period artifacts on display include personal items that belonged to Anthony Wayne, a peace pipe used during the signing of the Treaty of Greenville and rifles made exclusively for Wayne's army by the French. Reconstructed fort structures include two blockhouses, the stockade and the main gate.

NEIL ARMSTRONG AIR & SPACE MUSEUM

Visitor Information: Located at the intersection of I-75 and Bellefontaine Street in Wapakoneta, approximately 12 miles south of Lima. Take I-75 north from Dayton or south from Lima to exit 111 at Wapakoneta and the museum. Mailing Address: Box 1978, Wapakoneta, Ohio 45895. Telephone: (419) 738-8811. Hours: 9:30 am to 5:00 pm Monday through Saturday, 12:00 noon to 5:00 Sunday from March through November. Admission: $2.00 per adult, $1.00 per child.

Items on Display: A complete list was unavailable at press time, but the museum's collection is known to include the following: Uniforms, Aircraft (fixed wing), Space Craft, Space Exploration Displays.

Exhibits and artifacts relating to the first manned lunar landing in history and to the career and achievements of Neil Armstrong are on display at the Neil Armstrong Air & Space Museum. The Aeronca 7AC Champion in which Armstrong learned to fly is on display in the museum's main gallery, along with a Jupiter rocket engine and audio-visual programs. The Gemini spacecraft used by Armstrong and Major David Scot to accomplish NASA's first docking mission in

Neil Armstrong Air & Space Museum, continued

March, 1966, is on display in the Space Flight Gallery, as are Armstrong's Gemini and Apollo XI backup spacesuits and items relating to Armstrong's lifelong interest in aviation. Another gallery features exhibits about the air and space achievements of Ohio natives, including the Wright Brothers. Several multi-media presentations about the Apollo XI mission occur daily. Outside stands the F5D Skylancer that Armstrong flew for the Air Force and NASA during the 1960s.

103RD OHIO VOLUNTEER INFANTRY MUSEUM

Visitor Information: Located at 5501 East Lake Road in Sheffield Lake, approximately ten miles west of Cleveland on the shores of Lake Erie. Take I-90 west from Cleveland to the OH-611 exit. Go west onto OH-611 to the first stop light. Turn right (north) at the stop light onto Miller Road and drive approximately two miles to Lake Road. Turn left onto Lake Road and drive approximately one half mile to the museum grounds on your right. Signs at the parking area direct you to the museum. Mailing Address: 980 North Ridge Road, West Lorain, Ohio 44053. Telephone: (216) 233-7610. Hours: open by appointment only. Admission: free.

Items on Display: Uniforms, Field Equipment, Personal Documents, Official Documents, Maps, Photographs, Paintings/Drawings, Flags, Medals, Edged Weapons, Side Arms, Shoulder Arms, Ordnance, Field Artillery.

This museum is unique among Civil War museums—not so much for the period artifacts it displays, but for the origins and history of the organization that founded it. In 1867, veterans of the 103rd Ohio Volunteer Infantry Regiment held their first annual reunion. The reunions continued in subsequent years, and in 1888 became week-long affairs, dubbed "camp week" by the participants. To this day, camp week continues. Every August, descendants of veterans of the 103rd meet to renew old friendships and carry on the tradition established by their Civil War-veteran ancestors more than one hundred twenty years ago. The museum curators say they know of no other Civil War regiment that has done this.

In 1970, the 103rd Ohio Volunteer Infantry Regiment Memorial Foundation was established to create the museum that now preserves artifacts from the 103rd's service in the Civil War and memorabilia from camp-week reunions.

OHIO

U.S. AIR FORCE MUSEUM

Visitor Information: Located on Wright-Patterson Air Force Base, six miles northeast of downtown Dayton on East Springfield Street near Woodman Drive. Accessible from I-75 or I-675. Signs are posted. Mailing Address: Wright-Patterson Air Force Base, Ohio 45433-5000. Telephone: (513) 255-3284. Hours: 9:00 am to 5:00 pm daily. Closed Thanksgiving, Christmas and New Year's Day. Admission: free.

Items on Display: Uniforms, Unit Patches, Field Equipment, Personal Documents, Official Documents, Maps, Photographs, Paintings/Drawings, Flags, Battle Streamers, Medals, Side Arms, Shoulder Arms, Ordnance, Nuclear Weapons Displays, Missiles, Aircraft (fixed wing, rotary wing), Space Craft, Space Exploration Displays (under development as of Spring 1989), Medical Equipment (displays under development as of Spring 1989), Wheeled Vehicles.

The country's oldest and largest military aviation museum, the U.S. Air Force Museum is visited annually by one and a half million people. More than two hundred aircraft and missiles and thousands of other aviation-related artifacts from the pre-World War I era to the present are housed inside a 300,000 square foot building, a restored World War II Nissen hut, a two-hangar annex accessible by free shuttle bus and an outdoor air park.

The list of rare and unique aircraft on display includes the only remaining XB-70 bomber, the B-29 that dropped the atom bomb on Nagasaki, the world's only known World War I-type observation balloon on display, a 1909 Wright Flyer, a World War I Spad VII, a B-36 long-range bomber, a U-2 reconnaissance plane, an experimental X-15 and the A-1E fighter flown by Major Bernie Fisher on his Medal-of-Honor-winning mission in Vietnam. Memorabilia from the careers of General Billy Mitchell, General Jimmie Doolittle, Captain Eddie Rickenbacker and many other famous Army Air Force and Air Force aviators are on display as well.

USS COD

Visitor Information: Located on the shore of Lake Erie on North Marginal Road between East 9th Street and Burke Lakefront Airport in downtown Cleveland. Take the East 9th Street north exits off I-90, I-77 or the Cleveland Memorial Shoreway to North Marginal Road and the submarine. Mailing Address: Cod Coordinating Committee, 1089 East 9th Street, Cleveland, Ohio 44114. Telephone: (216) 566-8770. Hours: 10:00 am to 5:00 pm daily May through Labor Day. Admission: $3.00 per adult, $2.00 per student through high school.

OHIO

USS *Cod*, continued

Items on Display: Submarines/Submersible Vehicles.

One of 235 fleet-type submarines built during World War II, the USS *Cod* operated in the Pacific theater out of Australia and the Philippines. During her seven war patrols, the *Cod* sent ten Japanese warships and thirty merchant ships to the ocean floor and damaged many others. After serving in the Korean War, she ended her career as a Naval Reserve training vessel in the early 70s.

Other Military Museums, Historic Sites & Exhibits in Ohio

Crawford Auto-Aviation Museum, 10825 East Boulevard, Cleveland, Ohio 44106. Telephone: (216) 721-5722.

Fort Miami, 716 Askin Street, Maumee, Ohio 43537. Telephone: (419) 893-2201.

General Forrest Harding Memorial Museum, c/o Franklin Area Historical Society, 302 Park Avenue, Franklin, Ohio 45005. Telephone: (513) 746-8295.

Perry's Victory and International Peace Memorial, P. O. Box 549, Put-In-Bay, Ohio 43456. Telephone: (419) 285-2184.

Sherman House Museum, 137 East Main Street, Lancaster, Ohio 43130. Telephone: (614) 654-9923.

OKLAHOMA

FORT GIBSON MILITARY PARK

Visitor Information: Located at 110 East Ash in Fort Gibson, approximately ten miles northeast of Muskogee. Take the Fort Gibson exit off US-62 and drive through the business district on Lee Street. The park is at the end of Lee Street. Mailing Address: P. O. box 457, Fort Gibson, Oklahoma 74434. Telephone: (918) 478-2669/3355. Hours: 9:00 am to 5:00 pm Monday through Saturday, 1:00 pm to 5:00 pm Sunday. Closed Easter, Thanksgiving and Christmas. Admission: free.

Items on Display: Uniforms (replicas), Edged Weapons (replicas), Shoulder Arms (replicas), Field Artillery (replicas), Historic Structures (reconstructed and restored fort buildings).

In April of 1824, five 7th Infantry companies commanded by Colonel Mathew Arbuckle began constructing Fort Gibson on the banks of the Grand (Neosho) River. Initially the garrison's duties were similar to those of many western outposts during peacetime, with law enforcement its primary function. The passage of the Indian Removal Act of 1830, however, greatly expanded the garrison's role in the region and enhanced its importance.

The Indian Removal Act called for the relocation of Indians from the Southeastern United States to what is now Oklahoma. Because of its strategic location in the Indian removal process, Army officials made Fort Gibson 7th Infantry headquarters in 1831 and later headquarters of the Army's Department of the Southwestern Frontier. The fort served as a staging area for military ventures in the region, most of which were intended to maintain peace between the Plains Indian tribes and the thousands of Creek, Cherokee and Seminole Indians who arrived during the 1830s and 1840s. In 1857, its mission accomplished, the fort's garrison was removed and the lands it occupied turned over to the Cherokee Nation.

Union troops re-garrisoned the fort during the Civil War. In 1867, construction began on much-needed stone buildings to replace the original log structures. Construction work was completed by 1871 and the buildings remained in use until the fort was disestablished for the last time in 1890.

During the 1930s, the fort's original stockade and outbuildings were reconstructed and other structures from the fort's post-Civil War period were restored. Rooms in the stockade area today contain replicas of period furnishings, military equipment and personal

Fort Gibson Military Park, continued

effects. The stone barrack contains an exhibit about the life of the cavalry soldier of the 1870s.

FORT WASHITA

Visitor Information: Located 15 miles northwest of Durant on OK-199. From I-35 west of Ardmore, take US-70 east to Madill to OK-199 east to the fort. Mailing Address: Star Route, Box 213, Durant, Oklahoma 74701. Telephone: (405) 924-6502. Hours: 9:00 am to 5:00 pm Monday through Friday, 1:00 pm to 5:00 pm weekends. Admission: free.

Items on Display: Uniforms, Field Equipment, Edged Weapons, Side Arms, Shoulder Arms, Field Artillery, Historic Structure (reconstructed and restored fort buildings, fort ruins).

The U.S. Army established Fort Washita in 1841 in an effort to protect Choctaw and Chickasaw Indian settlements from renegade Plains Indian tribes. Many punitive expeditions against the Plains Indians, in particular the Comanches, were launched from Fort Washita. A number of prominent men served at the fort, including General Zachary Taylor, Captain George McClellan and Colonel Braxton Bragg, who later served as a general in the Confederate Army.

The U.S. Army abandoned the fort at the outbreak of the Civil War. Confederate troops promptly reoccupied the fort and used it as a supply depot until the end of the war.

Reconstructed and restored fort buildings and the site's visitor center contain pre-Civil War military artifacts.

45TH INFANTRY DIVISION MUSEUM

Visitor Information: Located at 2145 Northeast 36th Street, Oklahoma City, Oklahoma 73111. In Oklahoma City, take I-35 to the Northeast 36th Street exit west to the museum on the right. Telephone: (405) 424-5313. Hours: 9:00 am to 5:00 pm Tuesday through Friday, 10:00 am to 5:00 pm Saturday, 1:00 pm to 5:00 pm Sunday. Admission: free.

Items on Display: Uniforms, Unit Patches, Field Equipment, Personal Documents, Official Documents, Maps, Photographs, Paintings/Drawings, Dioramas, Flags, Battle Streamers, Medals,

OKLAHOMA
45th Infantry Division Museum, continued

Edged Weapons, Side Arms, Shoulder Arms, Machine Guns, Flame Throwers, Ordnance, Field Artillery, Coast-Defense Artillery, Air-Defense Artillery, Rockets/Rocket Launchers, Missiles, Aircraft (fixed wing, rotary wing), Space Exploration Displays, Amphibious Landing Craft, Communications Equipment, Medical Equipment, Tracked Vehicles, Wheeled Vehicles, Scale Models (aircraft, tracked vehicles, wheeled vehicles).

One of the country's exemplary state-operated military museums, the 45th Infantry Division Museum houses weapons and other artifacts from the Revolutionary War to Vietnam. The museum's Jordan B. Reaves collection of military weapons is one of the most extensive in the country, with weapons from all of the nation's major armed conflicts. The Bill Maudlin Room contains more than 200 original drawings by the two-time Pulitzer Prize winning correspondent. One room honors the nine 45th Infantry Division soldiers who won the Medal of Honor in World War II and Korea. Items used by divisional chaplains during World War II and Korea are on display in the Museum Chapel. Personal items that once belonged to Adolf Hitler, captured by 45th Infantry Division members near the end of World War II, are on display as well. More than 40 historic aircraft, tracked and wheeled vehicles and other pieces of military equipment are located on the museum grounds.

MUSKOGEE WAR MEMORIAL PARK
& USS *BATFISH*

Visitor Information: Located off the Muskogee-Broken Arrow Turnpike in Muskogee. Take the Port of Muskogee exit off the turnpike to the park. Mailing Address: P. O. Box 253, Muskogee, Oklahoma 74401. Telephone: (918) 682-6294. Hours: 9:00 am to 5:00 pm Monday through Saturday, 12:00 noon to 5:00 pm Sunday from March 15 to October 15. Admission: $1.50 per adult, $0.75 per child ages six and over.

Items on Display: Uniforms, Unit Patches, Field Equipment, Personal Documents, Official Documents, Maps, Photographs, Flags, Battle Streamers, Medals, Edged Weapons, Shoulder Arms, Field Artillery, Air-Defense Artillery, Submarines/Submersible Vehicles, Scale Models (aircraft, ships/boats).

The Muskogee War Memorial Park's museum houses military artifacts from World War I to the present. Big guns, two torpedoes and one depth charge device are on the museum grounds, as is the

OKLAHOMA
Muskogee War Memorial Park & USS *Batfish*, continued

USS *Batfish*, one of World War II's more distinguished submarines. During the war, the *Batfish* sank 14 Japanese vessels, including three Japanese submarines in 76 hours—an all-time record for an American submarine. Though she did not enter the war until 1944, the *Batfish* earned nine battle stars.

U.S. ARMY FIELD ARTILLERY
& FORT SILL MUSEUM

Visitor Information: Located at 437 Quanah Road, Fort Sill, Oklahoma 73503-5100. Take the Fort Sill exit off I-44 to Key Gate. Turn right onto Randolph Road to the Old Post area and the museum. Telephone: (405) 351-5123. Hours: 8:30 am to 4:30 pm daily. Admission: free.

Items on Display: Uniforms, Unit Patches, Field Equipment, Personal Documents, Official Documents, Maps, Photographs, Paintings/Drawings, Dioramas, Flags, Battle Streamers, Medals, Edged Weapons, Side Arms, Shoulder Arms, Ordnance, Nuclear Weapons Displays, Field Artillery, Rockets/Rocket Launchers, Aircraft (fixed wing, rotary wing), Communications Equipment, Tracked Vehicles, Wheeled Vehicles, Historic Structures [original post buildings (1869-1875)].

The Fort Sill Museum is a part of the Fort Sill National Historic Landmark area, where 26 of the post's original buildings still stand. Seven are open to the public and contain displays, weapons and other artifacts from the Civil War and Indian Wars periods through Vietnam. The museum has three major themes: the history of Fort Sill, the Indian Wars of the Southwest and the evolution of field artillery pieces.

Atomic Annie, the 280mm gun that fired the world's first atomic artillery round is on display at the museum's Cannon Walk, along with many other types of U.S. and foreign artillery pieces, rockets and rocket launchers, aircraft and other items. The Old Post Chapel, built in 1875, is the oldest existing house of worship in Oklahoma in continuous use since its founding.

Geronimo, the famous Indian chief who was imprisoned in the fort's guardhouse on several occasions, is buried about two miles from the fort. Ask museum personnel for directions.

OKLAHOMA

Other Military Museums, Historic Sites & Exhibits in Oklahoma

Black Kettle Museum, P. O. Box 252, Cheyenne, Oklahoma 73628. Telephone: (405) 497-3929.

Civil War Monument/Second Battle of Cabin Creek, Route 3, Box 216, Vinita, Oklahoma 74301. Telephone: (918) 782-3582.

Confederate Memorial Museum and Information Center, P. O. Box 245, Atoka, Oklahoma 74525. Telephone: (405) 889-7192.

Fort Towson Historic Site, Route HC-65, Box 5, Fort Towson, Oklahoma 74735. Telephone: (405) 873-2634.

J. M. Davis Gun Museum, P. O. Box 966, Claremore, Oklahoma 74018. Telephone: (918) 341-5707.

Mid-American Air Group/Frederick Air Museum, Industrial Park, Frederick, Oklahoma 73542. Telephone: (405) 335-2421.

Veterans' Museum, Route 3, Box 96, Wilburton, Oklahoma 74578. Telephone: (918) 465-2607/2890.

Veterans of Foreign Wars, National War Memorial, City Park, Bristow, Oklahoma 74010. Telephone: (918) 367-5720.

Washita Battlefield, c/o Black Kettle Museum, P. O. Box 252, Cheyenne, Oklahoma 73628. Telephone: (405) 497-3929.

OREGON

FORT STEVENS STATE PARK

Visitor Information: Located at the extreme northwestern tip of Oregon in the town of Hammond. Enter the town of Hammond and drive west from the only stop light in town for one half block, then turn right at the sign for Fort Stevens Historical Area and Visitors Center. Mailing Address: Hammond, Oregon 97121. Telephone: (503) 861-2000. Hours: 10:00 am to 6:00 pm daily during the summer months, 12:00 noon to 4:00 pm Wednesday through Sunday during the winter months. Admission: a $0.50 donation per person is requested.

Items on Display: Uniforms, Unit Patches, Field Equipment, Personal Documents, Maps, Photographs, Medals, Mines, Ordnance, Field Artillery, Communications Equipment, Medical Equipment, Wheeled Vehicles, Scale Models (ships/boats), Historic Structures (fort buildings, gun batteries).

The U.S. Army built Fort Stevens near the close of the Civil War. It remained an active post until 1947. Originally, Fort Stevens consisted of earthworks, gun emplacements and several buildings, all of which were surrounded by a moat, complete with drawbridge, to protect the fort from attack by land. In 1897 the fort underwent a massive refortification process during which eight concrete batteries were put in place.

On June 21, 1942, Fort Stevens came under fire for the first and last time when a Japanese submarine fired nine shells at the fort. The shelling caused no damage and the sub was out of range of the fort's heavy guns. Fort Stevens thus became the only installation in the continental United States to be attacked by a foreign power since the War of 1812.

Oregon State Parks began restoring and interpreting the fort's history for visitors after leasing the fort in 1975. The Fort Stevens museum is housed in a 1911 dormitory with artifacts and exhibits dating from the Civil War through World War II. All the fort's batteries are open to the public, though the guns themselves were removed after World War II.

OREGON

Other Military Museums, Historic Sites & Exhibits in Oregon

Fort Clatsop National Memorial, Route 3, Box 604-FC, Astoria, Oregon 97103. Telephone: (503) 861-2471.

Fort Dalles Surgeon's Quarters, Fifteenth Street and Garrison Street, The Dalles, Oregon 97058. Telephone: (503) 296-4547.

Fort Klamath Historical Frontier Post, Fort Klamath, Oregon 97626. Telephone: None.

Oregon Military Museum, Camp Withycombe, Oregon 97015. Telephone: (503) 657-6806.

PENNSYLVANIA

BRANDYWINE BATTLEFIELD PARK

Visitor Information: Located on US-1 between US-202 and PA-100 in Chadds Ford. Mailing Address: Box 202, Chadds Ford, Pennsylvania 19317. Telephone: (215) 459-3342. Hours: 9:00 am to 5:00 pm Tuesday through Saturday, 12:00 noon to 5:00 pm Sunday. Admission: $1.00 per adult, $0.75 per senior citizen and member of large group, $0.50 per child ages 6-17.

Items on Display: Uniforms, Field Equipment, Maps, Dioramas, Flags, Edged Weapons, Side Arms, Shoulder Arms, Ordnance, Field Artillery, Historic Structures (reconstructed Hq building and restored living quarters).

An audio-visual program at the Brandywine visitor center interprets the significance of the Battle of Brandywine and its role in the Philadelphia Campaign of 1777. Period artifacts, some excavated at the battlefield, are on display, including British and American muskets and swords, 1st Continental Regimental flags and a fife and other items used at the battle.

The house that served as General Washington's headquarters prior to the battle has been reconstructed and furnished to its 1770s appearance. The house in which French patriot LaFayette was quartered has been restored and may also be toured.

BUSHY RUN BATTLEFIELD

Visitor Information: Located on Bushy Run Road in Jeannette, ten to fifteen miles southeast of Pittsburgh. Take Route 66 north from Greensburg and turn left onto Route 993 west. Drive for three miles to the battlefield entrance on the right. Mailing Address: Bushy Run Road, Jeannette, Pennsylvania 15644. Telephone: (412) 527-5584. Hours: 8:30 am to 5:00 pm Tuesday through Saturday, 12:00 noon to 5:00 pm Sunday. Grounds are open till 8:00 during daylight savings time. Admission: fee charged.

Items on Display: Field Equipment, Paintings/Drawings, Edged Weapons, Shoulder Arms, Ordnance.

In August, 1763, a British force lead by Colonel Henry Bouquet defeated an Indian force at the Bushy Run Battlefield site. The British victory is said to have been the turning point in Pontiac's War. Exhibits at the site's visitor center interpret Pontiac's War and

PENNSYLVANIA
Bushy Run Battlefield, continued

the significance of the British victory at Bushy Run in detail. Period artifacts are on display.

CIVIL WAR LIBRARY & MUSEUM

Visitor Information: Located in downtown Philadelphia at 1805 Pine Street, Philadelphia, Pennsylvania 19103. Call for driving directions. Telephone: (215) 735-8196. Hours: 10:00 am to 4:00 pm Monday through Friday, weekends by appointment. Admission: $2.00 per person.

Items on Display: Uniforms, Field Equipment, Personal Documents, Official Documents, Maps, Photographs, Paintings/Drawings, Dioramas, Flags, Battle Streamers, Medals, Edged Weapons, Side Arms, Shoulder Arms, Field Artillery, Medical Equipment, Scale Models (ships/boats).

The Civil War Library and Museum was established on the day President Lincoln died by the Military Order of the Loyal Legion of the United States. The Legion consisted of Union officers who had participated in the Civil War. Today, membership is open to all descendants of honorably discharged Union officers or Union officers who died in battle.

The museum houses an impressive collection of Civil War-era militaria. The Meade Room is dedicated to Union Major General George G. Meade, commander of the Army of the Potomac. A beautiful gold sword and scabbard presented to the General by the Pennsylvania Reserve Corps is one of the items on display. Confederate forces artifacts are on display in the Confederate Reading Room, as are three flags that flew on board the Confederate raider CSS *Florida* and other items.

Upstairs in the Lincoln Room, hundreds of rare volumes about Lincoln and his presidency are available to qualified researchers and scholars. The room also houses rare photographs, busts and etchings of Lincoln. The Grant Room contains items relating to the military career of General Ulysses S. Grant, with one of his dress uniforms and examples of original correspondence on display. Histories of Union and Confederate regiments are on display in the Grant room as well. The Navy Room houses the Naval libraries of Thomas Skelton Harrison and Frederick Schrober and other items. On the third floor, arms, accouterments and medical equipment are housed in the Enlisted Men's Room and the Armory.

PENNSYLVANIA

FORT NECESSITY NATIONAL BATTLEFIELD

Visitor Information: Located 11 miles east of Uniontown on US-40. Mailing Address: RD 2, Box 528, Farmington, Pennsylvania 15437. Telephone: (412) 329-5512. Hours: 10:30 am to 5:00 pm daily (visitor center); 8:00 am to 5:00 pm daily (park). Admission: $1.00 per person ages 17-61, $3.00 maximum per family.

Items on Display: Uniforms (reproductions), Field Equipment, Personal Documents, Maps, Paintings/Drawings, Dioramas, Flags (reproductions), Edged Weapons, Side Arms, Shoulder Arms, Field Artillery, Historic Structure (reconstructed fort).

The first battle of the French and Indian War occurred at Fort Necessity on July 3, 1754, when a force of 600 French soldiers and 100 of their Indian allies attacked the British fort, which was commanded by George Washington. Both sides suffered badly during the battle, but the colonials more than their attackers. After negotiating with the French commander, Washington surrendered the fort under favorable terms. This was the first major event in Washington's military career and the only time he was forced to surrender under any circumstances. The French burned the fort to the ground after the British, with their arms and baggage, departed.

Exhibits and slide presentations at the fort's visitor center interpret the significance of the battle at Fort Necessity. Period artifacts and other items in the center focus on the fort's rediscovery by archaeologists and other related subjects.

GETTYSBURG NATIONAL MILITARY PARK

Visitor Information: Located off US-15 (business route) in Gettysburg. Signs are posted throughout the area. Mailing Address: Gettysburg, Pennsylvania 17325. Telephone: (717) 334-1124. Hours: 8:00 am to 5:00 pm daily. Closed Christmas and New Year's Day. Admission: free. Fee charged for electric map and cyclorama programs.

Items on Display: Uniforms, Personal Documents, Maps, Photographs, Paintings/Drawings, Dioramas, Flags, Medals, Edged Weapons, Side Arms, Shoulder Arms, Field Artillery, Communications Equipment, Medical Equipment.

Confederate General Robert E. Lee's Army of Northern Virginia attacked the Union forces led by General George G. Meade at Gettysburg on July 1, 1863. Three days later, when the battered and

PENNSYLVANIA
Gettysburg National Military Park, continued

diminished Confederate force began its retreat back to Virginia, it was, in the words of National Park Service officials, "emotionally and spiritually exhausted. Never again would Lee attempt an offensive operation of such magnitude. And Meade, though criticized for not pursuing Lee's troops, would forever be remembered as the man who won the battle that has come to be known as the High Water Mark of the Confederacy."

On November 19, 1863, President Lincoln delivered his famous address at the Soldiers' National Cemetery in Gettysburg. Fifteen thousand dignitaries, soldiers and civilians stood in silence as Lincoln, in the space of two minutes, in 272 well chosen words, affirmed his and the nation's commitment to the principles of liberty, freedom and political self-determination. At the Gettysburg Address Exhibit in the Cyclorama Center, visitors will be able to see either the original first or second draft of Lincoln's address, depending upon the time of their visit.

Park rangers lead walking tours of the battlefield, deliver talks and present programs to help visitors interpret the battle. The visitor center contains interpretive exhibits and Civil War artifacts. More exhibits, a ten-minute film—"From These Honored Dead"—and the Gettysburg Cyclorama are located in the Cyclorama Center.

INDEPENDENCE NATIONAL HISTORICAL PARK

Visitor Information: The Army-Navy Museum is located in Pemberton House on Chestnut Street between 3rd and 4th Streets. The Marine Corps Memorial Museum in New Hall is adjacent to the Army-Navy Museum. Administrative offices are located at 313 Walnut Street, Philadelphia, Pennsylvania 19106. Take I-95 to Delaware Avenue south to a left onto Dock Street. Follow Dock Street to a left onto Walnut Street. Follow Walnut Street to 5th Street and turn right. Follow 5th Street to Chestnut Street and turn right. The museums are on the right mid-way between 3rd and 4th Streets. The parking garage is on 2nd Street between Chestnut and Walnut Streets. The visitor center is across the street from the parking garage. Telephone: (215) 597-2458 (Pemberton House); (215) 597-8974 (visitor center). Hours: 9:00 am to 4:45 pm daily except for Christmas Day and the months of January and February. Visitors are advised to call ahead. Admission: free.

Items on Display: Uniforms, Field Equipment, Paintings/Drawings, Edged Weapons, Side Arms, Shoulder Arms, Ordnance, Field

PENNSYLVANIA
Independence National Historical Park, continued

Artillery, Coast-Defense Artillery, Navigational Equipment, Scale Models (ships/boats), Historic Structures.

Like its counterpart in Boston, the Independence National Historical Park is comprised of many historic structures, museums and monuments from or related to the pre- through post-Revolutionary period in American history. Exhibits at the two military museums in the park focus on Army, Navy and Marine Corps activities from the Revolutionary War through the years preceding the War of 1812.

PENNSYLVANIA MILITARY MUSEUM—28TH DIVISION SHRINE

Visitor Information: Located on US-322 in Boalsburg, just east of the city of State College. Take US-322 east to Boalsburg but do not take the Nittany Expressway. Stay on old US-322 into Boalsburg to the first red light. Take the first left after the light to the museum. Mailing Address: P. O. Box 148, Boalsburg, Pennsylvania 16827. Telephone: (814) 466-6263. Hours: 9:00 am to 5:00 pm Tuesday through Saturday, 12:00 noon to 5:00 pm Sunday. Admission: fee charged.

Items on Display: Uniforms, Unit Patches, Field Equipment, Personal Documents, Maps, Paintings/Drawings, Dioramas, Flags, Medals, Edged Weapons, Side Arms, Shoulder Arms, Machine Guns, Medical Equipment, Tracked Vehicles, Wheeled Vehicles.

According to museum officials, "the Pennsylvania Military Museum, through its collections and exhibits, preserves the record of Pennsylvania's participation and involvement in the nation's wars. The Museum has an extensive and varied group of weapons, uniforms, and other accoutrements of soldiers of the last two centuries."

World War II tanks, half-tracks and armored personnel carriers and a Spanish-American War ambulance are on display indoors and on the museum grounds.

VALLEY FORGE NATIONAL HISTORICAL PARK

Visitor Information: Located off the Pennsylvania Turnpike in Valley Forge. Take the turnpike to exit 24 (Valley Forge). Turn right at exit 24 onto Gulph Road. Drive approximately two miles to the

PENNSYLVANIA
Valley Forge National Historical Park, continued

intersection with PA-23. The park entrance is on the left. Mailing Address: Valley Forge, Pennsylvania 19481. Telephone: (215) 783-1077. Hours: 8:30 am to 5:00 pm daily. Admission: $1.00 per person ages 17-61 for admittance to historic houses.

Items on Display: Uniforms, Field Equipment, Edged Weapons, Side Arms, Shoulder Arms, Ordnance, Field Artillery, Historic Structures (restored redoubts, restored Hq building).

Exhibits in the visitor center at the Valley Forge National Historical Park focus on the Continental Army's encampment at Valley Forge during the harsh winter of 1877-1878. Original period artifacts are on display. Two partially restored redoubts and three reconstructed redoubts are on the site, as is General Washington's Hq building, an almost entirely original structure; the General's sleeping marquee; reconstructed soldiers' huts and Brigadier General Varnum's quarters.

Other Military Museums, Historic Sites & Exhibits in Pennsylvania

Clivedon and the Battle of Germantown, c/o Clivedon, Incorporated, 6401 Germantown Avenue, Philadelphia, Pennsylvania 19144. Telephone: (215) 848-1777.

Dandy First Museum, 103rd Engineer Battalion, 3205 Lancaster Avenue, Philadelphia, Pennsylvania 19104. Telephone: (215) 222-8117.

Flagship Niagara, 80 State Street, Erie, Pennsylvania 16507. Telephone: (814) 871-4596.

Farnsworth House Tour and Garret Museum, 401 Baltimore Street, Gettysburg, Pennsylvania 17325. Telephone: (717) 334-8838.

Fort Augusta, P. O. Box 1026, Harrisburg, Pennsylvania 17108. Telephone: (717) 787-6242.

Fort Bedford Museum, c/o Reverend Robert Sweet, Box 1976, Old Bedford Village, Bedford, Pennsylvania 15522. Telephone: (814) 623-1156.

Fort Loudoun, Box 181, Fort Loudoun, Pennsylvania 17224. Telephone: (717) 369-3318.

PENNSYLVANIA
Other Military Museums in Pennsylvania, continued

Fort LeBoeuf Museum, c/o Edinboro University of Pennsylvania, Department of Sociology, Anthropology and Social Work, Edinboro, Pennsylvania 16444. Telephone: (814) 732-2573.

Fort Ligonier, South Market Street, Ligonier, Pennsylvania 15658. Telephone: (412) 238-9701.

Fort Pitt Blockhouse, Point State Park, Pittsburgh, Pennsylvania 15222. Telephone: (412) 471-1764.

Fort Pitt Museum, Point State Park, Pittsburgh, Pennsylvania 15222. Telephone: (412) 281-9284.

Fort Roberdeau, Altoona, Pennsylvania 16603. Telephone: (814) 942-3916.

Hessian Powder Magazine Museum, c/o U.S. Army Military History Institute, Carlisle Barracks, Pennsylvania 17013-5000. Telephone: (717) 235-3434.

Lincoln Train Museum and Alexander Model Train and Military Rail Collection, Gettysburg, Pennsylvania 17325. Telephone: (717) 334-5678.

Mid-Atlantic Air Museum, R.D. 9, Box 9381, Reading, Pennsylvania 19605. Telephone: (215) 372-7333.

Military Edged Weapons Museum, 3562 Old Philadelphia Pike, Box 6, Intercourse, Pennsylvania 17534. Telephone: (717) 768-7185.

Museum of the First Troop—Philadelphia City Cavalry, The Armory, 23rd and Rumstead Streets, Philadelphia, Pennsylvania 19103. Telephone: (215) 654-1488.

National Civil War Wax Museum, 297 Steinwehr Avenue, Gettysburg, Pennsylvania 17325. Telephone: (717) 334-6245.

Omar N. Bradley Museum, c/o U.S. Army Military History Institute, Carlisle Barracks, Pennsylvania 17013-5000. Telephone: (717) 235-3434.

Soldiers and Sailors Memorial, Fifth and Bigelow Streets, Pittsburgh, Pennsylvania 15213. Telephone: (412) 621-4253.

PENNSYLVANIA
Other Military Museums in Pennsylvania, continued

Soldiers National Museum and Abe Lincoln Place, Gettysburg, Pennsylvania 17325. Telephone: (717) 334-4890.

USS *Becuna*, c/o Cruiser *Olympia* Association, P. O. Box 928, Philadelphia, Pennsylvania 19105. Telephone: (215) 922-1898

USS *Olympia*, c/o Cruiser *Olympia* Association, P. O. Box 928, Philadelphia, Pennsylvania 19105. Telephone: (215) 922-1898.

Valley Forge Museum, c/o Valley Forge Historical Society, Box 122, Valley Forge, Pennsylvania 19481. Telephone: (215) 783-0535.

Washington Crossing Historic Park, P. O. Box 103, Washington Crossing, Pennsylvania 18977. Telephone: (215) 493-4076.

Willow Grove Naval Air Station Air Park, Public Affairs Office, Naval Air Station, Willow Grove, Pennsylvania 19090. Telephone: (215) 443-1776.

RHODE ISLAND

NAVAL WAR COLLEGE MUSEUM

Visitor Information: Located at the Naval Education and Training Center on Coasters Harbor Island in Newport. Take RI-114 south to the Connell Highway or Kalbfus road east and follow signs to the museum. Mailing Address: Coasters Harbor Island, Newport, Rhode Island 02841-5010. Telephone: (401) 841-4052/1317. Hours: 10:00 am to 4:00 pm Monday through Friday year round, 12:00 noon to 4:00 pm weekends during the summer months. Admission: free.

Items on Display: Uniforms, Field Equipment, Personal Documents, Official Documents, Maps, Photographs, Paintings/Drawings, Flags, Medals, Edged Weapons, Scale Models (aircraft, ships/boats).

Exhibits at the Naval War College Museum focus on the histories of naval warfare and the Naval War College and naval activities in the Narragansett Bay region. The Naval War College itself is the oldest naval war college in the world and the Navy's highest educational institution. Artifacts on display date from the American Revolution through Vietnam.

NEWPORT ARTILLERY COMPANY MILITARY MUSEUM

Visitor Information: Located at 23 Clark Street in Newport. Call for directions. Mailing Address: P. O. Box 14, Newport, Rhode Island 02840. Telephone: (401) 846-8488. Hours: By appointment only. Admission: $2.00 per adult, $1.50 per child.

Items on Display: Uniforms, Unit Patches, Field Equipment, Personal Documents, Official Documents, Maps, Photographs, Paintings/Drawings, Dioramas, Flags, Battle Streamers, Medals, Edged Weapons, Side Arms, Shoulder Arms, Machine Guns, Ordnance, Field Artillery, Rockets/Rocket Launchers, Wheeled Vehicles, Scale Models (artillery), Historic Structure (armory).

One hundred twenty-three different nations are represented in the Newport Artillery Company Military Museum's collection of military artifacts and memorabilia. The museum houses one of the largest collections of foreign military uniforms anywhere, as well as a large number of weapons and other items from the Revolutionary War to the present. The armory building itself dates from 1836.

RHODE ISLAND

Other Military Museums, Historic Sites & Exhibits in Rhode Island

Butts Hill Fort, Sprague Street, Portsmouth, Rhode Island 02871. Telephone: None.

Fort Adams State Park, Harrison Avenue (Ocean Drive), Newport, Rhode Island 02840. Telephone: (401) 847-2400.

Fort Barton, c/o Curator, 51 Leonard Drive, Tiverton, Rhode Island 02878. Telephone: (401) 624-4543 (curator) -4277 (town hall).

Independent Company of Kentish Guards Armory, Pierce and Armory Streets, East Greenwich, Rhode Island 02818. Telephone: (401) 828-5731, 884-1519.

Rhode Island National Guard Heritage Hall, Benefit Street Arsenal, 176 Benefit Street, Providence, Rhode Island 02903. Telephone: (401) 277-2061.

Varnum Military Museum, Main and Division Streets, East Greenwich, Rhode Island 02818. Telephone: (401) 884-4110/8567.

SOUTH CAROLINA

COWPENS NATIONAL BATTLEFIELD

Visitor Information: Located 11 miles northwest of Gaffney, South Carolina, and I-85. Take SC-11 west from I-85 to the battlefield. Mailing Address: P. O. Box 308, Chesnee, South Carolina 29323. Telephone: (803) 461-2828. Hours: 9:00 am to 5:00 pm daily. Closed Christmas. Admission: $1.00 per person or $3.00 per family from May 1 to October 31. Persons under age 16, senior citizens and school groups admitted free.

Items on Display: Uniforms (reproductions), Paintings/Drawings, Flags (reproductions), Battle Streamers (reproductions), Edged Weapons, Side Arms, Shoulder Arms, Field Artillery (reproductions).

The battle at the Cowpens pitted a force of British regulars led by Banastre Tarleton against a tired but determined band of Continental soldiers and militiamen led by Daniel Morgan, one of the best field tacticians of the Revolution. The American victory at Cowpens in 1781 dealt a severe blow to the British cause, which, for all practical purposes, ended with Cornwallis' surrender at Yorktown later in the same year. The visitor center at the battlefield houses exhibits that interpret the battle and its consequences in detail. Reproduction and original period artifacts are on display.

FLORENCE AIR & MISSILE MUSEUM

Visitor Information: Located on US-301 north of the Florence Airport entrance. From I-95, take exit 170 and follow signs to the museum. Mailing Address: P. O. Box 1326, Florence, South Carolina 29503. Telephone: (803) 665-5118. Hours: 9:00 am to 6:00 pm daily. Admission: $4.00 per adult, $3.00 per child.

Items on Display: Uniforms, Unit Patches, Paintings/Drawings, Photographs, Personal Documents, Machine Guns, Rockets, Missiles, Aircraft (fixed wing, rotary wing), Space Craft, Space Exploration Displays, Satellites/Satellite Communications Displays, Tracked Vehicles, Scale Models (aircraft).

Dedicated to the Air Force and Air Corps personnel who have served their country since heavier-than-air flight became a reality, the Florence Air and Missile Museum has over 40 aircraft, missiles and rockets in its collection. A B-29 Superfortress, a C-124 Globemaster and a Titan I missile that stands 98 feet tall are on display, along with helicopters, jet fighters, trainers and cargo carriers. A Gemini

SOUTH CAROLINA
Florence Air & Missile Museum, continued

space capsule is also on display, along with Alan Shepard's space suit, space parachutes and Apollo launch-computer equipment. A special room is dedicated to the exploits and activities of the famous Lafayette Escadrille.

FORT JACKSON MUSEUM

Visitor Information: Located on Fort Jackson in Building 4442, Jackson Boulevard, 12 miles northeast of Columbia. Mailing Address: ATTN: ATZJ-PTM-P, Fort Jackson, South Carolina 29207-5325. Telephone: (803) 751-7419/7355. Hours: 1:00 pm to 4:00 pm Tuesday through Sunday. Closed all federal holidays.

Items on Display: Uniforms, Field Equipment, Personal Documents, Official Documents, Maps, Photographs, Paintings/Drawings, Flags, Medals, Edged Weapons, Side Arms, Shoulder Arms, Machine Guns, Mines, Ordnance, Field Artillery, Aircraft (rotary wing), Amphibious Landing Craft, Communications Equipment, Medical Equipment, Tracked Vehicles.

An extensive collection of military artifacts and memorabilia, some dating as far back as the Revolution, are on display at the Fort Jackson Museum. Selected exhibits chronicle the history of Fort Jackson, beginning with its establishment as Camp Jackson in 1917 and continuing up to the present.

FORT SUMTER NATIONAL MONUMENT

Visitor Information: Located a short distance east of Charleston at 1214 Middle Street, Sullivan's Island, South Carolina 29482. From US-17 take SC-703 to Sullivan's Island. Telephone: (803) 883-3123. Hours: 9:00 am to 6:00 pm during the summer months, 9:00 am to 5:00 pm other months. Admission: free.

Items on Display: Uniforms, Unit Patches, Field Equipment, Personal Documents, Official Documents, Maps, Photographs, Paintings/Drawings, Dioramas, Flags, Medals, Edged Weapons, Side Arms, Shoulder Arms, Ordnance, Field Artillery, Coast-Defense Artillery, Communications Equipment, Historic Structures (forts).

Exhibits at the Fort Sumter museum interpret the fort's history as a coast-defense fortification in the southeastern U.S. Special exhibits focus on the fort's capture by Confederate militia in 1861, the first overtly hostile military action of the Civil War. The U.S. flag that

SOUTH CAROLINA
Fort Sumter National Monument, continued

flew over the fort during that first battle is on display, as is the Confederate flag (actually a homemade South Carolina militia flag) that took the U.S. flag's place after the Confederate force supplanted its Federal counterpart. A visitor center at neighboring Fort Moultrie also houses interpretive displays and artifacts.

Many of the items in both the Fort Sumter and Fort Moultrie display areas were excavated on site, including 17 Civil War-era cannon at Fort Sumter and 20 artillery and siege guns at Fort Moultrie. Other items on display range from pre-Civil War edged weapons to World War II-era shoulder arms, ordnance and coast-defense artillery pieces.

NINETY SIX NATIONAL HISTORIC SITE

Visitor Information: Located two miles south of Ninety Six, South Carolina, off SC-248. From I-26, take SC-72 toward Greenwood for approximately 20 miles then follow signs to the site. Mailing Address: P. O. Box 496, Ninety Six, South Carolina 29666. Telephone: (803) 543-4068. Hours: 8:00 am to 5:00 pm daily. Closed Christmas and New Year's Day. Admission: free.

Items on Display: Uniforms, Maps (reproductions), Paintings/Drawings, Edged Weapons (reproductions and originals), Side Arms, Shoulder Arms (reproductions), Ordnance, Field Artillery, Historic Structures (restored fort, fort ruins, earthworks).

The site of several engagements between loyalist and patriot forces during the American Revolution, Ninety Six began as a stopping place on a major trade route out of Charleston. Traders named the site Ninety Six because they thought it was 96 miles from the old Cherokee town of Keowee in the foothills of the Blue Ridge Mountains. By the outbreak of the Revolution, Ninety Six was a small but active community with 12 houses, a courthouse and a jail.

In November of 1775, 1,800 loyalist troops attacked a much smaller band of patriots who were gathered at the Ninety Six site. After several days of hostilities, both sides agreed to a truce. The truce, however, had no lasting impact on the military fortunes of the surrounding region. Patriot forces soon organized an expedition that harried and then crushed loyalist forces present in the region at the time. Ninety Six saw more bloodshed in 1781 when an occupying army of loyalists, defending their territory from a star fort west of the town and a stockade fort on the east, fought back the onslaught of 1,000 regular army troops and a handful of militia led by one of

SOUTH CAROLINA
Ninety Six National Historic Site, continued

the Continental Army's most capable leaders, Nathanael Greene. Though loyalist forces won the day, the town and its fortifications were largely ruined once the battle ended with Greene's retreat. The loyalists burned the few buildings still standing before they marched for the coast.

The star fort's ruins and the siege lines constructed by the patriot forces have been excavated, while the stockade fort has been largely reconstructed. The Ninety Six visitor center houses original and reproduction period artifacts. Exhibits and an audio-visual program interpret the town's history and its importance in deciding the outcome of the Revolution.

PARRIS ISLAND MUSEUM

Visitor Information: Located a short distance south of Beaufort on the Parris Island Marine Corps Recruit Depot. From I-95 take the US-17 exit to US-21 into Beaufort. Follow signs to the Marine Corps Recruit Depot. Mailing Address: Marine Corps Recruit Depot, Parris Island, South Carolina 29905-5000. Telephone: (803) 525-2951. Hours: 10:00 am to 4:30 pm daily. Closed Thanksgiving, Christmas and New Year's Day. Admission: free.

Items on Display: Uniforms (reproductions and originals), Unit Patches, Field Equipment (reproductions and originals), Personal Documents, Official Documents, Maps, Photographs, Paintings/Drawings, Dioramas, Flags (reproductions), Medals, Edged Weapons, Side Arms, Shoulder Arms, Machine Guns, Flame Throwers, Mines, Ordnance, Field Artillery, Air-Defense Artillery, Rockets/Rocket Launchers, Scale Models (aircraft, ships/boats, amphibious landing craft).

Exhibits at the Parris Island Museum interpret the military and civilian histories of Parris Island, beginning with the landing of French Huguenots in 1562 to the present. The museum's principal displays focus upon the Spanish settlement of Santa Elena, a fortified village on Parris Island that Spanish colonists built in 1566 and occupied until 1587; the history of the Marine Corps Recruit Depot on Parris Island; contemporary training activities at the depot; and the history of the Marine Corps in the 20th century. An extensive collection of military artifacts from colonial times to the present is on display.

SOUTH CAROLINA

PATRIOTS POINT NAVAL & MARITIME MUSEUM

Visitor Information: Located in Charleston Harbor on US-17 North. Take I-26 south to Charleston and US-17 north to the museum. Signs are posted. Mailing Address: P. O. Box 986, Mt. Pleasant, South Carolina 29465. Telephone: (803) 884-2727. Hours: 9:00 am to 6:00 pm daily. Admission: $7.50 per adult, $4.00 per child.

Items on Display: Uniforms, Unit Patches, Field Equipment, Personal Documents, Official Documents, Maps, Photographs, Paintings/Drawings, Dioramas, Flags, Battle Streamers, Medals, Edged Weapons, Side Arms, Shoulder Arms, Mines, Ordnance, Air-Defense Artillery, Rockets/Rocket Launchers, Missiles, Aircraft (fixed wing), Ships/Boats, Amphibious Landing Craft (planned), Submarines/Submersible Vehicles, Scale Models.

Patriot's Point is one of the largest naval and maritime museums in the country, with five historic vessels in its collection. The USS *Yorktown*, known as the "Fighting Lady" during World War II, participated in many naval campaigns in the Pacific Theater. After the war, she patrolled the western Pacific, fought in Vietnam and in 1968 recovered the crew of Apollo VIII, the first manned craft to circle the moon. Many areas on board the carrier are open to the public, including the flight deck, the hangar deck, the bridge and the ship's hospital. Exhibits on board include a large collection of mines and artifacts from several other historic aircraft carriers.

The USS *Laffey*, a World War II-era destroyer, participated in the D-Day landings at Normandy four months after being commissioned. After D-Day, she was transferred to the Pacific. Off Okinawa, she was hit by five Japanese Kamikaze planes and three bombs in the space of one hour. In spite of the damage inflicted by the Japanese, the *Laffey's* crew still managed to shoot down 11 enemy planes before the attack ended. The Laffey also served in the Korean War and in the Atlantic Fleet before being decommissioned in 1975. Most ship areas are open to the public.

The USS *Clamagore*, a World War II-era submarine, was commissioned in 1945 and patrolled the Atlantic and the Mediterranean during her career. When decommissioned in 1975, she was one of the few remaining active-service diesel-powered submarines in the fleet. Exhibits about submarine warfare are on board.

The US Coast Guard Cutter *Comanche* is the oldest ship at Patriots Point and its newest arrival. Commissioned in 1934, the *Comanche*

SOUTH CAROLINA
Patriots Point Naval & Maritime Museum, continued

served in the Hudson River until World War II, when she was turned over to the Navy. During the war she operated as a convoy-escort and weather-patrol vessel. Decommissioned in 1947, she came to Patriots Point in 1984.

The *Savannah*, the world's first nuclear-powered merchant ship, was launched in 1959 and served for eight years as an experimental alternative to fossil fuel-burning cargo ships. The ship's upper decks and engine room are open to the public.

SOUTH CAROLINA CONFEDERATE RELIC ROOM & MUSEUM

Visitor Information: Located on the campus of the University of South Carolina, one block southeast of the state capitol building at the corner of Sumter and Pendleton Streets in the War Memorial Building, 920 Sumter Street, Columbia, South Carolina 29201. Telephone: (803) 734-9813. Hours: 8:30 am to 5:00 pm Monday through Friday. Weekends by appointment. Admission: free.

Items on Display: Uniforms, Unit Patches, Field Equipment, Personal Documents, Official Documents, Photographs, Dioramas, Flags, Battle Streamers, Medals, Edged Weapons, Side Arms, Shoulder Arms, Machine Guns, Ordnance, Space Exploration Displays, Satellite Communications Displays, Navigational Equipment, Medical Equipment, Scale Models (ships/boats).

The museum houses both military and general-history artifacts from Colonial times to the space age, including Confederate-era projectiles, a captured Japanese machine gun, a Confederate surgeon's chest and dental case, Apollo XVI astronaut General Charles Duke's flight jacket and items carried aboard the space shuttle on various NASA missions. Upper-gallery displays honor prominent South Carolina veterans.

SOUTH CAROLINA NATIONAL GUARD MUSEUM

Visitor Information: Located at 395 North Pike West, Sumter, South Carolina 29151-1028. Take US-76 east from Columbia to the intersection with US-521 in Sumter. At the intersection, go east on Frontage Road to the museum at the National Guard Armory. Telephone: (803) 773-4151. Hours: 8:00 am to 4:30 pm Monday through Friday as requested by visitors. Admission: free.

SOUTH CAROLINA
South Carolina National Guard Museum, continued

Items on Display: Uniforms (reproductions and originals), Unit Patches, Field Equipment, Official Documents, Maps, Photographs, Paintings/Drawings, Flags, Battle Streamers, Medals, Edged Weapons, Side Arms, Shoulder Arms, Machine Guns, Ordnance, Chemical/Biological Weapons Displays, Field Artillery, Coast-Defense Artillery.

Military artifacts and memorabilia from the American Revolution to the present are on display in South Carolina's National Guard Museum. Dedicated to the preservation of South Carolina's military heritage, the museum currently houses more than 8,000 documents, photographs, and clippings; and nearly 500 pieces of military equipment, including eight artillery pieces, captured German machine guns, Revolutionary War-era edged weapons and Civil War-era ordnance.

Other Military Museums, Historic Sites & Exhibits in South Carolina

Beaufort Museum, 713 Craven Street, Beaufort, South Carolina 29902. Telephone: (803) 525-7471.

Citadel Museum and Archives, The Citadel, Charleston, South Carolina 29409. Telephone: (803) 792-6846.

Kings Mountain National Military Park, P. O. Box 40, Kings Mountain, North Carolina 28086. Telephone: (803) 936-7921. (The park itself is located in South Carolina.)

Powder Magazine, Cumberland Street, Charleston, South Carolina 29401. Telephone: None.

SOUTH DAKOTA

BATTLESHIP *SOUTH DAKOTA* MEMORIAL

Visitor Information: Located at the intersection of 12th and Kiwanis Streets in Sioux Falls. Take exit 79 off I-29 and drive one mile east to the memorial. Mailing Address: 600 East 7th Street, Sioux Falls, South Dakota 57102. Telephone: (605) 339-7060. Hours: 9:00 am to 5 pm daily from Memorial Day to Labor Day. Admission: free.

Items on Display: Uniforms, Unit Patches, Field Equipment, Personal Documents, Official Documents, Maps, Photographs, Paintings/Drawings, Flags, Battle Streamers, Medals, Ordnance, Navigational Equipment, Scale Models (ships/boats).

The Battleship *South Dakota* Memorial houses artifacts, memorabilia and interpretive displays and exhibits about the distinguished history of one of World War II's most decorated fighting ships, the USS *South Dakota*. On two occasions the Japanese reported sinking the *South Dakota*, after which the battleship was frequently referred to in official and unofficial communications as "battleship X." Japanese eagerness to see the *South Dakota* out of commission is easy to understand, since the ship downed 64 enemy fighter planes in her wartime career, participated in nine shore bombardments and garnered 14 battle stars while participating in every major Naval battle in the Pacific.

FORT SISSETON STATE HISTORIC PARK

Visitor Information: Located in the northeast corner of South Dakota. Take exit 232 off I-29 in Sisseton and drive 25 miles west on SD-10, then six miles south on the county blacktop road to the fort. Signs point the way. Mailing Address: Rural Route 2, Box 51, Lake City, South Dakota 57247. Telephone: (605) 448-5701. Hours: 11:00 am to 7:00 pm daily from Memorial Day through Labor Days. Tours at other times of the year can be arranged by contacting the Park Manager. Admission: free.

Items on Display: Uniforms, Field Equipment, Personal Documents, Maps, Photographs, Paintings/Drawings, Flags, Edged Weapons, Shoulder Arms, Field Artillery, Historic Structure (fort).

Fort Sisseton was established in 1864 as a peacekeeping garrison after hostilities broke out between Indian inhabitants of the region and settlers. In addition to their routine patrol and peacekeeping

SOUTH DAKOTA

Fort Sisseton State Historic Park, continued

duties, soldiers at the fort escorted railroad survey crews, cattle drives and wagon trains on their way further west until 1889, when the fort was abandoned.

Many of the fort's original buildings have been restored and are open to the public. The visitor center/museum offers an interpretive audiovisual program, interpretive displays and exhibits about the fort and the history of the surrounding region.

OLD FORT MEADE MUSEUM

Visitor Information: Located one mile east of Sturgis, South Dakota, on SD-34/79. Mailing Address: Box 134, Ft. Meade, South Dakota 57741. Telephone: (605) 347-2818/3924. Hours: 9:00 am to 5:00 pm from May 15 through the Memorial Day weekend, 9:00 am to 8:00 pm from Memorial Day weekend through Labor Day, 9:00 am to 5:00 pm Labor Day through the last weekend in September. Admission: $1.00 per person over age 15.

Items on Display: Uniforms, Unit Patches, Field Equipment, Personal Documents, Official Documents, Maps, Photographs, Paintings/Drawings, Dioramas, Flags, Edged Weapons, Shoulder Arms, Medical Equipment, Historic Structure (fort).

Exhibits at the Old Fort Meade Museum interpret the history of Fort Meade beginning with its establishment in 1878 as a peacekeeping fort on the Dakota frontier. Selected displays focus on Lt. Col. George Armstrong Custer's 7th Cavalry, which reorganized following the Battle of the Little Big Horn and became the core of the fort's first permanent garrison; Comanche, the lone, equine survivor of Custer's ill-fated band, who was retired at Fort Meade with full military honors; the importance of veterinarians and horseshoers to a cavalry unit; P.O.W.s held at Fort Meade; and W.A.C.s stationed at the fort.

SOUTH DAKOTA AIR & SPACE MUSEUM

Visitor Information: Located ten miles east of Rapid City off I-90 on and near Ellsworth Air Force Base. Take exit 66 off I-90 and follow signs to the base's main gate. Mailing Address: Ellsworth Heritage Foundation, Inc., P. O. Box 871, Box Elder, South Dakota 57719. Telephone: (605) 385-5188. Hours: 9:00 am to 4:00 pm daily from May 16 to September 30; 9:00 am to 4:00 pm Monday through Friday, 9:00 am to 2:00 pm weekends from October 1 to May 15. Admission: free to the museum; a small fee is charged for bus

SOUTH DAKOTA
South Dakota Air & Space Museum, continued

transportation on base.

Items on Display: Uniforms, Unit Patches, Field Equipment, Personal Documents, Official Documents, Maps, Photographs, Paintings/Drawings, Flags, Battle Streamers, Medals, Ordnance, Missiles, Aircraft (fixed wing, rotary wing).

In 1989, the South Dakota Air and Space Museum moved off the grounds of Ellsworth, allowing visitors direct access to the museum and its large collection of aviation-related artifacts, exhibits and memorabilia. Bus tours of Ellsworth and its static aircraft displays depart from the museum on a regular basis, affording visitors, in the words of museum officials, a "windshield view of Air Force community life, plus a stop where the new B-1B bomber may be seen and photographed. A tour of the flight line will afford an upclose look at the KC-135 and EC-135 aircraft, plus another stop at the museum restoration hangar where the more ancient aircraft may be seen."

Aircraft on static display include a B-29 Superfortress, the Mitchell B-25 bomber that General Eisenhower used in Europe during World War II, an A-26 Invader and an F-101 jet fighter.

SOUTH DAKOTA NATIONAL GUARD MUSEUM

Visitor Information: Located at 303 East Dakota Avenue in Pierre. From Sioux Avenue, the main road through Pierre, turn south on Chapelle Street and drive one block to the museum. Mailing Address: P. O. Box 398, Pierre, South Dakota 57501. Telephone: (605) 224-9991. Hours: 1:00 pm to 5:00 pm Monday, Wednesday and Friday. Admission: free.

Items on Display: Uniforms, Unit Patches, Field Equipment, Personal Documents, Official Documents, Maps, Photographs, Flags, Medals, Edged Weapons, Side Arms, Shoulder Arms, Machine Guns, Ordnance, Field Artillery, Rockets/Rocket Launchers, Tracked Vehicles.

Artifacts and memorabilia from the history of South Dakota's National Guard are on display at the South Dakota National Guard Museum. Many of the items on display date back to the days of the South Dakota territorial militia units that evolved into today's modern Guard. Museum highlights include a Sherman tank, a horse-drawn field gun from Civil War days, a dress sword owned by George A. Custer, German and American machine guns from World Wars I

South Dakota National Guard Museum, continued

and II and a collection of South Dakota National Guard unit patches.

TENNESSEE

ABRAHAM LINCOLN LIBRARY & MUSEUM

Visitor Information: Located near the Virginia-Tennessee border on the grounds of Lincoln Memorial University, Harrogate, Tennessee 37752. Take I-75 to TN-63 east to Harrogate. Or take I-81 to TN-25E north in Moorestown to Harrogate. Telephone: (615) 869-3611 extension 354. Hours: 9:00 am to 4:00 pm Monday through Friday, 11:00 am to 4:00 pm Saturday, 1:00 pm to 4:00 pm Sunday. Admission: $2.00 per adult, $1.50 per senior citizen, $1.00 per child ages 6-12.

Items on Display: Uniforms, Field Equipment, Personal Documents, Official Documents, Maps, Photographs, Paintings/Drawings, Dioramas, Flags, Medals, Edged Weapons, Side Arms, Shoulder Arms, Ordnance, Medical Equipment, Scale Models (ships/boats).

The Abraham Lincoln Library and Museum contains the third largest collection of Lincolniana in the world. More than 250 original Lincoln documents comprise the core of the library's collection, which also includes the papers of John Worden, who captained the Union ironclad the *Monitor*; the Cassius Clay papers; and numerous diaries, lithographs, pamphlets, books and newspapers pertaining to the Civil War, the life and career of Abraham Lincoln and the lives and deeds of other individuals who played vital roles in shaping the Civil War era. Military artifacts from the Civil War period are also on display.

CARTER HOUSE & MUSEUM

Visitor Information: Located approximately 15 miles south of Nashville at 1140 Columbia Avenue (US-31S), Franklin, Tennessee. Take I-65 south from Nashville to TN-96 east and follow signs. Mailing Address: P. O. Box 555, Franklin, Tennessee 37064. Telephone: (615) 791-1861. Hours: 9:00 am to 4:00 pm Monday through Saturday, 2:00 pm to 4:00 pm Sunday. Admission: a moderate fee is charged.

Items on Display: Uniforms, Personal Documents, Official Documents, Maps, Photographs, Paintings/Drawings, Dioramas, Flags, Medals, Edged Weapons, Side Arms, Shoulder Arms, Medical Equipment, Historic Structure (Carter House).

Designed and built in 1830, the Carter House was commandeered by Federal troops in November of 1864 and served as their command post during one of the bloodiest battles fought during the waning

TENNESSEE

Carter House & Museum, continued

months of the Civil War. The Battle of Franklin pitted the tired, poorly provisioned Confederate troops under General John B. Hood against a superior force commanded by Union General John Schofield. Ironically, Hood and Schofield graduated together from West Point in 1853. Largely because of Hood's poor generalship and lack of sound tactical judgement, the battle was a disaster for the Confederate army, which suffered nearly three times as many casualties as the Union army and nearly ten times as many dead.

The visitor center and museum at the Carter House site contain exhibits that interpret the Battle of Franklin, and others that depict the day-to-day lives of people who lived in the Civil War era. Artifacts on display include the original casket of Confederate Colonel William M. Shy, who died in the Battle of Franklin; Confederate uniforms; an ammunition chest that was left on the Franklin battlefield; and an enormous oil-on-canvas painting in the Carter House auditorium that depicts key events in the battle. A number of other military artifacts from the period are on display.

FORT DONELSON NATIONAL BATTLEFIELD

Visitor Information: Located one mile west of Dover on US-79. Take US-79 west from Clarksville through Dover and look for signs to the battlefield. Mailing Address: P. O. Box 434, Dover, Tennessee 37058. Telephone: (615) 232-5348. Hours: 8:00 am to 4:30 pm daily. Closed Christmas. Admission: $1.00 per adult.

Items on Display: Uniforms, Field Equipment, Photographs, Flags, Medals, Edged Weapons, Side Arms, Shoulder Arms, Ordnance, Field Artillery, Medical Equipment, Historic Structure (earthworks).

The visitor center at the Fort Donelson National Battlefield houses a relatively small Civil War-era artifacts display that includes ten heavy artillery pieces, eight field guns, two uniform coats, three sabers, a surgical kit and other items.

Nearly two and a half miles of earthworks are located at the site. Constructed in 1861 and 1862, they were employed during the Battle of Fort Donelson in February of 1862.

FORT LOUDOUN STATE HISTORIC AREA

Visitor Information: Located one and half miles east of the intersection of US-411 and TN-361 near Vonore. Take US-129 south

TENNESSEE
Fort Loudoun State Historic Area, continued

from Knoxville to US-411 south to TN-360 east. Mailing Address: Route 2, Box 565, Vonore, Tennessee 37885. Telephone: (615) 884-6217. Hours: 8:00 am to 4:30 pm daily (visitor center); 8:00 am to dusk daily (fort). Admission: free.

Items on Display: Uniforms, Field Equipment, Official Documents, Maps (reproductions), Flags (reproductions), Medals, Side Arms, Shoulder Arms, Ordnance, Field Artillery, Historic Structure (partially reconstructed fort).

Built during the winter of 1756-1757, Fort Loudoun served as a much-needed British frontier garrison in Cherokee Indian territory for only four years. Initially the fort's presence strengthened the alliance between the British and the Cherokees; however, after relations between the two powers had deteriorated beyond repair, it became the focus of a military confrontation with disastrous results for the British. The Cherokees laid siege to the fort in 1760, cut British supply lines and waited. The British finally agreed to surrender and left the fort. The next morning, Cherokee warriors attacked the British camp, killing all but one officer and many enlisted personnel. Those in the British party left alive were taken as slaves.

A visitor center at the site houses an audio-visual room and exhibits that interpret the fort's history in detail. A number of military and civilian artifacts excavated at the site of the original fort are on display. The fort itself is being reconstructed and is open for self-guided tours.

SHILOH NATIONAL MILITARY PARK

Visitor Information: Located on TN-22, 50 miles south of I-40 and 110 miles east of Memphis via US-64. Take US-64 east from Memphis or west from Lawrenceburg to TN-22 south to the park. Or take TN-22 south from I-40 in Lexington to the park. Mailing Address: P. O. Box 61, Shiloh, Tennessee 38376. Telephone: (901) 689-5275. Hours: 8:00 am to 5:00 pm daily from Labor Day through Memorial Day; 8:00 am to 6:00 pm from Memorial Day through Labor Day. Admission: $1.00 per person age 16 and over.

Items on Display: Uniforms, Field Equipment, Official Documents, Maps, Paintings/Drawings, Dioramas, Flags, Edged Weapons, Side Arms, Shoulder Arms, Ordnance, Field Artillery, Medical Equipment.

Shiloh National Military Park, continued

More than 80,000 Union and Confederate troops clashed at Shiloh in March of 1862. The two-day-long battle pitted General Ulysses S. Grant's Army of the Tennessee against Confederate General Albert S. Johnston, whose surprise attack gave the Confederate troops the upper hand during the first day of battle. Overnight, however, Union troops regrouped and were reinforced by General Buell's Army of the Ohio. Johnston's forces attacked again the next morning, but the superior Union force gained the upper hand and forced the Confederates to retreat to Cornith.

The visitor center/museum at the site was redesigned in late 1988, with new exhibits that focus upon Union and Confederate soldiers, famous veterans of the battle at Shiloh, Civil War artillery, Civil War hospitals and other subjects.

STONES RIVER NATIONAL BATTLEFIELD

Visitor Information: Located 27 miles southeast of Nashville in the northwest corner of Murfreesboro. Take I-24 south from Nashville to TN-96 east (exit 78) to a left on US-41-70S. Three miles northwest of the center of Murfreesboro, cross the railroad track and turn right at the next intersection onto the Old Nashville Highway. Take the next left to the park. Mailing Address: Route 10, Box 495, Murfreesboro, Tennessee 37129. Telephone: (615) 893-9501. Hours: 8:00 am to 5:00 pm daily. Closed Christmas and New Year's Day. Admission: $1.00 per person. $3.00 maximum per vehicle. Under age 16 or over 61 admitted free.

Items on Display: Uniforms, Field Equipment, Personal Documents, Official Documents, Photographs, Dioramas, Flags, Medals, Edged Weapons, Shoulder Arms, Ordnance, Field Artillery, Historic Structure (earthworks).

The battle at Stones River pitted a large force of Federal troops lead by Major General William Rosecrans against an almost equally large Confederate force led by General Braxton Bragg. The battle began on the morning of December 31, 1862. When the last shots were fired on January 2 and General Rosecrans' Confederates retreated to the south, both sides claimed victory, though each had suffered enormous losses, with an estimated combined total of 23,000 men killed or wounded.

The oldest Civil War memorial in the nation was erected at Stones River in 1863 by survivors of one of the many brigades that

TENNESSEE
Stones River National Battlefield, continued

participated in the battle. The visitor center at the site houses interpretive exhibits and a number of period artifacts, including 21 pieces of field artillery on outdoor display and four more indoors. Brannon Redoubt, the largest of several earthen fortifications constructed in 1863 as part of Fortress Rosecrans, west of Murfreesboro, can also be viewed.

Other Military Museums, Historic Sites & Exhibits in Tennessee

Confederate Memorial Hall—Bleak House, 3148 Kingston Pike Southwest, Knoxville, Tennessee 37919. Telephone: (615) 522-2371.

Military Branch—Tennessee State Museum, 7th and Union, Nashville, Tennessee 37219. Telephone: (615) 741-2692.

TEXAS

ADMIRAL NIMITZ STATE HISTORIC PARK

Visitor Information: Located 20 miles north of I-10 at 340 East Main, Fredericksburg, Texas. Mailing Address: P. O. Box 777, Fredericksburg, Texas 78624. Telephone: (512) 997-4379. Hours: 8:00 am to 5:00 pm daily. Admission: $2.00 per person. A discount is extended to senior citizens.

Items on Display: Uniforms, Unit Patches, Field Equipment, Personal Documents, Official Documents, Maps, Photographs, Paintings/Drawings, Dioramas, Flags, Medals, Edged Weapons, Side Arms, Shoulder Arms, Machine Guns, Mines, Ordnance, Nuclear Weapons Displays, Field Artillery, Air-Defense Artillery, Rockets/Rocket Launchers, Aircraft (fixed wing), Ships/Boats, Submarines/Submersible Vehicles, Navigational Equipment, Military Intelligence/Covert Operations Displays, Communications Equipment, Tracked Vehicles, Scale Models (aircraft, ships/boats, tracked vehicles).

The Admiral Nimitz State Historic Park, located in Fleet Admiral Chester Nimitz's birthplace of Fredericksburg, Texas, consists of the Museum of the Pacific War, the History Walk of the Pacific War, the Peace Garden and the Nimitz Gallery of Combat Art. Numerous American and Japanese war relics are on display, including one of only two Japanese Shinhoto Chi-Ha tanks in existence, a Douglas A-24 dive bomber, a Grumman Avenger torpedo bomber and the USS *Pintado*, a Balao class submarine that sank 14 ships during World War II.

THE ALAMO

Visitor Information: Located in downtown San Antonio off I-35. Mailing Address: P. O. Box 2599, San Antonio, Texas 78299. Telephone: (512) 222-1693. Hours: 9:00 am to 5:30 pm Monday through Saturday, 10:00 am to 5:30 pm Sunday. Closed Christmas Eve and Day. Admission: free.

Items on Display: Uniforms, Field Equipment, Personal Documents, Official Documents, Maps, Photographs, Paintings/Drawings, Dioramas, Flags, Battle Streamers, Edged Weapons, Side Arms, Shoulder Arms, Coast-Defense Artillery, Medical Equipment, Historic Structure (fort).

TEXAS
The Alamo, continued

In 1836, when the numerically superior forces of Mexican dictator Santa Ana laid seige to, and eventually captured, the Alamo, legendary frontiersmen Davy Crockett and Jim Bowie were among the 189 men in the old, converted mission who made the ultimate sacrifice in defense of liberty. Largely through the continuing efforts of the Daughters of the Republic of Texas, the legacy of the Alamo continues to remind generation after generation that the timeless ideals of personal liberty and political self-determination must never be taken for granted.

Two buildings remain from the time of the Battle of the Alamo: the old church building and the Long Barrack. The Long Barrack Museum contains artifacts dating from the time of Texas' war for independence and exhibits that interpret that war.

BATTLESHIP *TEXAS* STATE HISTORICAL SITE

Visitor Information: Located approximately 15 miles east of Houston at 3527 Battleground Road, La Porte, Texas 77571. From I-610 (Houston Beltway), take TX-225 (La Porte Freeway) and follow signs to the site. Telephone: (713) 479-2411. Hours: 10:00 am to 5:00 pm daily. Closed Christmas. Admission: $2.00 per adult, $1.00 per child.

Items on Display: Uniforms, Field Equipment, Paintings/Drawings, Ships/Boats, Scale Models (ships/boats).

The USS *Texas* is the only surviving naval vessel that participated in both world wars. When commissioned in 1914, it was the most complex and powerful weapon of war ever constructed and served for 32 years, during which time its weapons and other systems were modified to keep pace with advances in technology. Self-guided tours of the 573-foot-long battleship cover the main deck and the second and third decks.

CONFEDERATE AIR FORCE FLYING MUSEUM

Visitor Information: Located in the extreme southern tip of the state, northwest of Brownsville, at 1 Heritage Way, Valley International Airport, in the city of Harlingen. From US-77 or US-83, take Loop 499 to Valley International Airport and the museum. Mailing Address: P. O. Box CAF, Harlingen, Texas 78551-0151. Telephone: (512) 425-1057. Hours: 9:00 am to 5:00 pm Monday through Saturday, 1:00 pm to 6:00 pm Sundays and holidays.

Confederate Air Force Flying Museum, continued

Admission: $3.00 per person age 13 and older, $1.50 per person ages 6-12.

Items on Display: Uniforms, Unit Patches, Field Equipment, Personal Documents, Official Documents, Maps, Photographs, Paintings/Drawings, Dioramas, Flags, Medals, Edged Weapons, Side Arms, Shoulder Arms, Machine Guns, Ordnance, Air-Defense Artillery, Aircraft (fixed wing, rotary wing), Scale Models (aircraft), Navigational Equipment, Communications Equipment, Tracked Vehicles, Wheeled Vehicles.

Museum officials describe the CAF Flying Museum as "a living history museum dedicated to preserving the history and heritage of World War II military aviation and airpower." The museum's collection includes "144 warplanes (fighters, bombers, transports, trainers, gliders, helicopter) of the U.S. Navy, Marines and Army Air Forces, the Royal Air Force, the German Luftwaffe and the Japanese Navy." All aircraft at the museum are either operational or are undergoing restoration and many are the last of their kind still in flying condition. The museum houses interpretive displays and an extensive collection of military artifacts, primarily from World War II, and features the "only known collection of original 'nose art' (fuselage sections rescued from demolition at war's end)."

CONFEDERATE RESEARCH CENTER & AUDIE MURPHY GUN MUSEUM

Visitor Information: Located between Forth Worth and Waco off I-35 east of Hillsboro on the Hill College Campus. Take I-35 south from Fort Worth or north from Waco to TX-22 east of Hillsboro to the Hill College Campus. Mailing Address: Hill College History Complex, P. O. Box 619, Hillsboro, Texas 76645. Telephone: (817) 582-2555. Hours: 8:00 am to 4:30 pm Monday through Friday. Admission: free.

Items on Display: Uniforms, Field Equipment, Personal Documents, Official Documents, Maps, Photographs, Paintings/Drawings, Dioramas, Flags, Medals, Edged Weapons, Side Arms, Shoulder Arms, Machine Guns, Ordnance, Communications Equipment, Medical Equipment, Scale Models (artillery pieces).

The Confederate Research Center contains more than 3,500 books, brochures and other publications about the Civil War, with an emphasis on the military history of the South. Capsule histories of

TEXAS
Confederate Research Center, continued

all Confederate regiments from five states, an extensive magazine and newspaper clipping file, an archive containing original maps, documents, letters and more comprise one of the most extensive collections of Confederate-related research materials in the U.S. The research center also houses a museum where U.S. and Confederate flags carried during the Civil War, detailed scale models of Confederate artillery pieces and artifacts from civil war battlefields can be viewed.

The Audie Murphy Gun Museum and Weaponry Library also serves as both museum and research facility, with more than 300 volumes about the history of weaponry on hand for the interested researcher. The museum's cornerstone, the Audie Murphy Exhibit, contains numerous artifacts and memorabilia from Murphy's wartime exploits and Hollywood successes and includes the part of a tank destroyer that Murphy stood on when he won his Medal of Honor. A collection of German and Japanese weapons and accoutrements, a display of Civil War carbines and an edged weapon display are available for viewing as well, in addition to other military artifacts from the Civil War through World War II.

FORT BLISS REPLICA MUSEUM

Visitor Information: Located on Fort Bliss in downtown El Paso. From I-10 north or south take the Chelsea Street exit north to Fort Bliss. Mailing Address: ATTN: ATZC-DPTM-M, Fort Bliss, Texas 79936. Telephone: (915) 568-4518. Hours: 9:00 am to 4:30 pm daily. Closed Easter, Thanksgiving, Christmas and New Year's Day. Admission: free.

Items on Display: Side Arms, Shoulder Arms, Field Artillery, Machine Guns, Wheeled Vehicles, Scale Model (fort).

The adobe buildings that house the Replica Museum's collection are one-half scale reproductions of the nearly twenty buildings that comprised the fort between 1854 and 1868. They contain numerous displays and photographs that document the history of Fort Bliss and the Army's involvement in the settlement of the southwest. The extensive firearms collection contains many pieces manufactured during the 1800s. Gatling guns, World War II artillery pieces, old wagons and other artifacts are on permanent display on the museum grounds.

TEXAS

FORT DAVIS NATIONAL HISTORIC SITE

Visitor Information: Located on the north side of Fort Davis, Texas, on TX-17 and TX-118. From I-10, take TX-17 south through Balmorhea. The site is 36 miles south of Balmorhea. Mailing Address: P. O. Box 1456, Fort Davis, Texas 79734. Telephone: (915) 426-3224. Hours: 8:00 am to 6:00 pm daily from Memorial Day through Labor Day, 8:00 am to 5:00 pm the rest of the year. Closed Christmas and New Year's Day. Admission: $3.00 per vehicle or $1.00 per person, whichever is less.

Items on Display: Uniforms, Field Equipment, Maps, Dioramas, Edged Weapons, Side Arms, Shoulder Arms, Field Artillery, Historic Structures (restored and original fort buildings).

Fort Davis was founded in 1854 and named in honor of Secretary of War Jefferson Davis. Soldiers at the fort guarded settlers in the region and travelers on the vital San Antonio-El Paso Road against Indian raids. They escorted mail carriers and protected railroad surveyors as well until the fort was abandoned in 1891. The fort's visitor center is located in a restored barracks where Indian Wars-period artifacts are on display, along with exhibits about the fort's history. During the summer months, park rangers and others dressed in period garb answer visitors' questions about life on the southwestern frontier in the later half of the 19th century.

FORT McKAVETT STATE HISTORIC SITE

Visitor Information: Located approximately 20 miles west of Menard. From I-10, take US-83 north toward Abilene. In Menard, take US-190 west for 17 miles, then drive south on FM-864 to the site. Mailing Address: P. O. Box 867, Fort McKavett, Texas 76841. Telephone: (915) 396-2358. Hours: 8:00 am to 5:00 pm daily. Closed Christmas. Admission: free.

Items on Display: Uniforms, Field Equipment, Personal Documents, Official Documents, Maps, Photographs, Paintings/Drawings, Dioramas, Flags, Battle Streamers, Edged Weapons, Side Arms, Shoulder Arms, Historic Structures (restored fort buildings).

Fort McKavett was an active post from 1852 to 1859 and from 1868 to 1883. Like Fort Davis, Fort Clark and many other frontier posts, Fort McKavett was established to protect settlers and travelers in the region from Indian raids and as a base of operations for mounting punitive expeditions against the Indians. Fifteen of the fort's original buildings have been restored, including the Officers' Quarters, the

TEXAS
Fort McKavett State Historic Site, continued

Headquarters building, barracks buildings and the hospital, where interpretive exhibits about the fort's history and period artifacts may be viewed.

FORT SAM HOUSTON MUSEUM

Visitor Information: Located in Building 123 on Fort Sam Houston in the city of San Antonio. From I-35, take the North New Braunfels Avenue exit north to Fort Sam Houston. Turn left (west) at the traffic light on Wilson Road then take the first right (north) at Liscum Road. Take the next left onto the S-4 Road and the museum will be 200 yards ahead on the right. Mailing Address: ATTN: AFZG-PTM-M, Fort Sam Houston, Texas 78234-5000. Telephone: (512) 221-4886. Hours: 10:00 am to 4:00 pm Wednesday through Sunday. Closed Thanksgiving, Christmas and New Year's Day. Admission: free.

Items on Display: Uniforms, Unit Patches, Field Equipment, Personal Documents, Official Documents, Maps, Photographs, Paintings/Drawings, Flags, Medals, Edged Weapons, Edged Weapons, Side Arms, Shoulder Arms, Machine Guns, Field Artillery, Aircraft (rotary wing), Communications Equipment, Tracked Vehicles, Wheeled Vehicles, Historic Structures (post buildings).

Chronologically arranged exhibits at the Fort Sam Houston Museum focus on the post's growth and development during the settlement and taming of the western frontier. The missions of the various units stationed here, including the 5th U.S. Army and the 2nd Infantry Division, are examined and explained through the use of photographs, maps, period uniforms and weapons and other items, many of which allow the visitor to gain some insight into what day-to-day life on a frontier Army outpost must have been like. Famous Americans who served at the post are the focus of another exhibit, among them Dwight D. Eisenhower, Theodore Roosevelt and Benjamin D. Foulois, who participated in the birth of military aviation when he piloted the Army's first aircraft at Fort Sam Houston's MacArthur Field. An extensive collection of World War II P.O.W. artifacts is on display as well.

TEXAS

HANGAR 9, EDWARD H. WHITE II MEMORIAL MUSEUM

Visitor Information: Located on Brooks Air Force Base in southeast San Antonio. From I-37 and Military Drive (Loop 13 south), take the Brooks Air Force Base exit. Pass the traffic light and Brooks is on the left. Enter through the first gate. Mailing Address: ATTN: 6570 ABG/MU, Brooks Air Force Base, Texas 78235-5000. Telephone: (512) 536-2203. Hours: 8:00 am to 4:00 pm Monday through Friday. Admission: free.

Items on Display: Uniforms, Paintings/Drawings, Aircraft (fixed wing), Scale Models (aircraft), Medical Equipment, Historic Structure (hangar).

The hangar that houses the Edward H. White Memorial Museum is the oldest wooden hangar in the Air Force. Constructed in 1917-18 and restored in 1969 by the citizens of San Antonio, it now has a place in the National Register of Historic Places and has been designated a National Historic Landmark. It houses the Museum of Flight Medicine with exhibits that examine the history of Brooks Air Force Base and the evolution of manned flight and aerospace medicine. Early space capsules and 20th-century medical research and testing equipment are on display.

HISTORY & TRADITIONS MUSEUM

Visitor Information: Located in Building 5206 on George Avenue on Lackland Air Force Base in southwest San Antonio. Take TX-90 west to Military Drive south. Enter through main gate number 2 (west). The museum is straight ahead. Mailing Address: AFMTC/LGM, Lackland Air Force Base, Texas 78236-5000. Telephone: (512) 671-3444/3055. Hours: 9:00 am to 6:00 pm Thursday through Monday. Closed Easter, Thanksgiving, Christmas and New Year's Day. Admission: free.

Items on Display: Uniforms, Field Equipment, Personal Documents, Official Documents, Photographs, Paintings/Drawings, Dioramas, Flags, Medals, Shoulder Arms, Machine Guns, Ordnance, Missiles, Aircraft (fixed wing, rotary wing), Scale Models (aircraft).

One of the finest Air Force museums in the American southwest, the History and Traditions Museum at Lackland houses exhibits and artifacts spanning the history of military aviation. Selected displays focus on the Women's Air Force Service Pilots; Air Force Medal of

TEXAS
History & Traditions Museum, continued

Honor recipients; Air Force service decorations and awards; the career of General Lackland; the Defense Language School; World War I clothing and memorabilia and much more. Guns and aircraft engines of many types, guided missiles, propellers, scale models and more than 65 aircraft from World II, Vietnam and Korea are on display as well.

NASA/LYNDON B. JOHNSON SPACE CENTER

Visitor Information: Located a short drive southeast of Houston. Take I-45 south from Houston to the NASA/Alvin exit east for approximately three miles on NASA Road 1 to the visitor entrance gate on the left. Mailing Address: Public Services Branch, Code AP4, Johnson Space Center, Houston, Texas 77058. Telephone: (713) 483-4241. Hours: 9:00 am to 4:30 pm daily. Closed Christmas. Admission: free.

Items on Display: Personal Documents, Official Documents, Photographs, Paintings/Drawings, Dioramas, Flags, Rockets/Rocket Launchers, Space Craft, Space Exploration Displays, Satellites/Satellite Communications Displays, Scale Models (spacecraft).

Perhaps the most renowned space-flight facility in the world, the Johnson Space Center has served, in the words of the center's director, "as the focal point for American's manned space flight programs." The center's mission includes "the design, development, and testing of spacecraft and associated systems for manned space flights; the selection and training of astronauts, payload and mission specialists; the planning and conducting of manned space flight missions; and the extensive development and participation in the areas of medical, scientific, and engineering experiments."

The visitor center in Building 2 houses moon rocks, space hardware and numerous space exploration exhibits. Gordon Cooper's Mercury capsule and the Apollo 17 Command Module are but two of the many artifacts on display. Building 9A houses the Space Shuttle Orbiter Training Facility, where full-scale Space Shuttle trainers are on display. The visitor viewing area in this building is restricted. In Building 31A, visitors can watch scientists as they study samples from the lunar surface. A number of moon rocks are on display. In Building 5 visitors may walk through Skylab trainers that astronauts used to prepare for missions that sometimes lasted three months. No visit to the center would be complete without a trip to Building 30

NASA/Lyndon B. Johnson Space Center, continued

and the Mission Control Center. In the control center's viewing room visitors receive a 30 minute presentation about the past, present and future of America's space program. Sign up for the next available briefing at the visitor center in Building 2.

OLD FORT CLARK GUARDHOUSE MUSEUM

Visitor Information: Located in Brackettville at Fort Clark Springs, half the distance between Del Rio and Uvalde off US-90. From I-10, take US-277/377 south to Del Rio. Take US-90 east from Del Rio to Brackettville. Mailing Address: c/o Fort Clark Historical Society, P. O. Box 1061, Brackettville, Texas 78832. Telephone: (512) 563-2709 (curator's residence). Hours: 1:00 pm to 4:00 weekends and by appointment. Admission: free.

Items on Display: Uniforms, Unit Patches, Field Equipment, Personal Documents, Official Documents, Maps, Photographs, Dioramas, Flags, Medals, Edged Weapons, Side Arms, Shoulder Arms, Field Artillery, Historic Structures (fort buildings).

Fort Clark served as an active Army post from 1852 until 1946. In the early days, troops at the fort guarded the San Antonio-El Paso Road against marauding Indians and protected the lives and property of settlers in the region. By the early 1870s, the Indian raids had become so frequent and brutal that Secretary of War W. W. Belknap and General Philip Sheridan road to Fort Clark and held secret meetings with the fort's commander, Colonel Mackenzie. Later, Mackenzie led 4th Cavalry soldiers and the famous Seminole-Negro Indian Scouts into Mexico on the first of many punitive expeditions against a number of tribes. By the early 1880s, the Indian trouble in Texas was largely over.

Fort Clark was an open post, rather than a walled fort. Many of its original structures still stand, though most are privately owned with interiors that have been entirely reconstructed. The museum, located in the fort's guardhouse, dates from 1873. Artifacts from the fort's history are on display.

2ND ARMORED DIVISION MUSEUM

Visitor Information: Located at the intersection of 27th Street and Battalion Avenue on Fort Hood, adjacent to the city of Killeen. From

TEXAS
2nd Armored Division Museum, continued

I-35 north or south between Dallas/Fort Worth and Austin, take US-190 west to Killeen and follow signs to Fort Hood. Mailing Address: P. O. Box 5009, Fort Hood, Texas 76546-5201. Telephone: (817) 287-3570. Hours: 9:00 am to 3:00 pm Monday through Friday, 12:00 noon to 3:30 pm weekends. Closed Easter, Thanksgiving, Christmas and New Year's Day. Admission: free.

Items on Display: Uniforms, Unit Patches, Field Equipment, Official Documents, Maps, Photographs, Paintings/Drawings, Dioramas, Flags, Medals, Edged Weapons, Side Arms, Shoulder Arms, Machine Guns, Mines, Ordnance, Field Artillery, Air-Defense Artillery, Rockets, Aircraft (rotary wing), Tracked Vehicles, Wheeled Vehicles, Scale Models (aircraft, tracked vehicles).

Exhibits at the 2nd Armored Division Museum interpret the history of the division from its activation in 1940 to the present. Items on display include General George S. Patton's general officers overcoat; UH-1B and UH-1C helicopters (found in front of unit headquarters); U.S., German and Vietcong/Northern Vietnamese Army machine guns; a French anti-tank mine; and 27 armored vehicles, trucks and artillery pieces on outdoor display.

3RD ARMORED CAVALRY REGIMENTAL MUSEUM

Visitor Information: Located in Building 2407 on Fort Bliss in El Paso. From I-10 north or south take the Chelsea Street exit north to Fort Bliss. Mailing Address: ATTN: ATZC-DPTM-M, Fort Bliss, Texas 79916-5300. Telephone: (915) 568-1922. Hours: 9:00 am to 4:30 pm Monday through Friday. Admission: free.

Items on Display: Uniforms, Unit Patches, Field Equipment, Personal Documents, Official Documents, Maps, Photographs, Paintings/Drawings, Flags, Battle Streamers, Edged Weapons, Side Arms, Shoulder Arms, Machine Guns, Aircraft (rotary wing), Tracked Vehicles.

Artifacts and interpretive exhibits at the 3rd Armored Cavalry Regimental Museum document the history of the 3rd, the "regiment of mounted riflemen." Selected displays focus on the 3rd Cavalry's involvement in the settling of the western frontier and feature small arms and edged weapons from the period. Thirty-six battle streamers from the Mexican-American War through World War II are on display, as well as a collection of regimental flags from 1846 to 1984 that museum officials describe as "probably the premier collection of

3rd Armored Cavalry Regimental Museum, continued

regimental standards in the entire U.S. Army."

U.S. ARMY AIR-DEFENSE ARTILLERY MUSEUM

Visitor Information: Located in Building 5000 on Fort Bliss in El Paso. From I-10 north or south take the Chelsea Street exit north to Fort Bliss. Mailing Address: ATTN: ATZC-DPTM-M, Building 5000, Fort Bliss, Texas 79916-5300. Telephone: (915) 568-5412. Hours: 9:00 am 4:30 pm daily. Closed Easter, Thanksgiving, Christmas and New Year's Day. Admission: free.

Items on Display: Uniforms, Field Equipment, Personal Documents, Official Documents, Maps, Photographs, Paintings/Drawings, Dioramas, Flags, Battle Streamers, Edged Weapons, Side Arms, Shoulder Arms, Machine Guns, Ordnance, Nuclear Weapons Displays, Coast-Defense Artillery, Air-Defense Artillery, Missiles, Aircraft (drones), Tracked Vehicles, Wheeled Vehicles, Scale Models (antiaircraft guns, missiles, missile systems).

The Air-Defense Artillery Museum is the only museum in the U.S. dedicated to the preservation of artifacts from the history of ground-based air-defense weaponry. Displays and exhibits inside a 10,000-square-foot building and examples of air-defense weapons on the grounds illustrate the history of American air defense from the early days of coast-mounted heavy guns to the present.

U.S. ARMY MEDICAL MUSEUM

Visitor Information: Located in Building 2264 on Fort Sam Houston in San Antonio. Take I-35 to the Fort Sam Houston exit on North New Braunfels Avenue. Take New Braunfels north to Stanley Road and turn right. The museum is two blocks east of the New Braunfels/Stanley Road intersection. Mailing Address: Academy of Health Sciences, ATTN: HSHA-SMM, Fort Sam Houston, Texas 78234-6100. Telephone: (512) 221-2358. Hours: 12:00 noon to 4:00 pm Monday through Friday. Admission: free.

Items on Display: Uniforms, Unit Patches, Field Equipment, Personal Documents, Official Documents, Maps, Photographs, Paintings/Drawings, Aircraft (rotary wing), Medical Equipment, Wheeled Vehicles.

U.S., German, Japanese, Russian and Vietnamese military medical equipment is on display at the Army Medical Museum, the official

TEXAS
U.S. Army Medical Museum, continued

museum of the U.S. Army Medical Department. The museum's mission, according to officials, is to "educate medical personnel and portray the history and development of the U.S. Army Medical Department from its establishment in 1775 to the present." Selected displays of uniforms, insignia, photographs and other items interpret the histories of the Army's six Medical Corps: Medical, Dental, Nurse, Veterinary, Medical Service and Medical Specialist. Of special interest is a document signed by President Lincoln appointing Phillip Adolphus as Assistant Surgeon General and a section of one of the beams from the Valley Forge Hospital used by George Washington and members of the colonial army during the harsh winter of 1777-1778.

U.S. ARMY MUSEUM OF THE NONCOMMISSIONED OFFICER

Visitor Information: Located at the intersection of Staff Sergeant Sims and Barksdale Streets on Biggs Field, Fort Bliss, in El Paso. From I-10 take the Airway exit north to Airport Road (Airway turns into Airport). From Airport Road turn right at the Biggs Field entrance and continue on the Boulevard of the Sergeants Major to Biggs Street. Turn left on Biggs then turn right three blocks later at Staff Sergeant Sims Street. The museum is ahead at the intersection with Barksdale Street.Mailing Address: ATTN: ATSS-S-M, Fort Bliss, Texas 79918-5000. Telephone: (915) 568-8646. Hours: 9:00 am to 4:00 pm Monday through Friday, 12:00 noon to 4:00 pm weekends. Admission: free.

Items on Display: Uniforms, Field Equipment, Official Documents, Maps, Photographs, Paintings/Drawings, Dioramas, Flags, Edged Weapons, Shoulder Arms, Machine Guns, Medical Equipment.

The NCO Museum's 60 exhibits interpret the history of the U.S. Army NCO and the evolution of the NCO's roles in war and peace from the Revolution to the present. Included in the collection is a 1782 edition of Baron Friedrich von Steuben's classic work, *Regulations for the Order and Discipline of the Troops of the United States*, which standardized NCO responsibilities and duties for the first time. Von Steuben's book served as the primary regulatory document for the Army's NCOs for thirty years. Uniforms, field equipment and documents from the Revolution to the present are on display along with many other items, including a horse's gas mask from World War I and a mock-up of a frontier barracks circa 1890.

Other Military Museums, Historic Sites & Exhibits in Texas

Audie Murphy Room, c/o W. Walworth Harrison Public Library, 3716 Lee Street, Greenville, Texas 75401. Telephone: (214) 455-2205/3812.

Breckenridge Aviation Museum, P. O. Box 388, Breckenridge, Texas 76024. Telephone: (817) 559-3201.

Confederate Museum, 603 Calhoun Street, P. O. Box 179, Richmond, Texas 77469. Telephone: (713) 342-8787.

Dyess Air Force Base Museum, 96 BMW/CV, Dyess Air Force Base, Texas 79607-5000. Telephone: (915) 696-2121.

Fannin Battleground State Historic Site, P. O. Box 66, Fannin, Texas 77960. Telephone: (512) 645-2020.

Fighting Air Command, P. O. Box 802402, Dallas, Texas 75380. Telephone: (214) 733-0047.

First Cavalry Division Museum, P. O. Box 5187, Fort Hood, Texas 76545-5000. Telephone: (817) 287-3626/4198.

Flying Tigers Air Museum, P. O. Box 118, Brookston, Texas 75421. Telephone: (214) 784-3613.

Fort Belknap Museum, Box 27, Route 1, Newcastle, Texas 76372. Telephone: (817) 549-1856.

Fort Concho National Historic Landmark, 213 East Avenue D, San Angelo, Texas 76903. Telephone: (915) 657-4441.

Fort Duncan Museum, c/o Fort Duncan Restoration Association, 546 Blanco Street, Eagle Pass, Texas 78852. Telephone: (512) 773-2748/6057.

Fort Griffin State Historic Park, Route 1, Box 125, Albany, Texas 76430. Telephone: (915) 762-3592.

Fort Groghan Museum, P. O. Box 74, Burnet, Texas 78611. Telephone: (512) 756-8281.

Fort House, 503 South Fourth, Waco, Texas 76706. Telephone: (817) 756-4161.

TEXAS
Other Military Museums in Texas, continued

Fort Lancaster State Historic Site, P. O. Box 306, Sheffield, Texas 79781. Telephone: (915) 836-4391.

Fort Mason Officers' Quarters, Spruce Street, Box 478, Mason, Texas 76856. Telephone: (915) 347-5725.

Fort Richardson State Historical Park, P. O. Box 4, Jacksboro, Texas 76056. Telephone: (817) 567-3506.

MSB 5 Minesweeper, c/o Pate Museum of Transportation, P. O. Box 711, Fort Worth, Texas 76101. Telephone: (817) 332-1161.

Silent Wings Museum, c/o Military Glider Pilots Association, P. O. Box 775, Terrell, Texas 75160. Telephone: (214) 563-0402.

Texas Confederate Museum, 112 East 11th Street, Austin, Texas 78701. Telephone: (512) 472-2596.

Texas National Guard Military Academy, Building 82, c/o The Adjutant General of Texas, ATTN: AGTX-CPH, P. O. Box 5218, Austin, Texas 78763-5218. Telephone: (512) 465-5659.

Texas Ranger Hall of Fame and Museum at Fort Fisher Park, P. O. Box 2570, Waco, Texas 76702-2570. Telephone: (817) 754-1433/1434.

U.S. Air Force Security Police Museum, 3280 TCHTS/LRC, Lackland Air Force Base, Texas 78236-5000. Telephone: (512) 671-2615.

USS *Cavalla*, USS *Stewart*, c/o City Park Board, Moody Center, 2100 Seawall Boulevard, Galveston, Texas 77550. Telephone: (409) 763-6564.

UTAH

FORT DOUGLAS MILITARY MUSEUM

Visitor Information: Located on Fort Douglas, on the northeastern outskirts of Salt Lake City. Call for specific driving directions. Mailing Address: Fort Douglas, Utah 84113-5000. Telephone: (801) 524-4154. Hours: 10:00 am to 12:00 noon and 1:00 pm to 4:00 pm Tuesday through Saturday. Admission: free.

Items on Display: A list was unavailable at press time.

Camp Douglas, later Fort Douglas, was established in the early 1860s by order of President Lincoln. Colonel Patrick Connor commanded the California Volunteers who built the fort on a hill overlooking Salt Lake City, home to Brigham Young and his Mormon followers. The garrison's two official missions were common to many frontier outposts: enforce peaceful relations between Indians and settlers and protect overland mail routes in the region. Its unofficial mission—to keep a watchful eye on the Mormons.

Today the fort serves as a Reserve/Guard post and a regional recruiting center. Adjacent to the original post commander's quarters, which dates from the 1860s, the museum houses exhibits about the fort's origins and its garrison's roles in the Spanish-American War, the two world wars and later periods.

HILL AIR FORCE BASE MUSEUM

Visitor Information: Located on Hill Air Force Base, approximately ten miles south of Ogden. Take exit 341 east off I-15 to the museum. Mailing Address: OOALC/XPH, Hill Air Force Base, Utah 84056-5990. Telephone: (801) 777-8623/6818. Hours: 9:00 am to 3:00 pm Monday through Friday, 10:00 am to 4:00 pm Saturday. Admission: free.

Items on Display: Uniforms, Unit Patches, Field Equipment, Photographs, Paintings/Drawings, Nuclear Weapons Displays, Rockets/Rocket Launchers, Missiles, Aircraft (fixed wing).

Exhibits at the Hill Air Force Base Museum focus on Air Force history and the history of the base from 1940 to the present. World War II, Korean War and Vietnam War-era artifacts are on display. More than 30 aircraft and missiles, once displayed outdoors, are now housed inside a new, 43,000-square-foot hangar. The aircraft collection includes bombers, fighters and cargo planes from World War II to the present.

VERMONT

NORWICH UNIVERSITY MUSEUM

Visitor Information: Located on the grounds of Norwich University in Northfield, approximately seven miles south of Montpelier. Take exit 5 off I-89 and drive west on Route 64 to Route 12. Turn north on Route 12 for approximately one mile to Northfield Village and the university. The museum is in White Hall. Mailing Address: Ainsworth Hall, Norwich University, Northfield, Vermont 05663. Telephone: (802) 485-2360. Hours: 2:00 pm to 4:00 pm weekdays when the university is in session. Admission: fee charged.

Items on Display: Uniforms, Photographs, Paintings/Drawings, Flags, Medals, Edged Weapons, Side Arms, Shoulder Arms.

Established in 1819, Norwich University is the oldest private military academy in the country. Exhibits at the Norwich University Museum interpret the university's history and the achievements of its graduates, including Admiral George Dewey, Alonzo Jackman and Grenville Dodge. Flags and the ship's wheel and bell from Admiral Dewey's flagship, the *Olympia*, are on display, along with Norwich uniforms, university medals and other items.

VERMONT MILITIA MUSEUM

Visitor Information: Located in Building 25 on Camp Johnson in Winooski, on the north side of Burlington. Take I-89 to the Winooski/Essex Junction exit east onto NH-15 for three miles to Camp Johnson and the museum. Mailing Address: Building 25, Camp Johson, Winooski, Vermont 05404-1697. Telephone: (802) 864-1360. Hours: 10:00 am to 3:00 pm Tuesday through Friday. Admission: free.

Items on Display: Uniforms, Unit Patches, Field Equipment, Personal Documents, Official Documents, Maps, Photographs, Paintings/Drawings, Flags, Medals, Edged Weapons, Shoulder Arms, Machine Guns, Field Artillery, Rockets/Rocket Launchers, Aircraft (fixed wing), Tracked Vehicles, Wheeled Vehicles.

Selected displays at the Vermont Militia Museum focus on the participation of Vermont Militia and Guard units in the making of American military history from the Revolutionary War to the 20th century. Food provisioning activities from the Civil War to the present, the Thompson submachine gun, Allied and enemy propaganda leaflets from World War II through Vietnam and

Vermont Militia Museum, continued

Vietnamese farming tools are the subjects of only a few of the museum's rotating exhibits. Aviation artifacts from World War I to the present may also be on display. Civil War artifacts on permanent display include edged weapons; a rare, four-button shirt worn by an NCO who was wounded in the shoulder; and a hand-made silk flag presented to a Vermont Volunteer unit during the Civil War.

All outdoor exhibits, including an F-4D Phantom and an M-47 "Bulldog" tank, are permanent.

Other Military Museums, Historic Sites & Exhibits in Vermont

Bennington Battle Monument, c/o Historic Preservation-Pavilion Building, Montpelier, Vermont 05602. Telephone: (802) 828-3226.

Hubbardton Battlefield and Museum, c/o Historic Preservation-Pavilion Building, Montpelier, Vermont 05602. Telephone: (802) 828-3226.

Mount Independence Historic Site, c/o Historic Preservation-Pavilion Building, Montpelier, Vermont 05602. Telephone: (802) 828-3226.

VIRGINIA

APPOMATTOX COURT HOUSE NATIONAL HISTORICAL PARK

Visitor Information: Located three miles north of Appomattox off VA-24. Mailing Address: P. O. Box 218, Route 24, Appomattox, Virginia 24522. Telephone: (804) 352-8987. Hours: 9:00 am to 5:00 pm daily. Closed federal holidays from November to February. Admission: $1.00 per person ages 17-61.

Items on Display: Field Equipment, Personal Documents, Official Documents, Maps, Photographs, Paintings/Drawings, Flags, Edged Weapons, Side Arms, Shoulder Arms, Ordnance, Field Artillery, Historic Structures (Civil War-era town).

Appomattox Court House National Historical Park preserves the site of General Robert E. Lee's surrender to Lt. General Ulysses S. Grant on April 9, 1865. Thirty historic structures at the site, with 18 restored and the remainder reconstructed, house over 4,000 artifacts from the Civil War era. Two 15-minute audio-visual slide programs at the visitor center/museum interpret the events that led to the South's surrender and the end of the bloodiest war ever fought on American soil. Historic structures include the Courthouse itself; the McLean House, where Grant and Lee met face to face; the Clover Hill Tavern Guesthouse; and the Clover Hill Tavern Kitchen, where an extensive selection of books about the Civil War may be purchased.

CASEMATE MUSEUM

Visitor Information: Located on Fort Monroe in Hampton, Virginia. Take the Fort Monroe/Mallory Street exit off I-64 in Hampton. Turn right at Mellen Street to the fort. Signs will direct you to the museum. Mailing Address: P. O. Box 341, Fort Monroe, Virginia 23651-5000. Telephone: (804) 727-3935/3391. Hours: 10:00 am to 5:00 pm daily. Closed Thanksgiving and Christmas. Admission: free.

Items on Display: Uniforms, Unit Patches, Field Equipment, Personal Documents, Official Documents, Maps, Photographs, Paintings/Drawings, Dioramas, Flags, Medals, Edged Weapons, Side Arms, Shoulder Arms, Ordnance, Field Artillery, Coast-Defense Artillery, Air-Defense Artillery, Medical Equipment, Scale Models (artillery), Historic Structure (fort).

Casemate Museum, continued

The Casemate Museum takes its unusual name from the small cells, or casemates, located within the massive stone walls of Fort Monroe, one of the largest stone forts ever constructed in the U.S. Several of the museums' exhibits, in fact, are housed in casemates, as is the Monitor and Merrimack display, which contains scale models of the two ironclads and information about their first, and perhaps most famous, confrontation with one another in Hampton Roads on March 9, 1862.

Another of Fort Monroe's casemates once served as a prison cell for Jefferson Davis, President of the Confederate State of America, after he was falsely accused of planning the assassination of President Lincoln. Visitors can view the casemate in which Davis was held, in addition to other exhibits and artifacts from the Civil War era and other periods in Fort Monroe's history, including a "living room" exhibit that recreates the living quarters of an officer's family circa 1900.

COLONIAL NATIONAL HISTORICAL PARK

Visitor Information: Located off I-64 on the Virginia Peninsula between the James and York Rivers. Take I-64 to the Colonial Parkway exit east to the Yorktown Battlefield; take I-64 to the Colonial Parkway exit west to Jamestown. Mailing Address: P. O. Box 210, Yorktown, Virginia 23690. Telephone: (804) 898-3400. Hours: daylight hours daily. Closed Christmas. Admission: free to the Yorktown Battlefield, $5.00 per car to Jamestown.

Items on Display: Field Equipment, Maps, Paintings/Drawings, Dioramas, Edged Weapons, Shoulder Arms, Field Artillery, Ships/Boats, Historic Structures (earthworks).

The Colonial National Historical Park consists of the Jamestown Historic Site and the Yorktown Battlefield. The two are connected to one another by the Colonial Parkway, which passes by Colonial Williamsburg.

Though not a military site, Jamestown does have a 17th-century shoulder arms display in its visitor center. The Yorktown Victory Center has shoulder-arms displays as well, in addition to other Revolutionary War-era relics, maps, interpretive exhibits and authentic artillery pieces, including several that were surrendered by British General Cornwallis at Yorktown in 1781. Historical markers, self-guided auto tour signs and leaflets available at the visitor

VIRGINIA
Colonial National Historical Park, continued

center's information desk all serve to interpret the events that took place here during the last major military engagement of the American Revolution.

DOUGLAS MacARTHUR MEMORIAL

Visitor Information: Located at 1 MacArthur Square, Norfolk, Virginia 23510. From I-64 east take I-264 to downtown Norfolk. Exit from I-264 onto City Hall Avenue east for two blocks. The memorial is on the left; parking is on the right. Telephone: (804) 441-2965. Hours: 10:00 am to 5:00 pm Monday through Saturday, 11:00 am to 5:00 pm Sunday. Closed Thanksgiving, Christmas and New Year's Day. Admission: free.

Items on Display: Uniforms, Unit Patches, Field Equipment, Personal Documents, Official Documents, Maps, Photographs, Paintings/Drawings, Flags, Medals, Edged Weapons, Side Arms, Shoulder Arms, Machine Guns, Ordnance, Scale Models (ships/boats).

Located in the former Norfolk city hall and courthouse building, the Douglas MacArthur Memorial is the final resting place for one of the United States' most important military leaders. The MacArthur Museum, housed in the memorial building itself, and the MacArthur Archives and Library, housed in a separate building on the grounds, were established to preserve and display artifacts, memorabilia and documents pertaining to the General's long and distinguished military career.

FORT WARD MUSEUM & HISTORIC SITE

Visitor Information: Located at 4301 West Braddock Road, Alexandria, Virginia 22304. Take the Seminary Road east exit off I-395. Go to the fourth traffic light on Seminary Road and turn left onto North Howard Street. Go three blocks and turn right onto West Braddock Road. The fort entrance is on the left. Telephone: (703) 838-4848. Hours: 9:00 am to 5:00 pm Tuesday through Saturday, 12:00 noon to 5:00 pm Sunday. Admission: free.

Items on Display: Uniforms, Field Equipment, Personal Documents, Official Documents, Photographs, Paintings/Drawings, Flags, Edged Weapons, Side Arms, Shoulder Arms, Ordnance, Field Artillery (reproductions), Rocket Launcher, Navigational Equipment, Medical Equipment, Historic Structure (reconstructed earthworks fort).

Fort Ward Museum & Historic Site, continued

According to museum officials, Fort Ward "was the 5th largest in a network of 68 major Union forts known as the Defenses of Washington which were built to protect the Federal capital of Washington, D.C. during the Civil War." The fort's northwest bastion and its earthen walls have been restored, while an officer's dwelling and the fort's ceremonial entrance gate have been reconstructed.

The Fort Ward Museum houses Civil War artifacts and memorabilia. Its library is "a specialized Civil War research facility" with approximately 2,000 volumes available for on-site research, in addition to periodicals and other related materials.

FREDERICKSBURG & SPOTSYLVANIA NATIONAL MILITARY PARK

Visitor Information: Located off I-95 in Fredericksburg. To reach the Fredericksburg Battlefield Visitor Center from I-95, take the Route 3 exit east and turn right onto Sunken Road or follow the brown signs to the center. Parking is on the left at the intersection with Lafayette Boulevard. To reach the Chancellorsville Visitor Center from I-95, take the Route 3 exit west and stay on Route 3 for seven miles. The visitor center is on the right. Mailing Address: P. O. Box 679, Fredericksburg, Virginia 22404. Telephone: (703) 373-4461. Hours: 8:30 am to 6:30 pm daily in the summer for the visitor centers; 9:00 am to 5:00 pm daily in the winter. Admission: fees are expected to be charged beginning sometime in 1989.

Items on Display: Uniforms, Field Equipment, Personal Documents, Official Documents, Photographs, Paintings/Drawings, Dioramas, Flags, Medals, Edged Weapons, Side Arms, Shoulder Arms, Ordnance, Field Artillery, Communications, Equipment, Medical Equipment, Historic Structures (earthworks).

This 5,644 acre military park is divided into seven units that encompass the sites of four major Civil War battlefields: the Battle of Fredericksburg, December 11-13, 1862; the Chancellorsville Campaign (comprised of the battles of Chancellorsville, Second Fredericksburg and Salem Church), April 27-May 6, 1863; the Battle of the Wilderness, May 5-6, 1864; and the Battle of Spotsylvania Court House, May 8-21, 1864. The Stonewall Jackson Shrine, located some 15 miles south of Fredericksburg, is part of the park as well.

Interpretive exhibits and artifact displays can be found in the visitor centers at the Fredericksburg and Chancellorsville Battlefields.

VIRGINIA
Fredericksburg & Spotsylvania Natl. Military Park, continued

Exhibit shelters are located at the Wilderness and Spotsylvania Court House sites. Historic buildings and earthworks are located throughout the park, as are interpretive walking tails and markers.

GEORGE C. MARSHALL LIBRARY & MUSEUM

Visitor Information: Located on the Parade Ground of the Virginia Military Institute in Lexington, Virginia. From I-81 take exits 51, 52, or 53 and follow signs to the museum. From I-64 take exits 12 or 13 and follow signs. Mailing Address: P. O. Box 1600, Lexington, Virginia 24450-1600. Telephone: (703) 463-7103. Hours: 9:00 am to 5:00 pm Monday through Saturday, 2:00 pm to 5:00 pm Sunday. The museum closes one hour earlier than the times listed from November 1 to March 1. Closed Thanksgiving, Christmas and New Year's Day. Admission: free.

Items on Display: Uniforms, Personal Documents, Official Documents, Photographs, Paintings/Drawings, Medals, Edged Weapons.

The George C. Marshall Museum and Library houses artifacts and exhibits from the life and career of General of the Army George C. Marshall, one of the 20th century's most prominent military leaders. The General's personal and public papers form the core of the library's extensive collection of books, manuscripts, and other documents, which also includes collections from the lives and careers of many of the General's personal friends and associates.

After graduating from the Virginia Military Institute in 1901, General Marshall rose from the Rank of 2nd Lieutenant to become General of the Army during World War II. After the war, he served as Special Representative of the President to China, as Secretary of State, as President of the American Red Cross and as Secretary of Defense. For his historic promulgation of the Marshall Plan for post-World War II Europe's economic recovery, he became, in 1953, the first professional soldier ever to receive the Nobel Peace Prize.

HAMPTON ROADS NAVAL MUSEUM

Visitor Information: Located in the Pennsylvania Building (G-29), Norfolk Naval Base, Norfolk, Virginia 23511-6002. To enter the base and visit the museum, you must either obtain a visitor's pass at the tour office on Hampton Boulevard or take the bus tour of the base which leaves from the tour office. To get to the museum from I-64,

Hampton Roads Naval Museum, continued

take naval base exit 564 (Admiral Taussig Boulevard) to gate 2 (Maryland Avenue). Follow Maryland Avenue to Dillingham Boulevard and turn right. Follow Dillingham to Farragut Avenue. The museum is at the corner of Dillingham and Farragut. Telephone: (804) 444-2243/3827. Hours: 9:00 am to 4:00 pm daily. Closed Thanksgiving, Christmas and New Year's Day. Admission: free.

Items on Display: Maps, Paintings/Drawings, Dioramas, Flags, Edged Weapons, Scale Models (aircraft, ships/boats, submarines).

Chronologically arranged displays at the Hampton Roads Naval Museum depict the naval history of the Hampton Roads area beginning with the Battle off the Virginia Capes during the American Revolution. Local pre-Civil War naval activities are highlighted by models and original prints of many of the ships constructed in the area, while an entire wing of the museum is devoted to Civil War naval operations, with an emphasis on the exploits of the famous ironclads, the *Monitor* and the *Merrimack* (renamed the CSS *Virginia* after it was captured by Confederate soldiers). Another wing is devoted to the ships and missions of NATO-alliance countries.

MANASSAS NATIONAL BATTLEFIELD PARK

Visitor Information: Located north of Manassas off I-66 at 6511 Sudley Road, Manassas, Virginia 22110. Take I-66 west from Washington, D.C., to exit 11 north (Route 234, Sudley Road). The visitor center is one half mile ahead on the right. Telephone: (703) 754-7107. Hours: 8:30 am to 5:00 pm daily during the winter months, 8:30 am to 6:00 pm during the summer months. Closed Christmas. Admission: $1.00 per person ages 17-61.

Items on Displays: Uniforms, Field Equipment, Personal Documents, Official Documents, Maps, Photographs, Paintings/Drawings, Flags, Edged Weapons, Side Arms, Shoulder Arms, Field Artillery, Ordnance, Medical Equipment.

In April of 1861, after secessionists gained control of the Union stronghold at Fort Sumter, President Abraham Lincoln responded by issuing an urgent call for volunteers. Able-bodied men were desperately needed by the federal Army if the Union was to be preserved. Three months later, a federal force of 35,000 men and boys, led by General Irvin McDowell, left Washington. Their mission was to capture Richmond, the Confederate capital, and thus, it was reasoned, bring a swift end to the civil strife that threatened the

VIRGINIA
Manassas National Battlefield Park, continued

very existence of an entire nation. All hopes for a swift end to the war, however, were shattered when McDowell's troops met the 22,000 Confederate soldiers commanded by General Pierre Beauregard at the Battle of First Manassas.

Reinforced immediately before and during the battle by 10,000 troops under General Joseph E. Johnston, the Confederate force, by day's end, proved victorious. By the following morning, the stunned Union troops had retreated behind the safety of Washington, D.C.'s formidable lines of defense.

More than 900 men and boys died during the Battle of First Manassas. When the opposing forces of North and South met again on the same field of battle during the Battle of Second Manassas, 3,300 died, and again the forces of the South were victorious. At that point in the war, the South was at the apex of its military and economic power. Northern resolve, however, failed to weaken. Three years later, not many miles away in Appomattox, Virginia, the South would lay down its arms in a defeat far more final and devastating than any its armies ever inflicted on the North.

The visitor center at the park houses Civil War artifacts and memorabilia, many excavated at the sites of the two Manassas battles. Pamphlets available at the visitor center explore the courses of the two battles in detail.

MUSEUM OF THE CONFEDERACY

Visitor Information: Located at 1201 East Clay Street, Richmond, Virginia 23219. Take the Broad Street exit off I-95 and follow signs to the museum. Telephone: (804) 649-1861. Hours: 10:00 am to 5:00 pm Monday through Saturday, 1:00 pm to 5:00 pm Sunday. Admission: $2.50 per adult, $1.00 per senior citizen or children ages 7-12.

Items on Display: Uniforms, Field Equipment, Official Documents, Maps, Photographs, Paintings/Drawings, Flags, Medals, Edged Weapons, Side Arms, Shoulder Arms, Field Artillery.

As its name implies, the Museum of the Confederacy houses relics and archival material from the stormy history of the Confederate States of America. One of the museum's key exhibits, "The Confederate Years," consists of a chronological survey of the Civil War with artifacts pertaining to the activities of Confederate soldiers

Museum of the Confederacy, continued

from enlisted personnel to general officers. The museum's collections curator also notes that the museum's collection is "the oldest and broadest collection (of its kind) that contains objects related to the principal leaders of the (Confederate) military: Lee, Stuart, Jackson, Hill, Johnston, etc." The museum's library research facilities contain a wealth of Confederate and general Civil War-related materials available for study and research by appointment.

NASA/LANGLEY RESEARCH CENTER

Visitor Information: Located 30 minutes east of Williamsburg and 30 minutes west of Norfolk. Westbound on I-64 take exit 63 (Route 134, Magruder Boulevard). Eastbound on I-64 take exit 62-B (Route 17 north). Follow the NASA directional signs. Mailing Address: NASA Visitor Center, Langley Research Center, Mail Stop 480, Hampton, Virginia 23665-5225. Telephone: (804) 865-2855. Hours: 8:30 am to 4:30 pm Monday through Saturday, 12:00 noon to 4:30 pm Sunday. Closed Easter, Thanksgiving, Christmas and New Year's Day. Admission: free.

Items on Display: Photographs, Paintings/Drawings, Space Craft, Space Exploration Displays, Scale Models (aircraft, space craft), Historic Structures (wind tunnels).

Since 1917, NASA/Langley has served as one of the world's most important aeronautical research facilities. Langley scientists and engineers have been responsible for a number of historic programs, including the X-1 and X-15 programs, out of which America's space programs developed, and Project Mercury, America's first manned space program. The original seven "right stuff" astronauts received their training at Langley. National Historic Landmarks on Langley include three wind tunnels, one dating from 1923, the Lunar Landing Research Facility and the Rendezvous and Docking Simulator.

Nearly 50 exhibits in the Langley Visitor Center focus on America's achievements in aeronautical and space engineering. The Apollo 12 Command Module, an early Mercury capsule, a Viking Mars Lander and other space artifacts are on display in the Space Gallery. Exhibits about wind tunnel research, aircraft development, future aircraft designs and other subjects are found in the Aeronautics Gallery.

VIRGINIA

NEW MARKET BATTLEFIELD PARK

Visitor Information: Located in Virginia's Shenandoah Valley. Take exit 67 off I-81 and follow signs. Mailing Address: P. O. Box 1864, New Market, Virginia 22844. Telephone: (703) 740-3101/3102. Hours: 9:00 am to 5:00 pm daily. Closed Christmas. Admission: $4.00 per adult, $1.50 per child ages 10-15.

Items on Display: Uniforms, Personal Documents, Maps, Photographs, Paintings/Drawings, Dioramas, Flags, Medals, Edged Weapons, Side Arms, Shoulder Arms, Ordnance, Field Artillery, Medical Equipment, Scale Models (ships/boats).

In 1864, a detachment of nearly 250 cadets from the Virginia Military Institute in Lexington, Virginia, was ordered to join a veteran force of Confederate soldiers in turning back a Union attempt to wrest the Shenandoah Valley from Confederate control. The desperate order was given by General John C. Breckinridge, commander of the Shenandoah Valley's Confederate forces. The order brought the V.M.I. cadets, most of them teenagers, under fire for the first time in what proved to be a Confederate victory at the Battle of New Market.

The battlefield's visitor center, the Hall of Valor, constructed at the battle site as a memorial to the V.M.I. cadets who participated, contains interpretive exhibits, audio-visual presentations and displays of period artifacts. A walking tour of the 160-acre park follows the path taken by the V.M.I. cadets on the day of the battle and includes a tour of the Bushong Farm, where many wounded soldiers were treated after the battle.

OLD GUARD MUSEUM

Visitor Information: Located adjacent to Arlington National Cemetery in Building 249, Sheridan Avenue, Fort Myer, Virginia 22211-5050. Take the Fort Meyer exit off Washington Boulevard at 2nd Street, or enter from Route 50 (Arlington Boulevard). Telephone: (202) 696-6670. Hours: 9:00 am to 4:00 pm Monday through Friday, 10:00 am to 2:00 pm Saturday. Admission: free.

Items on Display: Uniforms, Field Equipment, Paintings/Drawings, Maps, Photographs, Flags, Battle Streamers, Medals, Edged Weapons, Side Arms, Shoulder Arms, Machine Guns, Ordnance.

The Old Guard Museum chronicles the history of the Army's oldest active infantry unit, the 3rd United States Infantry. Artifacts and

Old Guard Museum, continued

memorabilia on display illustrate over two centuries of Old Guard participation in the shaping of American military history.

Selected exhibits focus on Guard involvement in the Mexican-American War, the Indian Wars of the western frontier, the Spanish-American War, the Philippines Insurrection of 1899-1902 and the Vietnam War.

Items on display include the national colors carried by the 3rd Infantry from 1896-1898, the centerpiece of the Spanish-American War display; a Vietcong modified K-50 submachine gun capable of firing 900 rounds per minute and a Chinese Communist M43 Type-56 submachine gun styled after the Soviet AK47 and used by the Vietcong, all part of the Vietnam display; a baton, fashioned from white pine used in the reconstruction of the White House after the War of 1812, presented to the Guard on April 10, 1952, by President Harry S. Truman to commemorate the Guard's many years of exemplary service to its country; and pictures of Guard members' participation in President John F. Kennedy's funeral, arranged around the casing of the first round fired over Kennedy's grave on November 25, 1963.

PETERSBURG NATIONAL BATTLEFIELD

Visitor Information: Located off I-95 east of Petersburg. Take exit 3 off I-95 onto Route 36 east (Washington-Wythe Streets) for two miles to the park. Mailing Address: Box 549, Route 36 East, Petersburg, Virginia 23804. Telephone: (804) 732-3531. Hours: 8:00 am to 7:00 pm daily during the summer season (though hours occasionally vary), 8:00 am to 5:00 pm during the winter season. Closed Christmas and New Year's Day. Admission: $1.00 per person ages 17-61.

Items on Display: Uniforms, Field Equipment, Personal Documents, Official Documents, Maps, Photographs, Paintings/Drawings, Dioramas, Flags, Medals, Edged Weapons, Side Arms, Shoulder Arms, Ordnance, Field Artillery, Communications Equipment, Medical Equipment, Historic Structures (fortifications).

The visitor center/museum at the Petersburg National Battlefield houses artifacts and interpretive exhibits about the Union campaign against Petersburg and its siege of the city, 1864-1865. A large number of original fortifications constructed between 1863-1865 and used during the siege have been preserved in the park. General

VIRGINIA
Petersburg National Battlefield, continued

Ulysses S. Grant's headquarters building has been reconstructed at the park's City Point Unit in Hopewell, where a diorama depicting the Union supply base located in Hopewell during the siege is also on display.

PORTSMOUTH NAVAL SHIPYARD MUSEUM

Visitor Information: Located in downtown Portsmouth facing Riverfront Park at 2 High Street. Take the Naval Hospital exit off I-264 and turn right at High Street. The museum is six blocks ahead. Mailing Address: P. O. Box 248, Portsmouth, Virginia 23705. Telephone: (804) 393-8591. Hours: 10:00 am to 5:00 pm Tuesday through Saturday, 1:00 pm to 5:00 pm Sunday. Closed Thanksgiving, Christmas and New Year's Day. Admission: free.

Items on Display: Uniforms, Field Equipment, Personal Documents, Official Documents, Maps, Photographs, Paintings/Drawings, Flags, Battle Streamers, Medals, Edged Weapons, Side Arms, Machine Guns, Medical Equipment, Models (ships/boats).

Artifacts and exhibits at the Portsmouth Naval Shipyard Museum depict the history of the Norfolk Naval Shipyard, located in Portsmouth. Called the Gosport Shipyard in the early days of the nation's history, Norfolk Naval Shipyard was the site of the first drydock in the country in the 1830s. A model of the original drydock is on display, along with a model of the shipyard as it appeared during World War II; models of military ships, many of which were constructed or serviced at the shipyard; and a broad range of other shipyard-related and general military artifacts and memorabilia.

PUBLICK MAGAZINE

Visitor Information: Located in Williamsburg. From I-64 take the Colonial Williamsburg exit and follow signs to the visitor center for information and tickets. Mailing Address: Colonial Williamsburg Foundation, Drawer C, Williamsburg, Virginia 23185. Telephone: (804) 229-1000, extension 2527 or 2836. Hours: 9:00 am to 5:00 pm daily from March 15 to January 1; times and days vary during the rest of the year. Admission: Colonial Williamsburg general admission ticket or a Patriot's Pass is required.

Items on Display: Uniforms (reproductions), Field Equipment (primarily reproductions), Flags (reproductions), Edged Weapons, Side Arms, Shoulder Arms (originals and reproductions), Ordnance, Field

Publick Magazine, continued

Artillery (originals and reproductions), Historic Structure (magazine).

The Publick Magazine is an original, 18th-century military warehouse built by Governor Alexander Spottswood in 1715. A reconstruction of the Williamsburg Guardhouse, originally built during the French and Indian War, stands nearby. The Magazine itself houses a collection of over 200 original British military small arms, including muskets, dragoons, pistols, and pole arms, in addition to a number of other original and reproduction military items from the colonial period.

RICHMOND NATIONAL BATTLEFIELD PARK

Visitor Information: Located at 3215 East Broad Street, Richmond, Virginia 23223. Southbound on I-95 take exit 10-A and follow signs. Northbound on I-95 take exit 10. Telephone: (804) 226-1981. Hours: 9:00 am to 5:00 pm daily. Closed Christmas and New Year's Day. Admission: free.

Items on Display: Uniforms, Field Equipment, Personal Documents, Paintings/Drawings, Flags, Edged Weapons, Side Arms, Shoulder Arms, Ordnance, Field Artillery, Medical Equipment, Historic Structures (forts and fortifications).

As the capital of the Confederacy, the city of Richmond, Virginia, was a key objective for Union military strategists and field tacticians for the entire length of the Civil War. The first of the Union's two, major, sustained drives on the capital occurred during 1862 and was commanded by General George B. McClellan. The second occurred during 1864 and was led by General Ulysses S. Grant.

The ten units that comprise the Richmond National Battlefield Park include Confederate forts and battle sites from both campaigns, one exhibit shelter at Cold Harbor and two visitor centers, one at Fort Harrison and the other at the site of the Chimborazo Confederate Hospital. Interpretive exhibits, artifacts and an audio-visual program, all at the Chimborazo Visitor Center, help orient visitors to the park and to the people, places, and events that comprise the history of the defense of Richmond.

VIRGINIA

U.S. ARMY QUARTERMASTER MUSEUM

Visitor Information: Located on Fort Lee, three miles east of Petersburg. From I-95 at Petersburg, take the Wythe Street exit and proceed east on VA-36 to the main entrance. Mailing Address: Fort Lee, Virginia 23801-5120. Telephone: (804) 734- 1854. Hours: 8:00 am to 5:00 pm weekdays, 11:00 am to 5:00 pm weekends. Closed Thanksgiving, Christmas and New Year's Day. Admission: free.

Items on Display: Uniforms, Unit Patches, Field Equipment, Photographs, Paintings/Drawings, Dioramas, Flags, Battle Streamers, Medals, Edged Weapons, Side Arms, Shoulder Arms, Machine Guns, Amphibious Landing Craft.

The Quartermaster Corps is the oldest service corps in the Army. It was founded just two days after the Army itself in 1775. Over the years, Quartermaster Corps responsibilities have included provision of food, clothing, transportation, aerial and petroleum supplies and mortuary services. Since 1962, Fort Lee has been the Army Quartermaster Center. The museum houses displays and artifacts from the entire history of the Corps. Highlights include General Ulysses S. Grant's wagon, a jeep used by General George Patton in Europe during World War II, extensive uniform and insignia collections and the most complete collection of Presidential flags ever assembled.

U.S. ARMY TRANSPORTATION MUSEUM

Visitor Information: Located 15 miles northeast of Newport News in Building 300, Besson Hall, Fort Eustis, Virginia 23692-5000. Take exit 60-A off I-64 and drive two miles to the fort. Obtain a visitor's pass at the gate. Drive one quarter mile past the gate and take a left after crossing the railroad tracks. Take another left at the stop sign. The museum is on the right. Telephone: (804) 878-1115/1182. Hours: 9:00 am 4:30 pm daily. Closed Easter and federal holidays except for Memorial Day, the 4th of July, and Labor Day. Admission: free.

Items on Display: Uniforms, Unit Patches, Field Equipment, Personal Documents, Official Documents, Maps, Photographs, Paintings/Drawings, Dioramas, Flags, Medals, Aircraft (fixed wing, rotary wing), Ships/Boats, Amphibious Landing Craft, Deep-Sea Exploration Displays, Navigational Equipment, Medical Equipment, Wheeled Vehicles, Scale Models (aircraft, ships/boats).

U.S. Army Transportation Museum, continued

A large and varied collection of Army sea-, air- and land-transportation vehicles from Revolutionary times to the present is on indoor and outdoor display at the U.S. Army Transportation Museum.

The museum is divided into four areas. In the main museum building, displays and exhibits chronicle the evolution and technological development of Army transportation vehicles. Items on display include a Conestoga wagon; small, functional rail cars; aircraft engines; the pilot's section of a Huey helicopter; deep-sea diving equipment and a collection of unit patches and other types of insignia worn by Army transportation personnel. The Rail and Truck Yard features Army railroad cars and more than 20 trucks and jeeps, including three Soviet trucks captured by American forces in Grenada. The Marine Park exhibit includes tugboats, J-boats and DUKWs (amphibious landing craft) dating from World War II to the present, in addition to a number of anchors and propellers from Army vessels. The Aircraft Pavilion contains more than 40 fixed- and rotary-wing aircraft from World War II to the present, including several experimental hovercraft.

U. S. MARINE CORPS AIR-GROUND MUSEUM

Visitor Information: Located on the Quantico Marine Corps Combat Development Command off I-95 south of Washington, D.C. From I-95 take the Quantico-Triangle exit or the Marine Corps Combat Development Command exit. Ask sentry on duty for directions from the gate. Mailing Address: Brown Field, Quantico, Virginia 22134-5001. Telephone: (703) 640-2606. Hours: 10:00 am to 4:00 pm Tuesday through Sunday from April 1 to November 28. Admission: free.

Items on Display: Uniforms, Unit Patches, Field Equipment, Maps, Photographs, Paintings/Drawings, Dioramas, Medals, Machine Guns, Ordnance, Field Artillery, Air-Defense Artillery, Rockets, Aircraft (fixed wing, rotary wing), Ships/Boats, Amphibious Landing Craft, Military Intelligence/Covert Operations Displays, Communications Equipment, Tracked Vehicles, Scale Models (aircraft, ships/boats), Historic Structures (hangars).

In 1913 the Marine Corps and the Navy conducted maneuvers in the Caribbean during which traditional ground forces and the new flying machines were deployed in a coordinated air-ground exercise for the first time in American military history. Today the Marine Corps Air-Ground Team consists of over 80,000 Marines divided into four

VIRGINIA
U.S. Marine Corps Air-Ground Museum, continued

divisions, each of which is armed with tanks and artillery and is supported by 250 to 350 aircraft. The Marine Corps Air-Ground Museum illustrates the historical development of the Air-Ground Team with extensive indoor and outdoor displays. Among the many aircraft in the museum's collection are the McDonnell FH-1 Phantom I, the Grumman F4F-4 Wildcat, the Chance-Vought F4U-4 Corsair and the Japanese-made Nakajima A6M2 model 21 Zero. The museum's indoor displays are housed in three iron expeditionary hangars used in Haiti and in Quantico circa 1919.

WAR MEMORIAL MUSEUM OF VIRGINIA

Visitor Information: Located at 9285 Warwick Boulevard, Huntington Park, Newport News, Virginia 23607. From I-64 take the Mercury Boulevard/James River Bridge exit south and follow US-258 to the intersection with US-60 (Warwick Boulevard). The museum is located immediately to the west of the Y.M.C.A. Telephone: (804) 247-8523. Hours: 9:00 am to 5:00 pm Monday through Saturday, 1:00 pm to 5:00 pm Sunday. Admission: free.

Items on Display: Uniforms, Unit Patches, Field Equipment, Personal Documents, Official Documents, Maps, Photographs, Paintings/Drawings, Flags, Battle Streamers, Medals, Edged Weapons, Side Arms, Shoulder Arms, Machine Guns, Flame Throwers, Mines, Ordnance, Chemical/Biological Weapons Displays, Field Artillery, Coast-Defense Artillery, Air-Defense Artillery, Rockets/Rocket Launchers, Military Intelligence/Covert Operations Displays, Communications Equipment, Medical Equipment, Tracked Vehicles, Wheeled Vehicles, Scale Models (aircraft, ships/boats, tracked vehicles).

Virginia's War Memorial Museum contains more than 60,000 artifacts from the history of the United States Military from 1775 to the present. Special exhibits focus upon the history of the Black soldier; the history of women in the military; military activities in the Hampton Roads area; the Axis powers; the evolution of weapons technology and the use of propagandistic images and art in the 20th-century with posters from many nations represented. Another exhibit (discreetly) depicts the history of military sanitation. Titled "Obeying the Call of Duty," it is located, appropriately enough, in the public rest-rooms.

More than 30 artillery pieces from 1860-1960 are on display outdoors. One is an M53 280mm atomic cannon. A research library at the

War Memorial Museum of Virginia, continued

museum has more than 20,000 volumes in its collection.

Other Military Museums, Historic Sites & Exhibits in Virginia

Culpepper Cavalry Museum, 133 West Davis Street, Culpepper, Virginia 22701. Telephone: (703) 825-8628.

George Washington's Office Museum, Cork and Braddock Streets, Winchester, Virginia 22601. Telephone: (703) 662-4412.

NASA/Wollops Flight Facility, Visitor Center, GSFC/Wollops Flight Facility, Wollops Island, Virginia 23337. Telephone: (804) 824-2298.

Sayler's Creek Battlefield Historical State Park, c/o Virginia Division of Parks and Recreation, 1201 Washington Building, Capitol Square, Richmond, Virginia 23219. Telephone: (804) 572-4623 (Staunton River State Park).

Staunton River Bridge Battlefield Historical State Park, c/o Virginia Division of Parks and Recreation, 1201 Washington Building, Capitol Square, Richmond, Virginia 23219. Telephone: (804) 572-4623 (Staunton River State Park).

Stonewall Jackson's Headquarters, 415 North Braddock Street, Winchester, Virginia 22601. Telephone: (703) 667-3242.

V.M.I. Museum, Virginia Military Institute, Lexington, Virginia 24450. Telephone: (703) 463-6232.

Virginia War Memorial, c/o Virginia Division of Parks and Recreation, 1201 Washington Building, Capitol Square, Richmond, Virginia 23219. Telephone: (804) 786-2132.

Warren Rifles Confederate Museum, 95 Chester Street, Front Royal, Virginia 22630. Telephone: (703) 636-2478.

WASHINGTON

BREMERTON NAVAL MUSEUM

Visitor Information: Located at 130 Washington Avenue, Bremerton, Washington 98310. Call for driving directions. Telephone: (206) 479-7447. Hours: 10:00 am to 5:00 pm Tuesday through Saturday, 1:00 pm to 5:00 pm Sunday. Admission: free.

Items on Display: Uniforms, Unit Patches, Field Equipment, Photographs, Paintings/Drawings, Dioramas, Flags, Battle Streamers, Medals, Edged Weapons, Machine Guns, Mines, Ordnance, Field Artillery, Navigational Equipment, Scale Models (aircraft, ships/boats).

Artifacts from all aspects of the nation's naval history are on display at the Bremerton Naval Museum. The museum's central collection focuses on the history of Puget Sound Naval Shipyard from 1891 to the present, with pictures, instruments, tools, models and other items relating to shipyard history and activities. Other displays center on the histories and exploits of the USS *Constitution*, the USS *Enterprise*, the USS *Missouri* and the USS *Washington*. Other items on display: penetrated ships' armor from the Spanish-American War and World War II, Korean bamboo cannon, many ships' bells, torpedoes and missiles.

COAST ARTILLERY MUSEUM AT FORT WORDEN

Visitor Information: Located at Fort Worden State Park in Port Townsend, approximately 30 miles north of Bremerton. Call for specific driving directions. Mailing Address: P. O. Box 574, Port Townsend, Washington 98368. Telephone: (206) 385-4730. Hours: 11:00 am to 5:00 pm daily from April 1 to Labor Day, weekends only from Labor Day to Memorial Day. Admission: $1.00 per adult.

Items on Display: Uniforms, Unit Patches, Field Equipment, Personal Documents, Photographs, Paintings/Drawings, Flags, Medals, Edged Weapons, Shoulder Arms, Machine Guns, Ordnance, Coast-Defense Artillery, Scale Models (artillery), Historic Structures (batteries, fort buildings).

From the early years of the 20th century until 1953, Fort Worden's heavy guns guarded the entrance to Puget Sound. Exhibits at the Coast Artillery Museum at Fort Worden State Park interpret 20th-century coast-defense activities in the Puget Sound area. One of the museum's central exhibits is a working scale model

Coast Artillery Museum at Fort Worden, continued

of a 12-inch disappearing gun. Another contains photographs of the big guns once in place at Fort Worden and a map indicating the locations of World War II-era coast-defense fortifications on both sides of the Strait of Juan de Fuca.

The park itself encompasses the entire fort site. Original fort batteries and many original post buildings still stand, with an interpretive display at Battery Kinzie.

COAST GUARD MUSEUM—NORTHWEST

Visitor Information: Located at 1519 Alaskan Way South, Seattle, Washington 98134. Call for driving directions. Telephone: (206) 286-9608. Hours: 10:00 am to 4:00 pm Monday, Wednesday and Friday, 1:00 pm to 5:00 pm weekends. Admission: free.

Items on Display: Uniforms, Unit Patches, Field Equipment, Personal Documents, Official Documents, Maps, Photographs, Paintings/Drawings, Flags, Battle Streamers, Medals, Edged Weapons, Side Arms, Shoulder Arms, Field Artillery, Scale Models (aircraft, ships/boats).

Coast Guard history and Northwestern U.S. maritime history are the Coast Guard Museum—Northwest's two principal themes. Artifacts date from the War of 1812 to the present. Among the items on display: the Coast Guard flag carried on board the first space shuttle flight, the bell from Admiral Peary's tug the *Roosevelt*, scale models of historic aircraft and ships, and numerous photographs. The museum's research facility houses more than 10,000 photographs, more than 2,000 documents and more than 1,000 books and other publications about Northwest maritime and Coast Guard history.

FAIRCHILD AIR FORCE BASE HERITAGE MUSEUM

Visitor Information: Located in Building 3511 on Fairchild Air Force Base. From Spokane, take US-2 west for 14 miles to the base's main gate. From the main gate drive straight ahead on Mitchell Street to Bong Street, just beyond the Air Park. Turn left on Bong and drive to the museum on the right. Mailing Address: 92 CSG/CDR, Fairchild Air Force Base, Washington 99011-5000. Telephone: (509) 247-2100. Hours: 10:00 am to 2:00 pm Monday, Wednesday, Friday and Saturday. Admission: free.

WASHINGTON
Fairchild Air Force Base Heritage Museum, continued

Items on Display: Uniforms, Unit Patches, Field Equipment, Personal Documents, Official Documents, Maps, Photographs, Paintings/Drawings, Flags, Medals, Edged Weapons, Side Arms, Shoulder Arms, Machine Guns, Mines, Ordnance, Rockets/Rocket Launchers, Missiles, Aircraft (fixed wing), Space Exploration Displays, Ships/Boats, Navigational Equipment, Communications Equipment, Medical Equipment, Wheeled Vehicles, Scale Models (aircraft), Historic Structure (1942 WAC Barracks).

Housed in a WAC Barracks built in 1942, the Fairchild Air Force Base Heritage Museum was established in 1980 to preserve artifacts from Fairchild's history, the histories of other local military installations past and present and military history in general. American, Chinese, Soviet, French, German, Japanese and Vietnamese weapons and other artifacts are on display, along with P.O.W. artifacts from World War II to Vietnam. The Aerospace Exhibit includes high-altitude flight suits, helmets and pictures of many American astronauts.

One of only two B-52s that has downed enemy aircraft is on outdoor display in the Air Park along with other historic aircraft and several missiles. One of the few remaining Air-Sea Rescue Drop Boats is also on display outdoors. This boat was dropped from the World War II-era B-29. A time capsule encased in a 500-pound bomb casing is buried in the Air Park area. The capsule will be opened in 2017.

FORT COLUMBIA STATE PARK

Visitor Information: Located two miles east of Chinook or two miles west of the north end of the Megler-Astoria Bridge on US-101. Take US-101 south from Aberdeen to the park. Mailing Address: P. O. Box 488, Ilwaco, Washington 98624. Telephone: (206) 642-3078 (winter); (206) 777-8221 (summer). Hours: variable. Call ahead. Admission: free.

Items on Display: Uniforms, Unit Patches, Field Equipment, Photographs, Shoulders Arms, Machine Guns, Historic Structure (restored fort).

Built in 1903, Fort Columbia was one of nearly 30 coast-defense units operating in northwestern Washington during the first four decades of the 20th century. The fort never came under fire and was decommissioned after World War II. Fourteen of the fort's original buildings stand. Most have been renovated. Selected exhibits in the

Fort Columbia State Park, continued

fort's visitor center, housed in a restored barracks, focus on the U.S. Army's coast artillery corps from the early years of the 20th century through World War II. Other exhibits focus on regional exploration and trade, Chinook Indian history and the Lewis and Clark expedition. The D.A.R. Museum at the site is located in the fort commander's home, with exhibits and period furnishings that reflect the military family's lifestyle in the first half of the 20th century.

FORT LEWIS MILITARY MUSEUM

Visitor Information: Located in Building 4320 on Fort Lewis, approximately ten miles south of Tacoma. Take exit 120 off I-5 to the fort. Mailing Address: Building 4320, Fort Lewis, Washington 98498-5000. Telephone: (206) 967-7206. Hours: 12:00 noon to 4:00 pm Tuesday through Sunday. Admission: free.

Items on Display: Uniforms, Unit Patches, Field Equipment, Personal Documents, Official Documents, Maps, Photographs, Paintings/Drawings, Dioramas, Flags, Battle Streamers, Medals, Edged Weapons, Side Arms, Shoulder Arms, Machine Guns, Field Artillery, Air Defense Artillery, Rockets/Rocket Launchers, Missiles, Amphibious Landing Craft, Medical Equipment, Tracked Vehicles, Scale Models (tracked vehicles).

The Fort Lewis Military Museum's four galleries focus on soldiers in the Northwest from 1804-1917 and the histories of the 9th Division, I Corps and Fort Lewis from 1918 to the present. The museum building dates from 1917 and is one of only two buildings extant from the World War I era. Many types of tracked vehicles, missiles and rockets are located on the museum grounds.

FORT SIMCOE STATE PARK

Visitor Information: Located 40 miles southwest of Yakima. Take Lateral A south from OR-22 south of Yakima. Turn west on Fort Road and follow signs to the park. Mailing Address: Route 1, Box 39, White Swan, Washington 98952. Telephone: (509) 874-2372. Hours: 8:00 am to 5:00 pm weekends or by appointment from October 1 to March 31; 6:30 am to dusk daily from April 1 to September 30. Admission: free.

Items on Display: Uniforms, Field Equipment, Official Documents, Maps, Photographs, Paintings/Drawings, Edged Weapons, Side Arms, Shoulder Arms, Field Artillery, Historic Structures (fort buildings).

WASHINGTON
Fort Simcoe State Park, continued

Fort Simcoe was established in 1856 in response to Indian hostilities that began in Washington in 1855. It remained an active Army post until 1859, when it was transferred to the Indian Agency. Five original fort buildings remain: the commanding officer's quarters, three captains' quarters and the blockhouse. Two of the buildings are opened to the public and are decorated with period furnishings. Ninth Infantry and Indian artifacts from the fort's active period are on display in the park's interpretive center.

McCHORD AIR MUSEUM

Visitor Information: Located on McChord Air Force Base, ten miles south of Tacoma. From Tacoma, take I-5 south to the base exit. Mailing Address: 62 MAW/CVM, McChord Air Force Base, Washington 98438-5000. Telephone: (206) 984-2485. Hours: 12:00 noon to 4:00 pm Tuesday through Sunday. Admission: free.

Items on Display: Uniforms, Field Equipment, Personal Documents, Maps, Photographs, Flags, Machine Guns, Aircraft (fixed wing), Navigational Equipment, Scale Models (aircraft).

Exhibits at the McChord Air Museum chronicle the history of the McChord Air Force Base and the units stationed there. One of the few remaining Douglas B-18A Bolo bombers is on display, along with a Douglas B-23 Dragon bomber, a Consolidated OA-10A Catalina, a Convair F-106A fighter, a beautifully restored Douglas C-47 Skytrain transport and other aircraft.

NAVAL UNDERSEA MUSEUM

Visitor Information: Located on the Naval Undersea Warfare Engineering Station (NUWES) in Keyport. From Tacoma, take WA-16 north to Gorst. WA-16 turns into WA-3. Follow WA-3 north around the water to the traffic light. Turn left at the light and drive to the Silverdale exit. Follow signs to the NUWES. Mailing Address: Keyport, Washington 98345-0580. Telephone: (206) 396-2894/6218. Hours: 8:00 am to 5:00 pm daily. Admission: free.

Items on Display: A complete list was unavailable at press time; however, the museum's collection is known to include the following: Uniforms, Paintings/Drawings, Mines, Ordnance, Submarines/Submersible Vehicles.

WASHINGTON

Naval Undersea Museum, continued

When the Naval Undersea Museum opens in December, 1989, it will become the only museum in the country dedicated to preserving the history of undersea exploration and the evolution of undersea technology. The famous Trieste II (known as the Trieste I before extensive modifications necessitated the name change), the bathyscaphe that dove to the bottom of the Marianas Trench in 1963, will be on display along with a Japanese Kaiten suicide submarine and numerous other artifacts and exhibits about the history of undersea exploration.

Other Military Museums, Historic Sites & Exhibits in Washington

Fort Casey State Park, 1280 South Fort Casey Road, Coupeville, Washington 98239. Telephone: (206) 678-4519.

Fort Flagler State Park, Nordland, Washington 98358. Telephone: (206) 385-1259.

Fort George Wright Historical Museum, West 4000 Randolph Road, Spokane, Washington 99204. Telephone: (509) 328-2970 extension 38.

Fort Simcoe at Mool-Mool, c/o Fort Simcoe at Mool-Mool Restoration Society, 1016 Larson Building, Yakima, Washington 98901. Telephone: (509) 248-2475.

Fort Spokane Visitor Center and Museum, Box 37, Coulee Dam, Washington 98116. Telephone: (509) 725-2727.

Fort Vancouver National Historic Site, 1501 East Evergreen Boulevard, Vancouver, Washington 98661. (206) 696-7655.

Lewis and Clark Interpretive Center, c/o Fort Canby State Park, P. O. Box 488, Ilwaco, Washington 98624. Telephone: (206) 642-3029.

Marshall House, 1313 Officers' Row, Vancouver, Washington 98860. (206) 693-3103.

Officers' Row, Evergreen Boulevard, Vancouver, Washington 98660. Telephone: (206) 699-2359.

WASHINGTON
Other Military Museums in Washington, continued

Old Fort Townsend, c/o Park Manager, Fort Worden State Park, Route 1, Box 574, Port Townsend, Washington 98368. Telephone: (206) 385-4730.

San Juan Island National Historical Park, P. O. Box 429, Friday Harbor, Washington 98250. Telephone: (206) 378-2240.

Schiffner Military Museum, Star Route, Box 193, Moses Lake, Washington 98837. Telephone: (509) 765-6374.

U.S. Army Corps of Engineers Chittenden Locks Visitor Center, 3015 Northwest 54th, Seattle, Washington 98124. Telephone: (206) 783-7059.

WEST VIRGINIA

CARNIFEX FERRY BATTLEFIELD STATE PARK

Visitor Information: Located on the Gauley River via WV-129. From Beckley, take US-19 north. After passing by the town of Mount Lookout, turn left onto WV-129 to the park. Mailing Address: Route 2, Box 435, Summersville, West Virginia 26651. Telephone: (304) 872-3773. Hours: 9:00 am to 5:00 pm from Memorial Day through Labor Day. Admission: free.

Items on Display: Specific information was not available at press time; however, relics from the battlefield are known to be on display.

On September 10, 1861, Union and Confederate forces engaged in a battle that had lasting repercussions on the future of West Virginia. When Union General William S. Rosecrans' troops defeated those lead by General John B. Floyd, Confederate hopes of controlling the Kanawha Valley and of suppressing the statehood movement in the region were lost. The restored Patterson House at the park houses relics from the battle.

FORT SAVANNAH MUSEUM

Visitor Information: Located at 200 North Jefferson Street (US-219) in Lewisburg, one and a half miles south of I-64 east of Beckley. Take I-64 to US-219 south to the museum. Mailing Address: P. O. Box 924, Lewisburg, West Virginia 24901. Telephone: (304) 645-3055. Hours: call for hours. Admission: a small fee may be charged.

Items on Display: Historic Structure (fort).

The Fort Savannah Museum consists of an original log fort built by the British in the 1760s. The fort served as a barracks during the War of 1812 and as a hospital during the Civil War. Non-military items on display in the fort include old tools, horse equipment, old Bibles, a copper still and—no kidding—a human skeleton with an arrowhead imbedded in its skull.

When I heard from the Fort Savannah Museum in 1988, they were temporarily closed because of a lack of funds. So call before going.

WEST VIRGINIA

HARPERS FERRY NATIONAL HISTORICAL PARK

Visitor Information: Located at the confluence of the Shenandoah and Potomac Rivers off US-340. Take US-340 southwest from Frederick, Maryland, or east from Charles Town to the park. Signs are posted. Mailing Address: Box 65, Harpers Ferry, West Virginia 25425. Telephone: (304) 535-6371 extension 6222. Hours: daylight hours daily. Admission: free.

Items on Display: A list of items in the Civil War Museum at the park was unavailable at press time. Many historic structures are located within the park's boundaries.

Harpers Ferry was a major regional center for industry and commerce from the early 1800s to the outbreak of the Civil War. The town did not gain national prominence, however, until the U.S. Armory in Harpers Ferry became the target of abolitionist John Brown's famous raid in October, 1859. Brown's subsequent capture and execution for treason and murder became the subject of heated debates across the nation and fueled the fires that lead to the Civil War.

Because of the town's strategic location near major rail lines and bridges across the Potomac, the town was occupied by Northern and Southern forces intermittently throughout the war. Actions by both sides left the town in ruins by war's end. Attempts to revitalize the town after the war were frustrated and finally doomed by massive floods.

Today, the National Park Service continues to renovate and reconstruct the old town. The Harper House, built by Robert Harper between 1755-1782, is the park's oldest original structure. Other historic structures at the park include the Stagecoach Inn (1826-1834), which serves as the park's visitor center; the Blacksmith Shop; the John Brown Museum, with interpretive exhibits and audio-visual programs about John Brown's raid; John Brown's Fort, a reconstruction of the Armory fire-engine house in which Brown and his party took refuge during the raid; and two Civil War Museums, which house period artifacts and exhibits that interpret the effects of the Civil War on the town and its people.

WEST VIRGINIA

Other Military Museums, Historic Sites & Exhibits in West Virginia

Droop Mountain Battlefield State Park, HC-64, Box 189, Hillsboro, West Virginia 24946. Telephone: (304) 653-4254.

Fort Ashby, Box 248, Fort Ashby, West Virginia 26719. Telephone: (304) 298-3319/3255/3926.

Fort Randolph, c/o West Virginia Department of Commerce, Tourism Division, State Capital—SP, Charleston, West Virginia 25305. Telephone: 1-800-CALL-WVA.

Point Pleasant Battle Monument State Park, P. O. Box 486, Point Pleasant, West Virginia 25550. Telephone: (304) 675-3330.

WISCONSIN

E.A.A. AIR ADVENTURE MUSEUM

Visitor Information: Located adjacent to Wittman Field at 3000 Poberezny Road, Oshkosh, Wisconsin 54903-3065. Take the WI-44 exit off US-41 to the field and the museum. Telephone: (414) 426-4800. Hours: 8:30 am to 5:00 pm daily. Closed Easter, Thanksgiving and Christmas. Admission: fee charged.

Items on Display: Photographs, Paintings/Drawings, Aircraft (fixed wing).

The Experimental Aircraft Association's museum houses historic aircraft and aviation artifacts and displays. The Eagle Squadron Hangar, a 41,000-square-foot hangar containing World War II aircraft and artifacts, was added to the museum in 1989. Each summer, the association hosts a convention and fly-in, during which many airworthy historic military and civilian aircraft participate in the association's air show.

FRANK A. PALUMBO CIVIL WAR MUSEUM

Visitor Information: Located in Lentz Hall on the grounds of Carthage College in Kenosha. Take I-94 to Highway 142 (Washington Road) east to Highway 32 (Sheridan Road). Turn left (north) on Sheridan and proceed to the college. Mailing Address: 2001 Alford Park Drive, Kenosha, Wisconsin 53141. Telephone: (414) 551-8500. Hours: variable. Admission: free.

Items on Display: Uniforms, Paintings/Drawings, Edged Weapons, Shoulder Arms.

The Civil War artifacts and accouterments on display at Carthage College are from the private collection of Frank A. Palumbo, a collector of Civil War-era items since the 1930s. The museum's 90-piece collection of Confederate currency includes counterfeit bills, several of which are of a higher quality than their genuine counterparts. Ten display cases contain Union and Confederate uniforms and related items. The museum also contains what officials describe as "the finest and most complete single collection" of stone lithography prints in the country

WISCONSIN

FORT CRAWFORD MEDICAL MUSEUM & MILITARY HOSPITAL

Visitor Information: Located at 717 South Beaumont Road, Prairie du Chien, Wisconsin 53821. Take US-18 west from Madison to Prairie du Chien. US-18 becomes Wisconsin Street in the town. From Wisconsin Street, turn left (south) onto South Main Street to the museum on the right. Telephone: (608) 326-6960. Hours: 10:00 am to 5:00 pm daily from May 1 to October 31. Admission: $2.00 per adult, $0.50 per child.

Items on Display: Uniforms, Dioramas, Edged Weapons, Shoulder Arms, Medical Equipment.

Part of the state of Wisconsin's Museum of Medical Progress, the Fort Crawford Medical Museum is a reconstructed, 19th-century military hospital. Nineteenth-century dentists' and physicians' offices have been recreated with original artifacts, as has a pharmacy from the 1890s. Dioramas about surgical techniques, created for the 1933 World's Fair in Chicago, are on permanent display, as are exhibits about Indian herbal remedies and other related subjects.

G.A.R. MEMORIAL HALL MUSEUM

Visitor Information: Located in Room 419 on the 4th floor of the State Capitol building in Madison. Take I-90 or I-94 to Madison and follow signs to the State Capitol. Mailing Address: State Capitol, Room 419 North, Madison, Wisconsin 53702. Telephone: (608) 266-1680. Hours: 9:00 am to 4:30 pm Monday through Friday year round and weekends May through September. Admission: free.

Items on Display: Uniforms, Field Equipment, Personal Documents, Official Documents, Maps, Photographs, Paintings/Drawings, Dioramas, Flags, Battle Streamers, Medals, Edged Weapons, Side Arms, Shoulder Arms, Field Artillery, Medical Equipment.

Though Wisconsin had not long been a state when the Civil War began, its citizens rallied behind the Union cause and responded to President Lincoln's call for volunteers. More than 80,000 men from the state volunteered. Eleven thousand never came home.

The G.A.R. Memorial Hall Museum was established to commemorate the state's Civil War veterans and to preserve the Civil War artifacts and memorabilia they brought home with them. Exhibits and artifacts from the Spanish-American War are also on display.

WISCONSIN

WISCONSIN VETERANS MUSEUM

Visitor Information: Located three miles south of Waupaca and 29 miles southeast of Stevens Point on WI-22 in King. From Stevens Point take US-10 east to US-22 south to King and the museum. Mailing Address: c/o G.A.R. Memorial Hall, Room 419 North, State Capitol, Madison, Wisconsin 53702. Telephone: (608) 266-1680. Hours: 9:00 am to 11:00 am to 1:00 pm to 4:00 pm daily. Admission: free.

Items on Display: Uniforms, Unit Patches, Field Equipment, Personal Documents, Maps, Photographs, Paintings/Drawings, Dioramas, Flags, Battle Streamers, Medals, Edged Weapons, Side Arms, Shoulder Arms, Machine Guns, Ordnance, Field Artillery, Medical Equipment.

Located on the grounds of the Wisconsin Veterans Home, the Wisconsin Veterans Museum houses artifacts from World War I to Vietnam, with interpretive exhibits that focus on various key aspects of the two world wars. The Wisconsin Veterans Home itself was established by Civil War veterans in 1887 and was the first facility of its kind to admit women.

USS *COBIA*/MANITOWOC MARITIME MUSEUM

Visitor Information: Located at 75 Maritime Drive in Manitowoc on the shores of Lake Michigan. Take I-43 to exit 79 east to Maritime Drive and the Manitowoc Maritime Museum. Mailing Address: c/o Manitowoc Maritime Museum, 75 Maritime Drive, Manitowoc, Wisconsin 54220. Telephone: (414) 684-0218. Hours: 9:00 am to 5:00 pm daily. Extended hours from Memorial Day through Labor Day. Closed Easter, Thanksgiving, Christmas and New Year's Day. Admission: fee charged.

Items on Display: A complete list was unavailable at press time; however, the museum's collection is known to include the following: Photographs, Flags, Weapons, Submarines/Submersible Vehicles.

One of twenty-eight submarines built at Manitowoc, the USS *Cobia* served with distinction in World War II, sinking 13 Japanese vessels during her six war patrols. The *Cobia* served as a training vessel from 1951-1954 and from 1959-1970. On August 23, 1970, she was dedicated as a memorial to submariners around the world. Visitors may take self-guided tours of the sub.

The Manitowoc Maritime Museum, which administers the submarine memorial, contains two exhibits relating to the submarine service.

WISCONSIN

USS *Cobia*/Manitowoc Maritime Museum, continued

One focuses on submarine-building activities in the area during the World War II era. Another, the Silent Service Exhibit, focuses on the submarine service during World War II and on the men who served. Original photos, American and Japanese flags, insignias and weapons obtained by submarine veterans are on display.

Other Military Museums, Historic Sites & Exhibits in Wisconsin

Fort Winnebago Surgeons' Quarters, W8687, State Highway 33 East, Portage, Wisconsin 53901. Telephone: (608) 742-2949.

Wisconsin National Guard Museum, P. O. Box 8111, Madison, Wisconsin 53708-8111. Telephone: (608) 241-6326.

WYOMING

FORT CASPAR MUSEUM

Visitor Information: Located on the west side of Casper off Mills Spur Road (Wyoming Boulevard) at 4001 Fort Caspar Road, Casper, Wyoming 82604. From I-25, take the Poplar Street exit south. Turn right at 13th Street and proceed to the museum. Telephone: (307) 235-8462. Hours: 9:00 am to 5:00 pm Monday through Friday, 2:00 pm to 5:00 pm Sunday from mid-September through mid-May; 9:00 am to 6:00 pm Monday through Friday, 9:00 am to 5:00 pm Saturday, 12:00 noon to 5:00 pm Sunday from mid-May through mid-September. Admission: free.

Items on Display: Uniforms, Field Equipment, Personal Documents, Official Documents, Photographs, Paintings/Drawings, Dioramas, Flags, Medals, Edged Weapons, Side Arms, Shoulder Arms, Field Artillery, Historic Structure (fort, reconstructed on original foundations).

In 1861 the Army dispatched a volunteer cavalry company to the area that is today Casper in response to increasing Indian raids in the area. From 1862 to 1865, this one-company military post was known as Platte Bridge Station. When Plains Indian tribes heard of the Sand Creek Massacre in Colorado Territory in 1865, they reacted as one might have expected—violently. The Platte Bridge Station garrison was reinforced shortly thereafter.

In July, 1865, Cheyenne and Sioux Indian tribes lead by Red Cloud attacked a small escort detachment from the fort. The detachment, lead by Lt. Caspar Collins, fought its way back to the fort, but several members of the detachment were killed, including Lt. Collins as he attempted to rescue a fallen comrade. The detachment had been ordered to escort a wagon train lead by Sgt. Amos Custard back to the fort. The wagon train was attacked shortly after the battle at Platte Bridge. Few of Custard's men survived.

In 1865, the Army changed the post's name from Platte Bridge Station to Fort Caspar to honor the fallen lieutenant. The Army abandoned the fort two years later. Exhibits in the fort's visitor center interpret Indian and civilian influence on the area, military life at Fort Caspar and other subjects of interest. Civil War-era military artifacts and those from later conflicts are on display.

WYOMING

FORT LARAMIE NATIONAL HISTORIC SITE

Visitor Information: Located three miles west of the township of Fort Laramie. From I-25, take County Road 160 east for 29 miles east to Fort Laramie Township then west (still on 160) for three miles to the park. Mailing Address: Fort Laramie, Wyoming 82212. Telephone: (307) 837-2221. Hours: 7:00 am to 7:00 pm daily during the summer months, 8:00 am to 4:30 pm during the winter months. Admission: fee charged.

Items on Display: Uniforms, Field Equipment, Personal Documents, Official Documents, Maps, Photographs, Paintings/Drawings, Flags, Medals, Edged Weapons, Side Arms, Shoulder Arms, Ordnance, Field Artillery, Medical Equipment, Historic Structures (fort buildings).

The Fort Laramie visitor center is housed in the old fort's commissary storehouse, with exhibits and artifacts relating to the Indian Wars period (1850-1890). Exhibits interpret the fort's punitive and peacekeeping roles during the Indian Wars. Artifacts include winter campaign gear, horse equipment, an 1840 Mountain Howitzer with limber and caisson, a wide variety of side and shoulder arms and other items.

FRANCIS E. WARREN AIR FORCE BASE MUSEUM

Visitor Information: Located in Building 210 on Francis E. Warren Air Force Base, adjacent to the city of Cheyenne. Take I-80 to I-25 north for two miles to gate #1. Mailing Address: 90 SMW/PA, Francis E. Warren Air Force Base, Wyoming 82005-5000. Telephone: (307) 775-2980. Hours: 1:00 pm to 4:00 pm weekends only. Admission: free.

Items on Display: Uniforms, Unit Patches, Field Equipment, Personal Documents, Official Documents, Photographs, Flags, Medals, Edged Weapons, Side Arms, Shoulder Arms, Machine Guns, Rockets/Rocket Launchers, Missiles, Aircraft (rotary wing).

Weapons and accouterments from the Mexican-American War through Vietnam are on display at the Francis E. Warren Air Force Base Museum. Period rooms on the museum's first floor reflect living and sleeping quarters and cooking facilities used by military personnel in the region between 1885-1900. An extensive military uniforms collection (1850-1945) and a photograph collection (1920-1945) are housed upstairs. Other items of interest include a World War I German aerial machine gun, a UH-1F helicopter and MX and ICBM missiles.

WYOMING

Other Military Museums, Historic Sites & Exhibits in Wyoming

Fort Bridger State Museum, P. O. Box 35, Fort Bridger, Wyoming 82933. Telephone: (307) 782-3842.

Fort Fetterman State Museum, Douglas, Wyoming 82633. Telephone: (307) 358-2864.

U.S. TERRITORIES & FOREIGN COUNTRIES

GERMANY

BLACKHORSE HISTORICAL CENTER— 11TH ARMORED CAVALRY REGIMENT

Visitor Information: Located in Building 7218 at Downs Barracks in Fulda. Take Autobahn A-7 to Fulda and the Fulda-Sud exit. Follow "U.S. Forces" signs to Downs Barracks. Mailing Address: Hq, 11th Armored Cavalry Regiment, ATTN: Blackhorse Historical Center, APO New York 09146-5000. Telephone: 0661-86-401; from the U.S. dial 011-49-661-86-401. Hours: 8:00 am to 5:00 pm Monday through Friday. Admission: free.

Items on Display: Uniforms, Unit Patches, Field Equipment, Photographs, Flags, Battle Streamers, Edged Weapons, Side Arms, Shoulder Arms, Machine Guns, Communications Equipment.

Artifacts and exhibits at the Blackhorse Historical Center chronicle the history of the 11th Armored Cavalry Regiment (ACR). Weapons captured by the regiment in Vietnam form the core of its Vietnam display. Other exhibits focus on the Mexican Punitive Expedition of 1916-1917, World War II-era uniforms and side arms and the strategic Fulda Gap, the area in which the 11th ACR now serves.

1ST ARMORED DIVISION MUSEUM

Visitor Information: Located four miles east of Ansbach in Katterbach. Take the E-12 Autobahn to the GE-14 exit and follow "U.S. Forces" signs to Katterbach Kaserne. Mailing Address: HQ, 1st Armored Division, APO New York 09326-5000. Telephone: 09802-832-866; from the U.S. dial 011-49-9802-832-866. Hours: 9:30 am to 5:00 pm Monday through Friday, 11:00 am to 3:00 pm second and last Saturdays of each month. Admission: free.

Items on Display: Uniforms, Unit Patches, Field Equipment, Personal Documents, Official Documents, Maps, Photographs,

GERMANY
1st Armored Division Museum, continued

Paintings/Drawings, Dioramas, Flags, Battle Streamers, Medals, Edged Weapons, Side Arms, Shoulder Arms, Machine Guns, Mines, Ordnance, Rockets/Rocket Launchers, Tracked Vehicles, Wheeled Vehicles, Scale Models (tracked vehicles).

Weapons and equipment used or captured by 1st Armored Division personnel from the 1930s to the present are on display at the division's museum. World War II-era tanks, scout cars and half-tracks are placed throughout the divisional area, with two scout cars and a half-track close to the museum.

MARNE MUSEUM

Visitor Information: Located one mile north of Würzberg on Leighton Barracks. Take the Frankfurt-Nürnberg Autobahn to the Heideingsfeld exit and follow signs to Leighton Barracks. Visitors must sign in at the gate. Mailing Address: HHC 3rd Infantry Division, Marne Museum, APO New York 09036-5000. Telephone: 0931-889-7337; from the U.S. dial 011-49-931-889-7337. Hours: 8:00 am to 5:00 pm Monday through Friday, 10:00 am to 4:00 pm Saturday. Admission: free.

Items on Display: Uniforms, Unit Patches, Field Equipment, Maps, Photographs, Dioramas, Flags, Battle Streamers, Medals, Edged Weapons, Side Arms, Shoulder Arms, Machine Guns, Flame Throwers, Field Artillery, Rockets/Rocket Launchers, Tracked Vehicles, Wheeled Vehicles.

Exhibits at the Marne Museum focus on the history of the Army's 3rd Infantry Division. The museum's collection of weaponry and equipment spans the years from World War I to the Korean Conflict. Tracked and wheeled vehicles and cannons of World War II vintage are on display outdoors. Indoors, American and foreign uniforms, weapons, flags and other items are on display. One exhibit features the military career of Audie Murphy, who earned more decorations for bravery than any other soldier in World War II.

SPEARHEAD MUSEUM

Visitor Information: Located in Building 521 on Drake Kaserne in Frankfurt. Driving north on the A5 Autobahn from the Frankfurter Kreuz, change to Autobahn 661 and drive in the direction of Bad Vilbel at the Bad Homburger Kreuz. Continue on 661 to the F. Preungesheim exit. You will see the U.S. base on the left. Exit the

GERMANY

Spearhead Museum, continued

Autobahn and turn left at the "T" intersection. Enter the base through the first open gate on the left. The museum is 50 yards from the gate on the left. Civilians must show passport or I.D. to be admitted. Mailing Address: Hq, 3rd Armored Division, ATTN: Spearhead Museum, APO New York 09039-5000. Telephone: 069-1549-8163; from the U.S. dial 011-49-69-1549-8163. Hours: 9:00 am to 5:00 pm Monday through Friday, 12:00 noon to 5:00 pm Saturday. Admission: free.

Items on Display: Uniforms, Unit Patches, Field Equipment, Personal Documents, Official Documents, Maps, Photographs, Dioramas, Flags, Battle Streamers, Medals, Edged Weapons, Side Arms, Shoulder Arms, Machine Guns, Flame Throwers, Mines, Field Artillery, Rockets/Rocket Launchers, Tracked Vehicles, Wheeled Vehicles, Scale Models (tracked vehicles).

The largest U.S. Army museum in Europe, the Spearhead Museum chronicles the history, traditions and achievements of the 3rd Armored Division from its activation in 1941 to the present. Items on display include World War II battle maps used by 3rd Armored Division personnel at Normandy and the Battle of the Bulge, a variety of modern Soviet land mines, U.S. and Soviet flame throwers and current uniforms and field equipment of Warsaw Pact and NATO countries. The museum's large collection of tracked and wheeled vehicles are displayed indoors and on the museum grounds.

Other Military Museums, Historic Sites & Exhibits in Germany

Berlin Brigade Museum, c/o Command Historian, U.S. Army Berlin, ATTN: AEBA-GCH, APO New York 09742-5000. Telephone: 030-819-9165/6215; from the U.S. dial 011-49-30-819-9165/6215.

GUAM

WAR IN THE PACIFIC
NATIONAL HISTORICAL PARK

Visitor Information: Located in seven separate areas on the Island of Guam. The T. Stell Newman Visitor Information Center is located on Marine Drive in Asan on the northwest coast of the island. Mailing Address: P. O. Box FA, Agana, Guam 96910. Telephone: (671) 477-9362/472-7240. Hours: 7:30 am to 3:30 pm Monday through Friday, 8:30 am to 2:00 pm weekends. Closed Thanksgiving, Christmas and New Year's Day. Admission: free.

Items on Display: Uniforms, Unit Patches, Field Equipment, Official Documents, Maps, Photographs, Paintings/Drawings, Flags, Edged Weapons, Side Arms, Shoulder Arms, Ordnance, Field Artillery, Coast-Defense Artillery, Air-Defense Artillery, Ships/Boats, Amphibious Landing Craft, Medical Equipment, Scale Models (aircraft, ships/boats, tracked vehicles).

In the words of National Park System officials, the War in the Pacific National Historical Park was established to "commemorate the bravery and sacrifice of those participating in the campaigns of the Pacific Theater of World War II and to conserve and interpret outstanding natural, scenic, and historic values and objects on the island of Guam." The story of the war in the Pacific is told by exhibits in the visitor center with an emphasis on the U.S. invasion and hard-fought capture of Guam in 1944. The park's seven separate units contain a variety of artifacts: various types of Japanese heavy guns, a World War I U.S. gun emplacement, pillboxes, foxholes and caves dug for the Japanese by forced labor.

This park is perhaps unique in the U.S. Park System because part of it lies under water. The ships, boats and amphibious assault craft mentioned above are all located off-shore. Most sank either during World War I or the 1944 U.S. invasion. Scuba divers will find a wealth of underwater artifacts to explore.

Visitors are cautioned not to climb on the guns or other artifacts and structures. Visitors are also cautioned not to touch ordnance found on land or under water. Beware! Much of this ordnance is live and extremely dangerous! If you find any ordnance, notify a park ranger. Also, do not attempt to open any sealed caves. Doing so is both illegal and dangerous.

GUAM

Other Military Museums, Historic Sites & Exhibits in Guam

Fort Nuestra Señora de la Soledad, c/o Guam Visitors Bureau, P. O. Box 3520, Agana, Guam 96910. Telephone (from the U.S.): 011-671-646-5278/9.

Fort Santa Agueda, c/o Guam Visitors Bureau, P. O. Box 3520, Agana, Guam 96910. Telephone (from the U.S.): 011-671-646-5278/9.

South Pacific Memorial Park, c/o Guam Visitors Bureau, P. O. Box 3520, Agana, Guam 96910. Telephone (from the U.S.): 011-671-646-5278/9.

KOREA

2ND INFANTRY DIVISION MUSEUM

Visitor Information: Located on Camp Casey in Tongduchon, north of Seoul. Enter Camp Casey through Gate 1. The museum is on Casey Boulevard. Civilians must be escorted by a military member to enter the camp. Mailing Address: 2X HHC-PAO-Museum, APO San Francisco 96224-5000. Telephone: 730-2277 (local); from the U.S. dial 011-82-2-730-2277. Hours: 8:00 am to 5:00 pm Tuesday through Friday, 8:00 am to 4:00 pm weekends. Admission: free.

Items on Display: Uniforms, Unit Patches, Field Equipment, Personal Documents, Official Documents, Maps, Photographs, Paintings/Drawings, Flags, Edged Weapons, Side Arms, Shoulder Arms, Machine Guns, Field Artillery, Communications Equipment.

Exhibits at the 2nd Infantry Division Museum chronicle the division's history and accomplishments, with numerous artifacts from the division's participation in the two world wars and the Korean War. Captured German and North Korean weapons and equipment are also on display. One exhibit commemorates President Ronald Reagan's visit to the area in 1983 with photos and the jacket worn by the President during his visit. Another exhibit memorializes two American officers who were killed during an unprovoked and unwarranted attack by North Korean soldiers in August, 1976.

If you pass through Seoul during your time in Korea, you will also want to visit the Korean War Museum. Uniforms, weapons, aircraft and other items of South Korean, North Korean, Soviet and American origin are on display.

PUERTO RICO

SAN JUAN NATIONAL HISTORIC SITE

Visitor Information: Located in Old San Juan on the northern coast of Puerto Rico. From Muñoz Rivera Avenue turn right onto Norzagaray Street. The forts are located along Norzagaray Street. Mailing Address: P. O. Box 712, Old San Juan, Puerto Rico 00902. Telephone: (809) 724-1974. Hours: 8:00 am to 6:00 pm daily. Admission: free.

Items on Display: Uniforms, Field Equipment, Official Documents, Photographs, Paintings/Drawings, Dioramas, Medals, Edged Weapons, Shoulder Arms, Ordnance, Field Artillery, Coast-Defense Artillery, Historic Structures (Spanish-built forts and city walls).

Spanish colonization of Puerto Rico began in 1508 when Juan Ponce de León established a Spanish colony at Caparra. In the decades that followed, hostile actions by foreign governments and pirates made clear the need for strong island fortifications. The fortification process that began in 1539 with the construction of Castillo de San Felipe del Morro continued for more than 350 years.

The Spanish built three forts to guard San Juan. All lie within the boundaries of the San Juan National Historic Site. Work began on Castillo de San Juan de la Cruz in 1610 (El Cañuelo), and on Castillo de San Cristóbal in 1634. Two of the forts remained active into the 1960s. When an armistice ended the Spanish-American War in 1898, Spanish officials peacefully transferred control of the forts to U.S. military personnel, thus closing a four-century-long chapter in the island's history. The site's museum houses many rare artifacts from the Spanish period.

Other Military Museums, Historic Sites & Exhibits in Puerto Rico

Museum of Military and Naval History, P. O. Box 4184, San Juan, Puerto Rico 00905. Telephone: (809) 724-5949 (Fine Arts Division of the Institute of Puerto Rican Culture. The museum itself has no telephone.)

OVERSEAS

Other Military Museums, Historic Sites & Exhibits Overseas

Saipan Museum, P. O. Box 1667, Saipan, Commonwealth of the Marianas 96950. Telephone: None.

Christiansted National Historic Site, P. O. Box 160, Christiansted, St. Croix, Virgin Islands 00820. Telephone: (809) 773-2107.

APPENDIX A

Historic Warships, Submarines & Boats

With some exceptions, the warships, submarines and boats listed below can be boarded by visitors. Historic naval ship and submarine tours normally are self-guided, though guided tours for groups can sometimes be arranged by writing or calling ahead of time.

ALABAMA

USS *Alabama* (Battleship), USS *Drum* (Submarine), c/o USS *Alabama* Battleship Commission, P. O. Box 65, Mobile, Alabama 36601. Telephone: (205) 433-2703.

CALIFORNIA

USS *Pampanito* (Submarine), c/o National Maritime Museum Association, Building 275, Presidio of San Francisco, San Francisco, California 94129. Telephone: (415) 441-5819.

USS *Roncador* (Submarine), c/o American Society of Military History, Patriotic Hall, 1816 South Figueroa Street, Los Angeles, California 90015. Telephone: (213) 746-1776.

CONNECTICUT

HMS *Rose* (Frigate replica), c/o Captain's Cove Seaport, 1 Bostwick Avenue, Bridgeport, Connecticut 06605. Telephone: (203) 335-1433.

USS *Nautilus* (Submarine), c/o *Nautilus* Memorial/Submarine Force Library and Museum, Naval Submarine Base, Groton, Connecticut 06349. Telephone: (203) 449-3174.

DELAWARE

U.S. Coast Guard Cutter *Mohawk*, c/o Mohawk Corporation, 901 Washington Street, Wilmington, Delaware 19801. Telephone: (302) 656-0400.

DISTRICT OF COLUMBIA

USS *Barry* (Destroyer), German Seehund Submarine, Italian Wet Sub, Japanese Kaitan Submarine, "Intelligent Whale" Submarine, c/o Navy Memorial Museum, Washington Navy Yard, Washington, D.C. 20374. Telephone: (202) 433-4882.

USS *Philadelphia* (Gondola Gunboat), c/o National Museum of American History, Smithsonian Institution, Washington, D.C. 20560. Telephone: (202) 357-1300.

Appendix A, continued

FLORIDA

USS *Requin* (Submarine), c/o USS *Requin* Submarine Memorial, P. O. Box 261704, Tampa, Florida 33685. Telephone: (813) 223-7981.

GEORGIA

CSS *Chattahoochee* (Gunboat), CSS *Jackson* (Muscogee) (Ironclad), c/o Confederate Naval Museum, P. O. Box 1022, Columbus, Georgia 31902. Telephone: (404) 327-9798.

HAWAII

USS *Arizona* (Battleship), c/o USS *Arizona* Memorial, National Park Service, Number 1 Memorial Place, Honolulu, Hawaii 96818. Telephone: (808) 422-2771.

USS *Bowfin* (Submarine), c/o Pacific Fleet Submarine Memorial, 11 Arizona Memorial Drive, Honolulu, Hawaii 96818. Telephone: (808) 422-2772.

ILLINOIS

U.S. Coast Guard Patrol Craft *McLaine*, c/o Marine Navigation and Training Association, 2333 North Newcastle Avenue, Chicago, Illinois 60635. Telephone: Information not available.

U-505 (German Submarine), c/o Chicago Museum of Science and Industry, 57th and Lake Shore Drive, Chicago, Illinois 60637. Telephone: (312) 684-1414.

LOUISIANA

CSS *Pioneer* (Submarine), c/o Louisiana State Museum, P. O. Box 2458, New Orleans, Louisiana 70716. Telephone: (504) 568-6968.

USS *Kidd* (Destroyer), c/o Louisiana Naval War Memorial, P. O. Box 44242, Baton Rouge, Louisiana 70804. Telephone: (504) 342-1942.

MAINE

USS *Bowdoin* (Schooner), c/o Schooner Bowdoin Association, P. O. Box 1117, Rockland, Maine 04841. Telephone: (207) 594-2301.

MARYLAND

US Frigate *Constellation*, Constellation Dock, Baltimore, Maryland 21202. Telephone: (301) 539-4018/1797.

Appendix A, continued

MARYLAND (continued)

USS *Torsk* (Submarine), U.S. Coast Guard Cutter *Taney*, U.S. Coast Guard Lightship *Chesapeake*, c/o Baltimore Maritime Museum, Pier #4, Pratt Street, Baltimore, Maryland 21202. Telephone: (301) 396-3854/5528.

USS X1 Midget Submarine, c/o U.S. Naval Academy Museum, Annapolis, Maryland 21402-5034. Telephone: (301) 267-2108.

MASSACHUSETTS

USS *Cassin Young* (Destroyer), USS *Constitution* (Frigate), c/o Boston National Historical Park, Charlestown Navy Yard, Boston, Massachusetts 02129. Telephone: (617) 242-0543 or 426-1812.

USS *Joseph P. Kennedy* (Destroyer), USS *Lionfish* (Submarine), USS *Massachusetts* (Battleship), LCM 56 (Landing Craft Mechanized), PT 619 and PT 796 (Patrol Torpedo Boats), c/o USS *Massachusetts* Memorial, Battleship Cove, Fall River, Massachusetts 02721. Telephone: (617) 678-1100.

MICHIGAN

Revolutionary War Sloop *Welcome*, P. O. Box 873, Mackinaw City, Michigan 49701. Telephone: (616) 436-5563.

Saginaw Gig Boat, c/o Saginaw County Historical Museum, 500 Federal Avenue, Saginaw, Michigan 48609. Telephone: (517) 752-2861.

USS *Silversides* (Submarine), c/o Great Lakes Naval and Maritime Museum, 349 West Webster Street, Muskegon, Michigan 49440. Telephone: (616) 755-1230.

YP 587 (Patrol Craft), c/o Naval Sea Cadets Corps, 26400 West Eleven Mile, Southfield, Michigan 40834. Telephone: (313) 352-6630.

MISSISSIPPI

USS *Cairo* (Ironclad), c/o Vicksburg National Military Park, 3201 Clay Street, Vicksburg, Mississippi 39180. Telephone: (601) 636-2199.

MISSOURI

USS *Inaugural* (Minesweeper), c/o St. Louis Concessions, Inc., 2241 Edwards, St. Louis, Missouri 63110. Telephone: (314) 771-9911.

Appendix A, continued

NEBRASKA

USS *Hazard* (Minesweeper), USS *Marlin* (Submarine), c/o Freedom Park, 2497 Freedom Park Road, Omaha, Nebraska 68111. Telephone: (402) 345-1959.

NEW HAMPSHIRE

USS *Albacore* (Auxiliary Submarine), c/o Port of Portsmouth Maritime Museum and Albacore Park, P. O. Box 4367, Portsmouth, New Hampshire 03801. Telephone: (603) 436-3680.

NEW JERSEY

Holland I (Submarine), Holland II *(Fenian Ram)* (Submarine), c/o Paterson Museum, 2 Market Street, Paterson, New Jersey 07501. Telephone: (201) 881-3874.

USS *Ling* (Submarine), c/o USS *Ling* Submarine Memorial Association, P. O. Box 395, Hackensack, New Jersey 07602. Telephone: (201) 342-3268.

NEW YORK

USS *Intrepid* (Aircraft Carrier), c/o *Intrepid* Sea-Air-Space Museum, West 46th Street and 12th Avenue, New York, New York 10036. Telephone: (212) 245-0072.

USS *Croaker* (Submarine), USS *Little Rock* (Cruiser), USS *The Sullivans* (Destroyer), PTF 17 (Fast Patrol Torpedo Boat), c/o Naval and Servicemen's Park, 1 Naval Park Cove, Buffalo, New York 14202. Telephone: (716) 847-1773.

NORTH CAROLINA

CSS *Neuse* (Ironclad Ram), c/o Caswell-*Neuse* State Historic Site, P. O. Box 3043, Kingston, North Carolina 28501. Telephone: (919) 522-2091.

USS *North Carolina* (Battleship), c/o USS *North Carolina* Battleship Commission, P. O. Box 417, Wilmington, North Carolina 28402. Telephone: (919) 762-1829.

OHIO

USS *Cod* (Submarine), c/o Cleveland Coordinating Committee, 1089 East 9th Street, Cleveland, Ohio 44144. Telephone: (216) 566-8770.

Appendix A, continued

OKLAHOMA

USS *Batfish* (Submarine), c/o Muskogee War Memorial Park Military Museum, P. O. Box 253, Muskogee, Oklahoma 74402. Telephone: (918) 682-6294.

PENNSYLVANIA

US Brig *Niagara*, 80 State Street, Erie, Pennsylvania 16507. Telephone: (814) 454-1740.

USS *Becuna* (Submarine), USS *Olympia* (Armored Cruiser), c/o Cruiser Olympia Association, P. O. Box 928, Philadelphia, Pennsylvania 19105. Telephone: (215) 922-1898.

SOUTH CAROLINA

U.S. Coast Guard Cutter *Comanche*, USS *Clamagore* (Submarine), USS *Laffey* (Destroyer), USS *Yorktown* (Aircraft Carrier), c/o Patriots Point Naval and Maritime Museum, P. O. Box 986, Mt. Pleasant, South Carolina 29464. Telephone: (803) 884-2727.

TEXAS

Admiral Nimitz Barge (Boat), USS *Pintado* (Submarine), c/o Admiral Nimitz State Historic Park, P. O. Box 777, Fredericksburg, Texas 78624. Telephone: (512) 997-4379.

MSB 5 (Minesweeper), c/o Pate Museum of Transportation, P. O. Box 711, Fort Worth, Texas 76101. Telephone: (817) 332-1161.

USS *Cavalla* (Submarine), USS *Stewart* (Destroyer Escort), c/o City Park Board, Moody Center, Seawall Boulevard, Galveston, Texas 77550. Telephone: (409) 763-6564.

USS *Texas* (Battleship), c/o Battleship *Texas* State Historical Site, 105 San Jacinto, LaPorte, Texas 77571. Telephone: (713) 479-2411.

WISCONSIN

USS *Cobia* (Submarine), c/o Manitowoc Maritime Museum, 75 Maritime Drive, East Door, Manitowoc, Wisconsin 54220-6823. Telephone: (414) 684-0218.

APPENDIX B

Museums Containing Coast Guard Artifacts

Museums not listed elsewhere in this book containing significant collections of Coast Guard artifacts are listed below. I would like to thank J. R. Ward, Chief, Community Relations Branch, Public Affairs Division, Office of Boating, Public and Consumer Affairs, and Commandant of the Coast Guard Admiral Paul A. Yost, Jr., for providing me with this information.

Calvert Marine Museum
P. O. Box 97
Solomons, Maryland 20688
Telephone: (301) 326-2042

Chesapeake Bay Maritime
Museum
St. Michaels, Maryland 21663
Telephone: (301) 745-2916

Columbia River Maritime
Museum
1792 Marine Drive
Astoria, Oregon 97103
Telephone: (503) 325-2323

Dunkirk Historical Lighthouse
Museum
1 Lighthouse Point Drive
P. O. Box 69
Dunkirk, New York 14048

East Brother Light Station
117 Park Place
Point Richmond, California
94801

East Hampton Town Marine
Museum
Bluff Road, P. O. Box 858
Amagansett, New York 11930
Telephone: (516) 267-6544

Great Lakes Historical
Museum
480 Main Street
Vermilion, Ohio 44089

Great Lakes Historical
Museum (continued)
Telephone: (216) 967-3467

Hampton Mariners Museum
120 Turner Street
Beaufort, North Carolina
28516
Telephone: (919) 728-7317

Hart Nautical Museum
265 Massachusetts Avenue
Cambridge, Massachusetts
02139
Telephone: (617) 253-4444

Hudson River Maritime Center
One Rondout Landing
Kingston, New York 12401
Telephone: (914) 338-0071

Kendall Whaling Museum
P. O. Box 297
Sharon, Massachusetts 02067
Telephone: (617) 784-5642

Lighthouse Society (U.S.)
130 St. Elmo Way
San Francisco, California
94127
Telephone: (415) 585-1303

Maine Maritime Museum
963 Washington Street
Bath, Maine 04530
Telephone: (207) 443-6311

Appendix B, continued

Mariners Museum
Newport News, Virginia 23606
Telephone: (804) 595-0368

Maritime Museum Association
   of San Diego
1306 North Harbor Drive
San Diego, California 92101

Mystic Seaport
Mystic, Connecticut 06355
Telephone: (203) 572-0711

National Maritime Museum at
   San Francisco
Foot of Polk Street
San Francisco, California
   94109
Telephone: (415) 776-1175

Ocean City Museum
Ocean City Museum
   Committee
P. O. Box 603
Ocean City, Maryland 21842

Old Dartmouth Historical
   Society
18 Johnny Cake Hill
New Bedford, Massachusetts
02740
Telephone: (617) 997-0046

Peabody Museum of Salem
East India Marine Hall
Salem, Massachusetts 01970
Telephone: (617) 745-1876

Penobscot Marine Museum
Searsport, Maine 04974
Telephone: (207) 548-6634

Philadelphia Maritime
   Museum
321 Chestnut Street
Philadelphia, Pennsylvania

Philadelphia Maritime
   Museum (continued)
19106
Telephone: (215) 925-5439

Radcliff Maritime Museum
The Maryland Historical
   Society
201 West Monument Street
Baltimore, Maryland 21201
Telephone: (301) 685-3750

South Street Seaport Museum
16 Fulton Street
New York, New York 10038
Telephone: (212) 766-9020

St. Augustine Lighthouse
   Museum
81 Lighthouse Avenue
St. Augustine, Florida 32084

Suffolk County Marine
   Museum
Box 1327
Sag Harbor, New York 11963
Telephone: (516) 725-0770

Suffolk Marine Museum
Montauk Highway
West Sayville, New York
   11796
(516) 567-1733

Thousand Islands Shipyard
750 Mary Street
Clayton, New York 13624
Telephone: (315) 686-4104

Virginia Beach Maritime
   Historical Museum
24th and Oceanfront
Virginia Beach, Virginia 23451

Appendix B, continued

Whaling Museum Society
P. O. Box 25
Cold Springs Harbor, New
    York 11724
Telephone: (516) 367-3418

APPENDIX C

American Military Cemeteries In the U.S. and Overseas

The cemeteries below are administered by the American Battle Monuments Commission. The commission has offices in Washington, D.C.; Rome, Italy; Garches, France; and Manila, Republic of the Philippines. The Washington address and phone number is: Casimir Pulaski Building, 20 Massachusetts Avenue, N.W., Washington, D.C. 20314-0300. Telephone: (202) 272-0533/0532. Winter season for the cemeteries below is October 1-April 15. Summer season is April 16-September 30.

World War I Cemeteries

Aisne-Marne, Belleau, France, 9:00 am to 5:00 pm daily winter season; 9:00 am to 6:00 pm daily summer season.

Brookwood, Brookwood, England, 9:00 am to 5:00 pm weekdays, 10:00 am to 6:00 pm weekends and holidays winter season; 9:00 am to 6:00 pm weekdays, 10:00 am to 12:00 noon and 3:00 pm to 6:00 pm weekends and holidays summer season.

Flanders Field, Waregam, Belgium, 8:00 am to 5:00 pm weekdays, 9:00 am to 5:00 pm weekends and holidays winter season; 8:00 am to 6:00 pm weekdays, 9:00 am to 6:00 pm summer season.

Meuse-Argonne, Romagne, France, 8:00 am to 5:00 pm weekdays, 9:00 am to 5:00 pm weekends and holidays winter season; 8:00 am to 6:00 pm weekdays, 9:00 am to 6:00 pm weekends and holidays summer season.

Oise-Aisne, Fere-en-Tardenais, France, 9:00 am to 5:00 pm weekdays, 10:00 am to 5:00 pm weekends and holidays winter season; 9:00 am to 6:00 pm weekdays, 10:00 am to 12:00 noon and 3:00 pm to 6:00 pm weekends and holidays summer season.

St. Mihiel, Thiacourt, France, 9:00 am to 5:00 pm weekdays, 10:00 am to 5:00 pm weekends and holidays winter season; 9:00 am to 6:00 pm weekdays, 10:00 am to 12:00 noon and 3:00 pm to 6:00 pm weekends and holidays summer season.

Somme, Bony, France, 9:00 am to 5:00 pm weekdays, 10:00 am to 5:00 pm weekends and holidays winter season; 9:00 am to 6:00 pm weekdays, 10:00 am to 6:00 pm weekends and holidays summer season.

Appendix C, continued

Suresnes, Paris, France, 8:00 am to 5:00 pm weekdays, 10:00 am to 5:00 pm weekends and holidays winter season; 8:00 am to 6:00 pm weekdays, 10:00 am to 6:00 pm weekends and holidays summer season.

World War II Cemeteries

Ardennes, Ardennes, Belgium, 8:00 am to 5:00 pm weekdays, 9:00 am to 5:00 pm weekends and holidays winter season; 8:00 am to 6:00 pm weekdays, 9:00 am to 6:00 pm weekends and holidays summer season.

Brittany, St. James, France, 8:00 am to 5:00 pm daily winter season; 8:00 am to 6:00 pm daily summer season.

Cambridge, Cambridge, England, 8:00 am to 5:00 pm daily winter season; 8:00 am to 6:00 pm daily summer season.

Epinal, Epinal, France, 8:00 am to 5:00 pm weekdays, 9:00 am to 5:00 pm weekends and holidays winter season; 8:00 am to 6:00 pm weekdays, 9:00 am to 6:00 pm weekends and holidays summer season.

Florence, Florence, Italy, 8:00 am to 6:00 pm daily winter and summer seasons.

Henri-Chapelle, Henri-Chapelle, Belgium, 8:00 am to 5:00 pm daily winter season; 8:00 am to 6:00 pm daily summer season.

Lorraine, St. Avold, France, 8:00 am to 5:00 pm daily winter season; 8:00 am to 6:00 pm daily summer season.

Luxembourg, Luxembourg City, Luxembourg, 9:00 am to 5:00 pm daily winter season; 9:00 am to 6:00 pm daily weekends and holidays.

Manila, Manila, Republic of the Philippines, 6:30 am to 4:45 pm daily winter and summer seasons.

Netherlands, Margarten, Holland, 8:00 am to 5:00 pm daily winter season; 8:00 am to 6:00 pm daily summer season.

Normandy, St. Laurent, France, 8:00 am to 5:00 pm daily winter season; 8:00 am to 6:00 pm daily summer season.

North Africa, Carthage, Tunisia, 8:00 am to 6:00 pm daily winter and summer seasons.

Appendix C, continued

Rhone, Draguignan, France, 9:00 am to 5:00 pm daily winter season; 8:00 am to 6:00 pm daily summer season.

Sicily-Rome, Nettuno, Italy, 8:00 am to 6:00 pm daily winter and summer seasons.

Many other military cemeteries are administered by the Veterans Administration. The V.A.'s main office is located at 810 Vermont Avenue, N.W., Washington, D.C. 20420, Telephone: (202) 233-4000 (main number). V.A. National Cemetery Area Offices are located at 730 Peachtree Street, N.E., Atlanta, Georgia 30365, Telephone: (404) 347-2121; P. O. Box 11720, 5000 Wissahickon Avenue, Philadelphia, Pennsylvania 19101, Telephone: (215) 951-7495/6; and 44 Union Boulevard, Box 25126, Denver, Colorado 80225, Telephone: (303) 980-2750.

Alexandria National Cemetery
209 Shamrock Avenue
Pineville, Louisiana 71360
Telephone: (404) 347-2121

Alexandria National Cemetery
1450 Wilkes Street
Alexandria, Virginia 22314
Telephone: (703) 690-2217

Alton National Cemetery
600 Pearl Street
Alton, Illinois 62003
Telephone: (314) 263-8691/2

Annapolis National Cemetery
800 West Street
Annapolis, Maryland 21401
Telephone: (301) 644-9696/7

Balls Bluff National Cemetery
Leesburg, Virginia 22075
Telephone: (703) 825-0027

Baltimore National Cemetery
5501 Frederick Avenue
Baltimore, Maryland 21228
Telephone: (301) 644-9696/7

Barrancas National Cemetery
Naval Air Station
Pensacola, Florida 32508
Telephone: (904) 452-4196/3357

Bath National Cemetery
VA Medical Center
Bath, New York 14810
Telephone: (607) 776-2111
  ext. 293

Baton Rouge National
  Cemetery
220 North 19th Street
Baton Rouge, Louisiana 70806
Telephone: (504) 398-0788

Bay Pines National Cemetery
P.O. Box 477
Bay Pines, Florida 33504
Telephone: (813) 398-9426

Beaufort National Cemetery
1601 Boundary Street
Beaufort, South Carolina
  29902
Telephone: (803) 524-3925

Appendix C, continued

Beverly National Cemetery
R.D. #1, Bridgeboro Road
Beverly, New Jersey 08010
Telephone: (609) 877-5460

Biloxi National Cemetery
P.O. Box 4968
Biloxi, Mississippi 39535
Telephone: (601) 388-6668

Black Hills National Cemetery
P.O. Box 640
Sturgis, South Dakota 57785
Telephone: (605) 347-3830

Calverton National Cemetery
210 Princeton Boulevard
Calverton, New York 11933
Telephone: ((516) 727-5410

Camp Butler National
Cemetery
R.R. #1
Springfield, Illinois 62707
Telephone: (217) 522-5764

Camp Nelson National
Cemetery
6980 Danville Road
Nicholasville, Kentucky 40356
Telephone: (606) 885-5727

Cave Hill National Cemetery
701 Baxter Avenue
Louisville, Kentucky 40204
Telephone: (502) 893-3852

Chattanooga National
Cemetery
1200 Bailey Avenue
Chattanooga, Tennessee 37404
Telephone: (615) 855-6590/91

City Point National Cemetery
10th Avenue and Davis Street
Hopewell, Virginia 23860
Telephone: (804) 222-1490

Cold Harbor National
Cemetery
Route 156 North
Mechanicsville, Virginia 23111
Telephone: (804) 222-1490

Cornith National Cemetery
1551 Horton Street
Cornith, Mississippi 38834
Telephone: (601) 286-5782

Crown Hill National Cemetery
700 West 38th Street
Indianapolis, Indiana 46208
Telephone: (317) 674-3321
  ext. 546/7

Culpeper National Cemetery
305 U.S. Avenue
Culpeper, Virginia 22701
Telephone: (703) 825-0027

Cypress Hills National
Cemetery
625 Jamaica Avenue
Brooklyn, New York 11208
Telephone: (516) 249-7300

Danville National Cemetery
1900 East Main Street
Danville, Illinois 61832
Telephone: (217) 442-8000
  ext. 391

Danville National Cemetery
377 North First Street
Danville, Kentucky 40442
Telephone: (606) 885-5727

Appendix C, continued

Danville National Cemetery
721 Lee Street
Danville, Virginia 24541
Telephone: (804) 636-2661

Dayton National Cemetery
VA Medical Center
4100 West Third Street
Dayton, Ohio 45428
Telephone: (513) 262-2115
Telephone: (513) 268-6511
   ext. 2748/9

Eagle Point National Cemetery
2763 Riley Road
Eagle Point, Oregon 97524
Telephone: No commercial
   phone

Fayetteville National Cemetery
600 Government Avenue
Fayetteville, Arkansas 72701
Telephone: (501) 443-4301
   ext. 584

Finn's Point National
Cemetery
R.F.D. No. 3, Fort Mott Road,
Box 542
Salem, New Jersey 08079
Telephone: (609) 935-3628

Florence National Cemetery
803 East National Cemetery
   Road
Florence, South Carolina
   29501
Telephone: (803) 669-8783

Florida National Cemetery
P.O. Box 337
Bushnell, Florida 33513
Telephone: (904) 793-7740

Fort Bayard National
Cemetery
P.O. Box 189
Fort Bayard, New Mexico
   88036
Telephone: (505) 537-5794

Fort Bliss National Cemetery
P.O. Box 6342
Fort Bliss, Texas 79906
Telephone: (915) 541-7674/7467

Fort Custer National Cemetery
15501 Dickman Road
Augusta, Michigan 49012
Telephone: (616) 731-4164

Fort Gibson National
Cemetery
Fort Gibson, Oklahoma 74434
Telephone: (918) 478-2334

Fort Harrison National
Cemetery
8620 Varina Road
Richmond, Virginia 23231
Telephone: (804) 222-1490

Fort Leavenworth National
Cemetery
Fort Leavenworth, Kansas
   66027
Telephone: (913) 682-1748/9

Fort Logan National Cemetery
3698 South Sheridan
   Boulevard
Denver, Colorado 80235
Telephone: (303) 761-0117

Fort Lyon National Cemetery
VA Medical Center
Fort Lyon, Colorado 81038
Telephone: (303) 456-1260
   ext. 231

Appendix C, continued

Fort McPherson National
Cemetery
HCO 1, Box 67
Maxwell, Nebraska 69151
Telephone: (308) 582-4433

Fort Meade National Cemetery
VA Medical Center
Fort Meade, South Dakota
57785
Telephone: (605) 347-3830

Fort Mitchell National
Cemetery
P.O. Box 2517
Phenix City, Alabama 36868
Telephone: (205) 855-4731

Fort Richardson National
Cemetery
P.O. Box 5-498
Fort Richardson, Alaska 99505
Telephone: (907) 862-4217

Fort Rosecrans National
Cemetery
Point Lima, P.O. Box 6237
San Diego, California 92106
Telephone: (619) 553-2084

Fort Sam Houston National
Cemetery
1520 Harry Wurzbach Road
San Antonio, Texas 78209
Telephone: (512) 221-2136

Fort Scott National Cemetery
P.O. Box 917
Fort Scott, Kansas 66701
Telephone: (316) 223-2840

Fort Smith National Cemetery
522 Garland Avenue and
South 6th Street
Fort Smith, Arkansas 72901
Telephone: (501) 783-5345

Fort Snelling National
Cemetery
7601 34th Avenue, South
Minneapolis, Minnesota 55450
Telephone: (612) 726-1127/8

Glendale National Cemetery
8301 Willis Church Road
Richmond, Virginia 23231
Telephone: (804) 222-1490

Golden Gate National
Cemetery
1300 Sneath Lane
San Bruno, California 94066
Telephone: (415) 589-7737
Telephone: (415) 761-1646

Grafton National Cemetery
431 Walnut Street
Grafton, West Virginia 26354
Telephone: (304) 265-2044

Hampton National Cemetery
Cemetery road at Marshall
Avenue
Hampton, Virginia 23669
Telephone: (804) 723-7104

Hampton National Cemetery
VA Medical Center
Hampton, Virginia 23669
Telephone: (804) 723-7104

Hot Springs National
Cemetery
VA Medical Center
Hot Springs, South Dakota
57747
Telephone: (605) 745-4101

Houston National Cemetery
10410 Veterans Memorial
Drive
Houston, Texas 77038
Telephone: (713) 653-3112

Appendix C, continued

Indiantown Gap National
Cemetery
P.O. Box 187
Annville, Pennsylvania 17003
Telephone: (717) 865-5254

Jefferson Barracks National
Cemetery
101 Memorial Drive
St. Louis, Missouri 63125
Telephone: (314) 263-8691/2
Telephone: (314) 263-8720/1/2/3

Jefferson City National
Cemetery
1024 East McCarty Street
Jefferson City, Missouri 65101
Telephone: (314) 263-8691/2

Keokuk National Cemetery
1701 J Street
Keokuk, Iowa 52632
Telephone: (319) 524-1304

Kerrville National Cemetery
VAMC - 3600 Memorial
Boulevard
Kerrville, Texas 78028
Telephone: (404) 347-2121
ext. 227

Knoxville National Cemetery
939 Tyson Street, N.W.
Knoxville, Tennessee 37917
Telephone: (615) 673-4560
Telephone: (615) 673-4573

Leavenworth National
Cemetery
P.O. Box 1694
Leavenworth, Kansas 66048
Telephone: (913) 682-1748/9

Lebanon National Cemetery
R.R. #1, Box 616
Lebanon, Kentucky 40033
Telephone: (502) 692-3390

Lexington National Cemetery
833 West Main Street
Lexington, Kentucky 40508
Telephone: (606) 885-5727

Little Rock National Cemetery
2523 Confederate Boulevard
Little Rock, Arkansas 72206
Telephone: (501) 374-8011

Long Island National
Cemetery
Farmingdale
Long Island, New York 11735
Telephone: (516) 249-7300

Los Angeles National
Cemetery
950 South Sepulveda
Boulevard
Los Angeles, California 90049
Telephone: (213) 824-4311

Loudon Park National
Cemetery
3445 Frederick Avenue
Baltimore, Maryland 21229
Telephone: (301) 644-9697

Marietta National Cemetery
500 Washington Avenue
Marietta, Georgia 30060
Telephone: (404) 428-5631

Marion National Cemetery
VA Medical Center
Marion, Indiana 46952
Telephone: (317) 674-3321
ext 546/7

Appendix C, continued

Massachusetts National
 Cemetery
Bourne, Massachusetts 02532
Telephone: (508) 563-7113/4

Memphis National Cemetery
3568 Townes Avenue
Memphis, Tennessee 38122
Telephone: (901) 386-8311

Mill Springs National
 Cemetery
Rural Route 2, P.O. Box 172
Nancy, Kentucky 42544
Telephone: (606) 636-6470

Mobile National Cemetery
1202 Virginia Street
Mobile, Alabama 36604
Telephone: (904) 452-4196

Mound City National
 Cemetery
Junction - Highway 37 and 51
Mound City, Illinois 62963
Telephone: (314) 263-8691/2

Mountain Home National
 Cemetery
P.O. Box 8
Mountain Home, Tennessee
 37684
Telephone: (615) 327-5360

Nashville National Cemetery
1420 Gallatin Road, South
Madison, Tennessee 37115
Telephone: (615) 327-5360

Natchez National Cemetery
61 Cemetery Road
Natchez, Mississippi 39120
Telephone: (601) 445-4981

National Memorial Cemetery
 of Arizona
23029 North Cave Creek Road
Phoenix, Arizona 85024
Telephone: Not available

National Memorial Cemetery
 of the Pacific
2177 Puowaina Drive
Honolulu, Hawaii 96813
Telephone: (808) 541-1427/8

New Albany National
 Cemetery
1943 Ekin Avenue
New Albany, Indiana 47150
Telephone: (502) 893-3852

New Bern National Cemetery
1711 National Avenue
New Bern, North Carolina
 28560
Telephone: (919) 637-2912

Philadelphia National
 Cemetery
Haines Street and Limekiln
 Pike
Philadelphia, Pennsylvania
 19138
Telephone: (609) 877-5460

Port Hudson National
 Cemetery
20978 Port Hickey Road
Zachary, Louisiana 70791
Telephone: (504) 389-0788

Prescott National Cemetery
VA Medical Center
500 Highway 89 North
Prescott, Arizona 86301
Telephone: (602) 445-4860

Appendix C, continued

Puerto Rico National Cemetery
P.O. Box 1298
Bayamon, Puerto Rico 00619
Telephone: (809) 785-7281

Quantico National Cemetery
P.O. Box 10
Triangle, Virginia 22172
Telephone: (703) 690-2217

Quincy National Cemetery
36th and Maine Street
Quincy, Illinois 62301
Telephone: (319) 524-1304

Raleigh National Cemetery
501 Rock Quarry Road
Raleigh, North Carolina 27601
Telephone: (919) 832-0144

Richmond National Cemetery
1701 Williamsburg Road
Richmond, Virginia 23231
Telephone: (804) 222-1490

Riverside National Cemetery
22495 Van Buren Boulevard
Riverside, California 92508
Telephone: (714) 653-8417

Rock Island National Cemetery
Rock Island Arsenal
Rock Island, Illinois 61299
Telephone: (309) 782-6715

Roseburg National Cemetery
VA Medical Center
Roseburg, Oregon 97470
Telephone: (503) 440-1000

St. Augustine National
Cemetery
104 Marine Street
St. Augustine, Florida 32804
Telephone: (904) 793-7740

Salisbury National Cemetery
202 Government Road
Salisburg, North Carolina
28144
Telephone: (704) 636-2661

San Antonio National
Cemetery
517 Paso Hondo Street
San Antonio, Texas 78202
Telephone: (512) 221-2136

San Francisco National
Cemetery
P.O. Box 29012
Presidio of San Francisco
San Francisco, California
94129
Telephone: (415) 561-2008
Telephone: (415) 561-2986

Santa Fe National Cemetery
501 North Guadalupe Street
P.O. Box 88
Santa Fe, New Mexico 87504
Telephone: (505) 988-6400

Seven Pines National
Cemetery
400 East Williamsburg Road
Sandston, Virginia 23150
Telephone: (804) 222-1490

Sitka National Cemetery
P.O. Box 1065
Sitka, Alaska 99835
Telephone: (303) 980-2750

Springfield National Cemetery
1702 East Seminole Street
Springfield, Missouri 65804
Telephone: (417) 881-9499

Appendix C, continued

Staunton National Cemetery
901 Richmond Avenue
Staunton, Virginia 24401
Telephone: (703) 825-0027

Togus National Cemetery
VA Medical and Regional
Office Center
Togus, Maine 04330
Telephone: (207) 623-8411
Telephone: (617) 563-7113

West Virginia National
Cemetery
c/o Grafton National Cemetery
431 Walnut Street
Grafton, West Virginia 26354
Telephone: (304) 265-2044

Willamette National Cemetery
P.O. Box 66147
11800 S.E. Mount Scott
Boulevard
Portland, Oregon 97266
Telephone: (503) 273-5252/50

Wilmington National Cemetery
2011 Market Street
Wilmington, North Carolina
28403
Telephone: (919) 343-4877

Winchester National Cemetery
401 National Avenue
Winchester, Virginia 22601
Telephone: (703) 825-0027

Wood National Cemetery
Milwaukee, Wisconsin 53295
(414) 671-8161/2

Woodlawn National Cemetery
1825 Davis Street
Elmira, New York 14901
Telephone: (607) 776-2111
ext. 293

Zachary Taylor National
Cemetery
4701 Brownsboro Road
Louisville, Kentucky 40207
Telephone: (502) 893-3852

APPENDIX D

Military Sites in the National Park System

The National Park System uses a wide variety of titles to identify sites associated with military history in the United States and its possessions: national military park, national battlefield park, national battlefield site, national battlefield, national monument, national historic site, and so on. Museums or visitor centers displaying military artifacts are found at many of the sites listed, as are original, restored, and/or reconstructed fortifications and other historic structures.

ALABAMA

Horseshoe Bend National Military Park
Route 1, Box 103
Daviston, Alabama 36256

ARIZONA

Fort Bowie National Historic Site
P. O. Box 158
Bowie, Arizona 85605

ARKANSAS

Fort Smith National Historic Site
P. O. Box 1406
Fort Smith, Arkansas 72902

Pea Ridge National Military Park
Pea Ridge, Arkansas 72751

CALIFORNIA

Fort Point National Historic Site
P. O. Box 29333
Presidio of San Francisco, California 94129

FLORIDA

Castillo de San Marcos National Monument
1 Castillo Drive
St. Augustine, Florida 32084

Appendix D, continued

FLORIDA, (continued)

Fort Caroline National Memorial
12713 Fort Caroline Road
Jacksonville, Florida 32225

Fort Jefferson National Monument
c/o Everglades National Park
P. O. Box 279
Homestead, Florida 33030

Fort Matanzas National Monument
c/o Castillo de San Marcos National Monument
1 Castillo Drive
St. Augustine, Florida 32084

Gulf Islands National Seashore
(Fort Pickens, Fort Barrancas,
Advanced Redoubt)
P. O. Box 100
Gulf Breeze, Florida 32561

GEORGIA

Andersonville National Historic Site
Andersonville, Georgia 31711

Chickamauga and Chattanooga
National Military Park
P. O. Box 2128
Fort Oglethorpe, Georgia 30742

Fort Frederica National Monument
Route 4, Box 286-C
St. Simons Island, Georgia 31522

Fort Pulaski National Monument
Kennesaw Mountain National Battlefield Park
P. O. Box 1167
Marietta, Georgia 30061

GUAM

War in the Pacific National Historical Park
P. O. Box FA
Agana, Guam 96910

Appendix D, continued

HAWAII

USS *Arizona* Memorial
c/o Pacific Area Office
National Park Service
Box 50165
Honolulu, Hawaii 96850

INDIANA

George Rogers Clark National Historical Park
401 S. Second Street
Vincennes, Indiana 47591

KANSAS

Fort Larned National Historic Site
Route 3
Larned, Kansas 67550

Fort Scott National Historic Site
Old Fort Boulevard
Fort Scott, Kansas 66701

LOUISIANA

Jean Lafitte National Historical Park and Preserve
U.S. Customs House
423 Canal Street, Room 206
New Orleans, Louisiana 70130

MARYLAND

Antietam National Battlefield
Box 158
Sharpsburg, Maryland 21782

Fort McHenry National Monument
and Historic Shrine
Baltimore, Maryland 21230

Fort Washington Park
National Capital Parks, East
1900 Anacostia Drive SE
Washington, DC 20019

Appendix D, continued

MARYLAND (continued)

Monocacy National Battlefield
c/o Antietam National Battlefield
Box 158
Sharpsburg, Maryland 21782

MASSACHUSETTS

Boston National Historical Park
Charlestown Navy Yard
Boston, Massachusetts 02129

Minute Man National Historical Park
P. O. Box 160
Concord, Massachusetts 01742

Springfield Armory National Historic Site
1 Armory Square
Springfield, Massachusetts 01105

MISSISSIPPI

Brices Crossroads National Battlefield Site
c/o Natchez Trace Parkway
R.R. 1, NT-143
Tupelo, Mississippi 38801

Gulf Islands National Seashore
(Fort Massachusetts)
3500 Park Road
Ocean Springs, Mississippi 39564

Tupelo National Battlefield
c/o Natchez Trace Parkway
R.R. 1, NT-143
Tupelo, Mississippi 38801

Vicksburg National Military Park
3201 Clay Street
Vicksburg, Mississippi 39180

MISSOURI

Wilson's Creek National Battlefield
Postal Drawer C
Republic, Missouri 65738

Appendix D, continued

MONTANA

Big Hole National Battlefield
P. O. Box 237
Wisdom, Montana 59761

Custer Battlefield National Monument
P. O. Box 39
Crow Agency, Montana 59022

NEW JERSEY

Morristown National Historical Park
Washington Place
Morristown, New Jersey 07960

NEW MEXICO

Fort Union National Monument
Watrous, New Mexico 87753

NEW YORK

Castle Clinton National Monument
Manhattan Sites
National Park Service
26 Wall Street
New York, New York 10005

Fort Stanwix National Monument
112 E. Park Street
Rome, New York 13440

General Grant National Memorial
Manhattan Sites
National Park Service
26 Wall Street
New York, New York 10005

Saratoga National Historical Park
R.D. 2, Box 33
Stillwater, New York 12170

NORTH CAROLINA

Guilford Courthouse National Military Park
P. O. Box 9806
Greensboro, North Carolina 27429

Appendix D, continued

NORTH CAROLINA (continued)

Kings Mountain National Military Park
P. O. Box 31
Kings Mountain, North Carolina 28086

Moores Creek National Battlefield
P. O. Box 69
Currie, North Carolina 28435

NORTH DAKOTA

Fort Union Trading Post National Historic Site
Buford Route
Williston, North Dakota 58801

PENNSYLVANIA

Fort Necessity National Battlefield
R.D. 2, Box 528
Farmington, Pennsylvania 15437

Gettysburg National Military Park
Gettysburg, Pennsylvania 17325

Independence National Historical Park
313 Walnut Street
Philadelphia, Pennsylvania 19106

Valley Forge National Historical Park
Valley Forge, Pennsylvania 19481

PUERTO RICO

San Juan National Historic Site
P. O. Box 712
Old San Juan, Puerto Rico 00902

SOUTH CAROLINA

Cowpens National Battlefield
P. O. Box 308
Chesnee, South Carolina 29323

Fort Sumter National Monument
1214 Middle Street
Sullivans Island, South Carolina 29482

Appendix D, continued

SOUTH CAROLINA (continued)

Ninety Six National Historic Site
P. O. Box 496
Ninety Six, South Carolina 29666

TENNESSEE

Fort Donelson National Military Park
P. O. Box F
Dover, Tennessee 37058

Shiloh National Military Park
Shiloh, Tennessee 38376

Stones River National Battlefield
Route 10, Box 495
Old Nashville Highway
Murfreesboro, Tennessee 37130

TEXAS

Fort Davis National Historic Site
P. O. Box 1456
Fort Davis, Texas 79734

Palo Alto Battlefield National Historic Site
P. O. Box 191
Brownsville, Texas 78520

VIRGINIA

Appomattox Court House
National Historical Park
P. O. Box 218
Appomattox, Virginia 24522

Colonial National Historical Park
P. O. Box 210
Yorktown, Virginia 23690

Fredericksburg and Spotsylvania County
Battlefields Memorial National Military Park
P. O. Box 679
Fredericksburg, Virginia 22404

Appendix D, continued

VIRGINIA (continued)

Manassas National Battlefield Park
P. O. Box 1830
Manassas, Virginia 22110

Petersburg National Battlefield
P. O. Box 549
Petersburg, Virginia 23803

Richmond National Battlefield Park
3215 East Broad Street
Richmond, Virginia 23223

WASHINGTON

San Juan Island National Historical Park
P. O. Box 429
Friday Harbor, Washington 98250

WEST VIRGINIA

Harpers Ferry National Historical Park
P. O. Box 65
Harpers Ferry, West Virginia 25425

WYOMING

Fort Laramie National Historic Site
Fort Laramie, Wyoming 82212

APPENDIX E

NASA Installations/Visitor Centers

NASA/Goddard Space Flight Center, Visitor Center & Museum, Code 130, Greenbelt, Maryland 20771. Telephone: (301) 286-8981.

NASA/Lyndon B. Johnson Space Center, Olin Teague Visitor Center, Public Services Branch, Code AP4, Johnson Space Center, Houston, Texas 77058. Telephone: (713) 483-4241.

NASA/Jet Propulsion Laboratory, 4800 Oak Grove Drive, ATTN: Visitor Control, Building 249, Pasadena, California 91109. Telephone: (818) 354-5533.

NASA/John F. Kennedy Space Center, PA-VIC, Kennedy Space Center, Florida 32899. Telephone: (407) 867-2363.

NASA/Langley Research Center, Visitor Center, Mail Stop 480, Hampton, Virginia 23665-5225. Telephone: (804) 865-2855.

NASA/Marshall Space Flight Center, Marshall Space Flight Center, Alabama 35812. Telephone: (205) 837-3400.

NASA/John C. Stennis Space Center, Visitor Center, John C. Stennis Space Center, Mississippi 39529. Telephone: (601) 688-3341.

NASA/Wollops Flight Facility, Visitor Center, GSFC/Wollops Flight Facility, Wollops Island, Virginia 23337. Telephone: (804) 824-2298/1344.

INDEX

—NOTES—

CENTRAL ORDER COUPON
Military Living Publications
P.O. Box 2347, Falls Church, VA 22042-0347, Telephone: (703) 237-0203

Publications	Qty.	Publications	Qty.
Military Space-A Air Opportunities Around the World*. *The one everyone is talking about!* **$15.45.**		Assignment Washington: A Guide to Washington Area Military Installations. *A "must" book for every Capital area military family!* **$8.45.**	
Temporary Military Lodging Around the World*. *Our all-time best seller!* **$11.45.**		U.S. Forces Travel & Transfer Guide Europe & Near East Areas*. *The complete military guide to Europe!* **$16.45.**	
Military RV, Camping & Rec Areas Around the World*. *You can have fun with this book!* **$9.45.**		U.S. Military Museums, Historic Sites & Exhibits*. *A great, practical book. Wonderful gift!* **$26.45 (hardcover).**	
U.S. Forces Travel & Transfer Guide U.S.A. & Caribbean Areas*. *This book should be in every car!* **$10.45.**		U.S. Military Museums, Historic Sites & Exhibits*. *The only all-military museum book!* **$16.45.**	
Military Living's R&R Space-A Report. *The world-wide travel newsletter.* 5 yrs.—$42.00 2 yrs.—$20.00 3 yrs.—$27.00 1 yr. —$12.00 (6 issues)		Military Living. *Local Washington area magazine.* 3 yrs.—$16.00 1 yr.—$7.00 2 yrs.—$12.00 (12 issues)	

* If you are an R&R Space-A Report Subscriber, you may deduct $1.00 per book. (No discount on the R&R Report itself.)

Total: $_____

VA addressees add 4.5 % sales tax: $_____
(Books only)

For 1st Class Mail, add $1.00 per book.
Mail Order Price are for the U.S., APO & FPO addresses. Please consult Publisher for International Mail Price. Sorry, no billing. GREAT FUND RAISERS! Please write for wholesale rates.

Total Amount Enclosed: $_____

We're as close as your telephone...by using our Telephone Ordering Service. We honor American Express, Mastercard and VISA. Call us at **(703) 237-0203 or FAX—(703) 237-2233** and order today!. Sorry, no collect calls. Or...fill out the the mail-order coupon below.

Name: _____

Street: _____

City/State/ZIP: _____

Phone: (____) _____

Signature: _____

Rank: _____ or Rank of Sponsor: _____

Branch of Service: _____

Active Duty: ____   Retired: ____   Widower: ____   100% Disabled Veteran: ____   Guard: ____

Reservist: ____   Other: ____

Card No.: _____   Card Expiration Date: _____
Mail check/money order to: Military Living Publications, P.O. Box 2347, Falls Church, VA 22042-0347.

—NOTES—

CENTRAL ORDER COUPON
Military Living Publications
P.O. Box 2347, Falls Church, VA 22042-0347, Telephone: (703) 237-0203

Publications	Qty.	Publications	Qty.
Military Space-A Air Opportunities Around the World*. *The one everyone is talking about!* **$15.45.**		Assignment Washington: A Guide to Washington Area Military Installations. *A "must" book for every Capital area military family!* **$8.45.**	
Temporary Military Lodging Around the World*. *Our all-time best seller!* **$11.45.**		U.S. Forces Travel & Transfer Guide Europe & Near East Areas*. *The complete military guide to Europe!* **$16.45.**	
Military RV, Camping & Rec Areas Around the World*. *You can have fun with this book!* **$9.45.**		U.S. Military Museums, Historic Sites & Exhibits*. *A great, practical book. Wonderful gift!* **$26.45 (hardcover).**	
U.S. Forces Travel & Transfer Guide U.S.A. & Caribbean Areas*. *This book should be in every car!* **$10.45.**		U.S. Military Museums, Historic Sites & Exhibits*. *The only all-military museum book!* **$16.45.**	
Military Living's R&R Space-A Report. *The world-wide travel newsletter.* 5 yrs.—$42.00 2 yrs.—$20.00 3 yrs.—$27.00 1 yr. —$12.00 (6 issues)		Military Living. *Local Washington area magazine.* 3 yrs.—$16.00 1 yr.—$7.00 2 yrs.—$12.00 (12 issues)	

* If you are an R&R Space-A Report Subscriber, you may deduct $1.00 per book. (No discount on the R&R Report itself.)

Total: $_____

VA addressees add 4.5 % sales tax: $_____
(Books only)

For 1st Class Mail, add $1.00 per book.
Mail Order Price are for the U.S., APO & FPO addresses. Please consult Publisher for International Mail Price. Sorry, no billing. GREAT FUND RAISERS! Please write for wholesale rates.

Total Amount Enclosed: $_____

We're as close as your telephone...by using our Telephone Ordering Service. We honor American Express, Mastercard and VISA. Call us at **(703) 237-0203 or FAX—(703) 237-2233** and order today!. Sorry, no collect calls. Or...fill out the the mail-order coupon below.

Name: _____

Street: _____

City/State/ZIP: _____

Phone: (_____) _____

Signature: _____

Rank: _____ or Rank of Sponsor: _____

Branch of Service: _____

Active Duty: _____   Retired: _____   Widower: _____   100% Disabled Veteran: _____   Guard: _____

Reservist: _____   Other: _____

Card No.: _____   Card Expiration Date: _____
Mail check/money order to: Military Living Publications, P.O. Box 2347, Falls Church, VA 22042-0347.

—NOTES—